THE CELL
Chemistry and function

THE CELL

Chemistry and function

Roger H. Trumbore, Ph.D.

Associate Professor of Biology,
State University of New York at Binghamton
Binghamton, New York

With 88 figures and
a 16-plate section of electron micrographs

The C. V. Mosby Company

Saint Louis   1966

To
Phyllis, Karen, and Michael

Preface

The rigorous curriculum of a major in the biological sciences often does not permit the luxury of a separate course in biochemistry. This was part of the motivation behind *The Cell: Chemistry and Function.* More basic than this is the strong belief that one cannot fully comprehend physiological processes without understanding the biochemical principles behind them. One can learn by rote, but the real understanding must come from a knowledge of the basic physical and chemical fundamentals.

By synthesizing the disciplines of biochemistry and cell biology into a single unit, this text attempts to serve two purposes. For those students who do not have formal course training in biochemistry, it is hoped that the text will give a foundation in the underlying concepts of this field, which should enable the intricacies and interrelationships between chemistry and cell physiology to be understood and appreciated more fully. On the other hand, if a student has some training in biochemistry, the first portion of the book will serve as a refresher course. Hopefully, it will still be instructive since the material is presented from the viewpoint of a biologist.

The idea of combining biochemistry with cell physiology is certainly not new; after all, much of physiology *is* chemistry. However, the approach which this book takes is to give the complete foundation in the biochemical concepts before applying them to the functional aspects of the cell.

The level of the book is predicated on two premises. First, the acceleration and more in-depth approach to biology which is prevalent in the high schools and lower college courses affords the higher level courses the luxury of not having to review too much of the basic, background material. Second, it is assumed that biology majors have had some exposure to organic chemistry. These requirements should not be interpreted as being stringent for the student. Past experience has shown that the biology and chemistry majors fare equally well in a course taught in the format of this book.

A textbook designed to be readable does not pretend to present a complete literature survey of all the material discussed. It is hoped that by selection of general references and some pertinent cited works the concepts and flow of ideas involved in cell physiology can better project across to the student. I do not deplore heavily referenced texts, but I do feel that a teaching text, like a set of lectures, should deemphasize the cited literature. General references are included at the end of most chapters, and many of the ones selected give excellent literature surveys which the student may use if he wishes to go beyond the scope of this book.

This textbook takes its origin from a set of lecture notes developed while I was teaching both in small liberal arts schools and in a university complex, from contact with many interested students, from an idea of how a subject should be handled, and from a desire for expression. Students are an excellent sounding board for ideas, and the reverberations often show discord. Deep appreciation is extended to those students who offered suggestions with sincerity and warmth. The encouragement of my colleagues should not go unmentioned.

No one man is responsible for the ideas which appear in a textbook. They are assimilated, converted, or borrowed from the researchers and theoretical scientists who originally shared their data and thoughts with others. It is to these men and women that any author should offer hearty thanks.

Thanks should also be extended to the following individuals who helped make this book possible. To Mr. James F. Burch, Jr., medical illustrator, who did the line drawings, and to Dr. Paul F. Doolin and Dr. Kevin D. Barron, who contributed the electron micrographs and photomicrographs, I am deeply grateful. My appreciation is also extended to Sir John Eccles, Dr. Daniel E. Koshland, Jr., and Dr. John P. Hannon for use of illustrations from previously published works.

The typing and retyping of a manuscript is a most thankless task. With affection, I acknowledge my wife, Phyllis, as the typist. Without her confidence and gentle encouragement, this book might never have been.

Roger H. Trumbore
Binghamton, New York

Contents

Section **III**

The physiochemical environment

Section **IV**

Bioenergetics

13. Fundamental thermodynamics in biological systems, 125

14. Enzymes, catalysis, and kinetics, 135

15. High-energy bonds and coupled reactions, 156

Section **V**

Intermediary metabolism

21. Electron transport chains and oxidative phosphorylation, 229

22. Bioluminescence, 242

23. Photosynthesis, 250

Section **VI**

The functional cell

Section **VII**

Cell processes

Section **VIII**

Control mechanisms

Section I

Introduction

The contrast between the cell as envisaged by Schleiden and Schwann in the 1800's and the cell as we know it today demonstrates the remarkable advance in knowledge about this basic unit of life. The dynamics of the functioning cell would astound the early microscopist whose acquaintance with his subject was only through a cold glass. As knowledge about the cell grew, the approach to further investigation was continually modified. The modern approach to investigation of the cell is to knit together the information from various disciplines into a comprehensive net of knowledge.

This introductory section points out the importance of the merger between structure and function. Chapter 1 defines the necessity for this approach. Chapter 2 reviews the basic characteristics and structures of the cell, and Chapter 3 attempts to reiterate the importance of the approach by developing the historical trends as they derived from various sources.

1

The scope and approach of cell physiology

INTRODUCTION

Cell physiology is primarily concerned both with elucidation and application of biochemical pathways to the overall physiology of the cell and with the study of those phenomena which are peculiar to the cell. This exciting field meshes biochemistry and cytology into a dynamic physiological unit.

Cell physiology, like all branches of physiology, is based on the tenet that structure and function can be integrated, the confluence resulting in a view-in-depth of the life processes. In the cell, structure is microscopic and submicroscopic; function lies at the molecular and macromolecular levels. And therein lie the reasons for building a base of biochemical data and insight before imposing the peculiarities of structural orderliness into the system.

RELATIONSHIP OF CELL PHYSIOLOGY TO OTHER AREAS OF PHYSIOLOGY

The dynamics and functions of the living cell and the application of explicit chemical reactions to these processes are important in the modern approach to the study of physiology at any level. Investigations of purely cellular phenomena are restricted to cell physiology.

The etymology of the word *physiology* defines the term literally as the science of nature. In loose translation, physiology is the study of function. It is the Why and How of the What's of biology. Cell physiology is only one aspect of this broad, basic division of the life sciences. Physiological studies can be made at every level of the hierarchy of the biotic world (Table 1-1). As a result, there are many separate areas of physiology, but with overlap between the areas.

3

Table 1-1. Hierarchy of organization and physiological studies which apply at each level

Level	Physiological study
Living world	Physiological ecology
Communities	Physiological ecology; comparative physiology
Species	Comparative physiology
Organisms	Comparative, animal, and plant physiology
Organ systems	Animal and plant physiology
Organs	Animal and plant physiology; histology
Tissues	Histology; cytology
Cells	Cytology; cell physiology
Molecular aggregates	Cell physiology; molecular biology
Molecules	Cell physiology; molecular biology
Atoms	Molecular biology

Gross physiology deals with reactions of the whole organism. Although these reactions may be cellular in origin, this field is primarily concerned with the more overt reactions of the organism as a unit. The basic dichotomy of gross physiology is into animal and plant physiology. Animal physiology is the study of the individual organ systems of the animal and how they are integrated to produce a functional organism. The organ systems are cells and cell products; therefore the processes that occur at the whole animal level reflect back to those occurring at the level of the cell. Similarly, plant physiology is the study of the functional plant and its approach to the operational whole. The fundamental process of photosynthesis, which is a cellular phenomenon, is one area of intense research and study.

These two basic fields have spawned satellite areas of study. Medical physiology is the animal physiology of man, whereas microbial physiology is the study of the function of bacteria, fungi, and protists. Inclusion of the last term illustrates overlap of cell, animal, and plant physiology.

There are also areas of physiology at the supraorganism level. Comparative physiology is the study of various organisms that perform the same fundamental processes of life. The diversity of nature has allowed penetration of organisms into every ecological niche, and each niche gives rise to new modes of performing basic functions. Physiological ecology is the study of the particular adaptation of each organism to its ecological niche.

TERMINOLOGY

The problem of terminology in cell physiology is aggravated because the terms used come from different roots—the chemical and the biological. One has to be just as facile with such expressions as *entropy* and *electron spin* as he does with *endoplasm* and *encystment*. The situation is exacerbated by two further complications. First, the study of function presupposes some knowledge of the structural characteristics of the material discussed. Second, the frustration of synonyms and near-synonyms, which crops up in any field, is no exception in cell physiology. Many groups of investigators have their own dialects, and

Table 1-2. Nutritional spectrum of cells

Classification	Requirement
Autotrophs	No organic carbon; nitrogen usually in form of NH_3, NO_2, or NO_3
Chemoautotrophs	Energy source for maintenance derived from oxidation of inorganic chemicals
Photoautotrophs	Energy source for maintenance derived from light
Heterotrophs	Require organic carbon; nitrogen and other requirements vary
I	Use atmospheric nitrogen
II	Fixed inorganic nitrogen
III	Organic nitrogen
IV	Organic nitrogen; vitamins
V	Organic nitrogen; vitamins; other additives
Paratrophs	Require the presence of living material (e.g., *Rickettsia* and viruses)

individual idiosyncrasies of nomenclature are common. There are no taxanomic rules of physiological terminology and, thus, synonymity results.

BASIC PROCESSES OF THE CELL

All cells exhibit the attributes of life and thus carry out a series of fundamental activities. It is the specialized adaptations for these basic processes which characterize any one cell. The trait which transcends all other features of living material is the highly ordered scheme in which life exists. This organization places an energy stress on the cell to maintain its homeostatic state. Maintenance of the homeostatic state encompasses the process of nutrition, which is a broad term for the production and storage of energy in the cell. The means by which cells draw in metabolites from the environment and convert them to utilizable energy with the release of waste material and by-products are so varied as to preclude generalizations. The fundamental tenet of nutrition, which is the conversion of available external energy to usable internal energy, underlies all nutritional schemes (Table 1-2).

The other basic processes are involved in the ability of the cell to adapt to the environment and still maintain or regain cellular homeostasis. The ability to respond to the environment, and the resultant series of responses, is an important parameter of adaptation. Irritability, conductivity, and contractility are three physiological properties derived from response to the environment. The phenomena of growth, division, and differentiation are responses of a different magnitude. Nonetheless, they are just as basic as any other processes. Growth is primarily a prerequisite to division and differentiation. Division ensures continuity of life, and differentiation allows cells to exist in one environment by virtue of their specialized microenvironments.

Implicit to the basic processes of cells is control. The highly ordered biological system necessitates precision of control over the various activities of the cell. Without regulation, the other fundamentals are meaningless.

APPROACHES TO THE STUDY OF CELL PHYSIOLOGY

Much of the study of cell physiology is beyond the realm of investigation at the level of the whole, intact cell although this level of study can be used in many exciting areas. The science which elucidates many of the phenomena of the cell is molecular biology, the attempt to explain the workings of the cell at the macromolecular and molecular levels. A whole new field of study has been created and along with it has come the demand that technology produce the tools to further this exploration. Each new segment of information opens another facet of knowledge, which leads to new hypotheses that can be proved only by more sophisticated techniques. Biophysical and biochemical techniques are finding their way into the study of cell physiology. The ultracentrifuge, electron and interference microscopes, and radiological techniques are all tools of cell physiologists. The past decade has seen more overlap of techniques among the sciences than in any other period of history.

Very often, in cell physiology a theory is but a transient idea. The difficulties in extrapolating beyond the limits of experimentation lead to many hypotheses that later prove to be wrong as data and techniques are improved. The tremendous diversity of form suggests equal diversity of function. Data accumulated from study of the erythrocyte, for example, may not be applicable to *Euglena*. And yet, universal features are shared by all cells. Experimentation, coupled with intuitive guesses and an element of serendipidity, is slowly yielding the answers to both the ubiquitous and specialized processes of the cell.

WHERE THE CHALLENGES LIE

Among the many stimulating facets of cell physiology are six major areas of challenge. The final integration of structure and function can only be done after the biochemical and cytological evidences of these areas are complete and meshed into unified understanding. The areas of challenge are these:

1. Molecular biology—Total comprehension of molecular interaction has to be uncovered before satisfactory theories can arise.
2. The problem of energy transfer and transformation—The cell must be able to convert from one energy form (light, chemical, osmotic, surface, and mechanical energy) to another and transfer these energies to drive physiological reactions.
3. Mechanism of adaptation by cell processes—The means by which the generalized and specific processes of the cell adjust to change is an important area of physiological research.
4. Structure-function relationship at the subcellular level—Knowledge of how organelles are modified for their particular function would give better insight into cell function itself.
5. How the cell exerts control over its processes—The areas of control include genetic, biochemical and structural; the latter includes the whole story of regulatory transport of material.
6. What effects microenvironment has on the functional cell—The physio-

chemical and biological environments have direct effects on the functional capacity of the cell.

THE CELL—CHEMISTRY AND FUNCTION

As the title implies, understanding of cell physiology is built on a firm base of biochemical concepts, which are applied to the functional aspects of the cell. Treatment of the chemistry is by a *biologist* for the *biology student*. Since much of cell physiology *is* chemistry, the background is of prime importance for some comprehension of the intricacies of the cell. The concepts developed in each section build on the knowledge assimilated from previous chapters.

No book of this nature is definitive on any one subject, and the student should realize that works in greater depth do exist. In a field that moves as rapidly as cell physiology, the current literature must be continually searched for new ideas and theories. Much of the literature is conflicting and any science student is cautioned against accepting all that he reads without further investigation and thought. The cited literature has been kept to a minimum to facilitate reading. At this level, development of understanding is the major criterion. General references are included at the end of each chapter for further reading in topics of interest.

General references

Davson, H. 1959. A textbook of general physiology. 2nd ed. Little, Brown & Co., Boston.
DeRobertis, E. L. P., W. W. Nowinski, and F. A. Saez. 1965. Cell biology. 4th ed. W. B. Saunders Co., Philadelphia.
Giese, A. C. 1962. Cell physiology. 2nd ed. W. B. Saunders Co., Philadelphia.
Langley, L. L. 1961. Cell function. Reinhold Publishing Corp., New York.

2

Cell organization and structure

N **INTRODUCTION**

Not long after Schleiden and Schwann proposed their biological maxim of the cell theory, biologists came to realize that this wondrous cell could only function as a unit because of its many distinct structures. The long, tedious microscopic analysis of the internal organization and structure began with the simple light microscope and culminated with the electron microscope, with which resolutions of 5 to 10 angstroms were possible. The entire spectrum of the cell, from the whole to its individual micromolecules, was revealed. Concurrently, biochemists were devoting much time to the study of the overt chemical reactions of the cell. Frustrated with the inconsistencies of data, they began to be aware of the importance of structure to the functional chemistry of the cell. The results of microscopic and chemical dissection of the structure of the cell are merging into a body of knowledge which gives great insight into the dynamics of the living system. Resynthesis of the mechanisms of the processes of the cell depends on both structure and function. Usefulness of one without the other is limited.

MACROANATOMY OF THE CELL

Cursory examination of the cells of any series of living organisms quickly reveals that there seem to be no generalizations that one can make concerning their size, shape, and other macroanatomical features. The variety and diversity of morphological types are as numerous as the assortment of functions which the cells can perform.

Cell size

Cell size ranges from 0.2 μ to 200 cm in diameter. This range is deceptive because cells at the upper end of the range include the eggs of birds and reptiles, which are in a class by themselves. The smallest cells are the bacteria whose size does not ever approach visible levels; at the other extreme are some neurons which have processes several meters in length.

8

Table 2-1. Size range of cells

Cell type	Largest dimension (microns)
Protein molecule	0.007
Viruses	0.07 to .10
Coccal bacterium	0.2
Bacillar bacterium	0.5 to 2.5
Erythrocyte	8
Liver cell	20
Euglena	100 to 200
Ostrich egg	2×10^5
Neuron (process)	2×10^6

Proportionally, the volume of cells varies considerably also. In many instances, adaptation to its particular existence determines the size and volume of the cell. There are, however, some basic conditions which are factors in determining the size of cells adapted for the same existence. Some investigators claim that the nuclear-cytoplasmic ratio is a limiting factor in cell volume, and that if the volume is such that the ratio is at a minimum, the cell will divide. Regardless of the veracity of this hypothesis, the nucleus-to-cytoplasm ratio is important. The nucleus is a control device for the cell, and in that capacity it must exert regulation over cytoplasmic processes. If the amount of cytoplasm becomes maximum, the control mechanism is weakened, and the result is a more inefficient cell.

Corollary to the nuclear-cytoplasmic relationship is the relation between surface area and surface volume. Simple geometric analysis can prove that the surface of a sphere does not increase as rapidly as the volume. To the cell, this means that as it becomes larger greater stress is placed on the transport mechanisms to ensure a steady supply of metabolites. If the transport mechanisms on the surface of the cell are biological phenomena with a definite rate of reaction, the exchange per unit volume of material decreases as the cell enlarges. This places a strain on the function of the membrane, and at some point, the exchange will lag behind the needs, and the cell either will not get enough metabolites in or will not be able to move enough toxic by-products out. Therefore, the rate at which material can be moved through the surface dictates, to some degree, the maximum size the cell can attain.

The third criterion is the rate of activity within the cell. A more quiescent cell does not place the demand on obtaining nutritional compounds that a highly active cell does, and as a result, a more slowly paced cell could theoretically be larger than its more active counterpart. Finally, the ability to control is the overriding factor. As long as the cell is capable of maintaining a homeostatic state through its regulatory mechanisms, cell size is no problem. When the control devices fail, the cell has exceeded its functional size.

At the other end of the spectrum, a fully functional cell cannot be less than a certain minimum in size. The necessity for packing in all of the macromolecules and molecules which are critical to function precludes the cell's being extremely small. It has been proposed that smaller cells such as bacteria have multifunctional enzymes that overcome this size difficulty.

Cell shape

Imagine any geometric or quasigeometric figure. There is probably a cell that corresponds to it in shape. The unicellular forms probably have the greatest variety of shapes because they are not in close contact with other cells when they develop. Most cells spurn the simple sphere as a shape, but there are several whose shape approaches this basic figure. Most cells have experimented with a variety of shapes ranging from the amorphous blob of some of the amebas to the elaborate, stalked structures of some of the algae.

Several factors control the shape of organisms. Plant cells and protozoans with rigid outer walls can maintain more definite and ageometric shapes. Most animal cells and some plant cells have more pliable outer coverings. Their shape is controlled more by physical laws such as the law of minimal surface tension. The characteristic shape of cells can be modified by changing the environment in which they exist. For example, the addition of a compound which reduces surface tension causes many cells to assume a basic shape that more nearly resembles the sphere. In multicellular forms, an important factor in cell shape is the location of the cell in respect to surrounding cells. Cells packed tightly together in layers or sheets have characteristic shapes which differ from cells which are isolated from each other by a semirigid matrix. The design of the latter is much more flexible.

The activities which cell types perform also affect their shape. Motile cells, for example, need a different shape from that of sessile or immobile cells.

Specialized cell features

Many cells develop structural characteristics which are so specialized that they are more than just an aspect of the general shape.

Consider the various modifications for motility which are seen in the cell. Cilia and flagella are found at all levels in both animals and plants. Elongate

Table 2-2. Diversity of cell type as indicated by some derivatives of undifferentiated cells

Undifferentiated cell	Differentiated derivatives
Procambium	Cambial cells
	Parenchyma
	Sclereids
	Fibers
	Tracheids
	Sieve cells
Mesenchyme	Blood cells
	Chondroblasts
	Osteoblasts
	Fibroblasts
	Muscle cells: striated, visceral, and cardiac

rhizoids of sessile cells are no less a modification. Fenestrations in the tracheid walls and arborization of neurons are further examples.

Specializations such as these are unique to many cell types and reflect the function and evolution of these cells. Variations of all types exist, and thus depicting of a simple, typical cell is impossible. Diversity, however, is part of the life plan (Table 2-2).

MICROANATOMY OF THE CELL

In spite of the many aberrations and innovations in the external morphology of most cells from the "typical cell," the microanatomy of all cells shares some common features. Differentiation of the internal anatomical features is less extreme than variations in the external structure. This is because all cells must undergo the same basic processes in order to survive, a fact which necessitates more unification of microanatomy.

All cells have some outer, delimiting membrane; most, in addition, have a nucleus and a series of specialized organelles. The internal features include such structures as the endoplasmic reticulum and microsomal fraction, the Golgi body, the lysosomes, the mitochondria, the centrosomes, and an assortment of vesicles, plastids, or inclusions. All of these have been described in satisfactory detail in intact cells (Plate 1, p. 303).

The nucleus appears almost amorphous upon staining, at least in the resting cell. The only visible structures are the nucleolus and nuclear membrane. The chromosomal material is dispersed throughout the proteinaceous matrix of the nucleus. Only when the cell gets ready to divide are the chromosomes visible in a stained cell. It is at this point that they clump into distinctive shapes.

The elaborate membrane system of the cell involves three of the cell organelles. The bulk of the membranes belong to the endoplasmic reticulum. This reticulum courses throughout the cell. The membranes are so aligned as to appear to be in channels. Parallel rows of membranes characterize a cluster known as the Golgi body. Small vesicles of membranes similar, or identical, to these are called the lysosomes (Plate 2, p. 304).

Distinct, double-membraned, large particles in the cell are the mitochondria. These organelles, the largest cytoplasmic structures in animal cells and second only to the chloroplasts of plant cells in size, are characterized by a double wall whose inner layer is folded into fingerlike projections in the center of the organelle (Plate 3, p. 305).

Other structures that can be seen microscopically are the centrosomes, which are related to the cilia and flagella, pinocytotic vesicles, or infoldings of the plasma membrane, and plastids or vacuoles of various kinds. All material not seen to have a particulate structure is called matrix.

The morphological characteristics just described are those that can be "seen" through microscopes, inclusive of a light microscope to an electron microscope. Determination of the function of these structures cannot be done with microscopes alone. There are two basic methods for correlating the function of a structure with the structure as viewed through a microscope.

When it is applicable, cytochemistry is an excellent tool to specifically locate various enzymes and other molecular components, using staining techniques. With the light microscope, dyes are used to localize the various substances. At the more refined level of the electron microscope, material which locates substances by making them appear more electron dense is used. The light and dark areas on an electron photomicrograph result from the relative density of the material to the electron beam (Plate 1, p. 303). The search continues for materials with which to localize particular substances. The technique is limited by the sparsity of such substances.

The second widely used tool is separation of cellular components by breaking the cell apart and differentially centrifuging the resulting mixture. The result is an operational fraction which can be equated with fair accuracy to structural units of the cell. The fractionation procedure and the medium used vary and different results are achieved with different procedures and media. For any given procedure and medium, the separation is reproducible.

The large particulate matter of the cell can be separated with relative ease. At low *g* forces, the nuclei spin down quite readily. The nuclear fraction is free from most contamination. That which does occur comes from materials that stick to the nuclear membrane. At higher speeds, the chloroplasts and then the mitochondria come down. The range in size of the mitochondria makes it very difficult to free that fraction from contamination.

At still higher speeds, the microsomal fraction spins down. During the early use of this technique and before the advent of high-resolution electron microscopes, the microsomal fraction was considered to contain distinct structures called *microsomes*. As techniques improved, it was discovered that the microsome fraction was actually a mixture of small mitochondria, lysosomes, membranes of the endoplasmic reticulum with associated ribosomes, and Golgi bodies. More precise centrifugation removes the mitochondria, but the other components remain. The term *microsomal fraction* is an operational definition, and activities purported to be associated with this fraction may actually be in any of the components of the fraction. Most of the materials in the microsomal fraction, however, are components of the intracellular membrane system.

The material which remains after the microsomal fraction has been centrifuged out is called the supernatant and contains the soluble components of the cell—lipoids and small macromolecules which do not spin down because of their smaller size.

Once any of these fractions is isolated, biochemical studies can be performed on it. The assay for enzyme content and physiochemical properties can be determined, and the structural units of the cell can thus be analyzed for their biochemical characteristics.

FUNCTIONS OF THE CELL

The cell is a physiological unit as well as a structural one, which means that it can perform physiological activities which are different from any single subcellular structure alone. It is a well-known fact in chemistry that each level of organization has properties different from its component parts. The actions and activities of potassium chloride are distinct from the properties of potassium or chlorine alone. This tenet holds true throughout the hierarchy of biology, as well. A macromolecule performs differently from the individual molecules in its makeup. By extension, the intact cell must have processes different from any single part of the whole. This fact is one which must be kept in mind when the function of the individual subcellular structures is determined. A structure may not behave in exactly the same manner as the whole, integrated cell.

The basic functions of the cell were outlined in Chapter 1. The biochemical basis and mechanisms of the cellular processes, the functions of the subcellular structures, and their ramifications will be explored in the remainder of the book.

General references

Bayliss, L. E. 1960. Principles of general physiology. 5th ed. John Wiley & Sons, Inc., New York. Vol. 2.

Bourne, G. H. 1951. Cytology and cell physiology. 2nd ed. Oxford University Press, London.

Brachet, J. 1961. The living cell. Sci. Am. (Sept.) p. 50.

Brachet, J., and A. E. Mirsky (editors). 1959-1961. The cell. Academic Press, Inc., New York. 6 vol.

Davson, H. 1959. A textbook of general physiology. 2nd ed. Little, Brown & Co., Boston.

DeRobertis, E. L. P., W. W. Nowinski, and F. A. Saez. 1965. Cell biology. 4th ed. W. B. Saunders Co., Philadelphia.

Giese, A. C. 1962. Cell physiology. 2nd ed. W. B. Saunders Co., Philadelphia.

Kuyper, Ch. M. A. 1962. The organization of cellular activity. Elsevier Publishing Co., New York.

Langley, L. L. 1961. Cell function. Reinhold Publishing Corp., New York.

Loewy, A. G., and P. Siekevitz. 1963. Cell structure and function. Holt, Rinehart & Winston, New York.

Picken, L. 1960. The organization of cells. Oxford University Press, London.

Swanson, C. P. 1960. The cell. Prentice-Hall, Inc., Englewood Cliffs, N. J.

Waddington, C. H. 1959. Biological organisation. Pergamon Press, Inc., New York.

3

Cell physiology—past, present, and future

INTRODUCTION

Cell physiology is a field with a short past, a dynamic present, and an exciting future. One of the youngest branches of the biological sciences, cell physiology has exploded to occupy a prominent position in the overall picture of biology. The major frontiers are in this field, but only because there are more unknowns to uncover. Study of the cell has come a long way from the cell theory.

Molecular biology has many connotations, but its strictest meaning is the explanation of living processes at the molecular level. Cell physiology lends itself to investigation at the molecular level. The macromolecules of the cell have attractive properties for study; their most provocative characteristic for the inquiring scientist is their total disrespect for the laws which govern most material. The physical properties of macromolecules are so unique that an entire area of biocolloids was created to investigate their physical laws. Macromolecules do not obey all of the chemical laws either. Reactions proceed which appear thermodynamically unfeasible; the basic system in which biology operates is different from chemical systems (open versus closed). The biological structure has not been completely revealed. As a result, a multidisciplinary approach is necessary to unlock the many secrets of the cell.

All living things have a past, a present, and a future. Cell physiology is a living, dynamic entity; it has a history, it is a vital force, and it will be an area of ever-increasing excitement and reward.

THE PAST

The history of any field of science serves two important purposes. As an introduction to the subject, a historical account gives an insight into the general trends and major ideas through which the field has progressed from inception to the present. To one who is acquainted with the field, the history offers an interesting survey of what has transpired, and in retrospect, historical facts can more easily be placed in their proper perspective.

Theories, facts, ideas, and investigators were all borrowed from the various disciplines when cell physiology was established as a separate facet of the life sciences. The history reflects this divergent background. Scientists associated with major ideas of cell physiology often had had their training in either some other phase of biology or, as was often the case, in physics and chemistry. Although the roots of cell physiology suggest a spurious existence, the field has become fixed as a legitimate science.

The development of such a science depends on the intuition, drive, and insight of many men and women. In a capsule summary such as this, it is impossible to name all of the investigators who have contributed to the field. All legitimate facts and ideas, regardless of their scope, add to the core of knowledge. Major ideas could not have been spawned without the background of information from other sources. Each new bit of information and each new technique added another facet and opened the way for new ideas and theories.

The story of the confluence of the various disciplines into the new field of cell physiology is fascinating, and the major trends and developments over the years are indeed noteworthy. These will briefly be discussed. Since as we have just said, it is impossible to list all who participated in the development of the present state of knowledge, only those whose contributions were of such significance as to merit reward will be named (Table 3-1). These men and women and their achievements reflect the progress of cell physiology during the past decades.

Cytological studies

As in many biological disciplines, cell physiology derived its first segment of knowledge from recognition of the structure of the cell. Before the advent of the magnifying glass and the microscope, the smallest structures known to man were those which he could see with the naked eye. Robert Hooke and Antoni van Leeuwenhoek changed that. Establishment of the cell as a basic structural unit of life (the *cell theory* of Schleiden and Schwann) and as a continuum of life (*"Ommis cellula e cellula,"* as Virchow stated) provided the impetus needed to initiate morphological investigations at the cellular level. Painstaking early work had surprising results. By the turn of the century, most of the subcellular particles had been described in detail. As microscopes improved and their resolution became better, the details could be refined more and more. The phase and interference microscopes aided the study of living cells. Contrasts of internal structure could finally be attained without the use of dyes. Cells could thus be seen in their natural state and could be compared with stained specimens. Resolution remained the major problem, however. All of these microscopes were limited in the depth to which they could probe the cell. The ultraviolet microscope partially alleviated the problem, but the electron microscope ranks right behind the light microscope as the major contribution to morphological study of the cell. A whole new world opened up when this instru-

Table 3-1. Nobel Prizewinners who have contributed to the field of cell physiology

Year	Nobel recipient	Field	Cited contribution	Importance to cell physiology
1901	W. K. Roentgen	Physics	Discovery of x-rays	Provided tool for research
1901	J. H. van't Hoff	Chemistry	Elucidated laws of chemical dynamics and osmosis	Gave background for quantitative approach to kinetics of reactions; allowed application of osmotic laws to biological membranes
1902	E. Fischer	Chemistry	Structural analysis of sugars and purines	Provided basis for carbohydrate chemistry
1903	A. Becquerel, P. Curie, and M. Curie	Physics	Discovery of radioactivity and study of uranium	Opened new field of research
1903	S. A. Arrhenius	Chemistry	Theory of ionization in electrolytes	Contributed to understanding of chemical reactions
1906	C. Golgi and S. Ramón y Cajal	Physiology	Structure of nerve tissue	Described internal structure of cell in great detail (classic description)
1907	E. Buchner	Chemistry	Discovered fermentation by means of zymase occurs without whole cell	First work hinting at enzyme as area of study
1908	E. Rutherford	Chemistry	Radioactive particles	Gave impetus to field of radiation research
1909	W. Ostwald	Chemistry	Studies of catalysis, chemical equilibria, and reaction rates	Contributed to understanding of chemical reactions; provided basis for later studies on proteins as catalysts
1910	A. Kossel	Physiology	Chemistry of cell	Among first to use cell as research area
1912	P. Sabatier	Chemistry	Methods of hydrogenating organic compounds	Impetus to organic synthesis
1914	M. von Laue	Physics	X-ray diffraction	Technique useful in determining structures of macromolecules
1915	R. Willstätter	Chemistry	Studies on chlorophyll	Basic work on pigments
1918	M. Planck	Physics	Quantum theory	Applications in all fields
1920	W. Nernst	Chemistry	Heat changes during chemical reactions	Fundamental thermodynamics; also worked in electropotentials on membrane
1921	A. Einstein	Physics	Relativity; law of photoelectric effect	Work had impact on all fields
1921	F. Soddy	Chemistry	Research on isotopes	Foundations for isotope chemistry
1922	N. Bohr	Physics	Atomic structure and radiations	Widespread importance

Table 3-1. Nobel Prizewinners who have contributed to the field of cell physiology, cont'd

Year	Nobel recipient	Field	Cited contribution	Importance to cell physiology
1922	F. W. Aston	Chemistry	Discovery of many isotopes with mass spectrograph	Gave added impetus to isotope studies
1922	A. V. Hill and O. Meyerhof	Physiology	Discovered heat production in muscle Correlated oxygen use and production of lactic acid in muscle	Basic work on metabolism of cells
1923	F. Pregl	Chemistry	Microanalysis of organic compounds	Opened many doors to more refined work
1923	F. G. Banting, and J. J. R. Macleod	Physiology	Discovery of insulin	Showed that structure of protein not beyond determination
1925	R. Zsigmondy	Chemistry	Work on colloidal solutions	Basic work, quite definitive in some areas
1926	T. Svedburg	Chemistry	Work on dispersion systems	Definitive work; developed technique which provided more tools for research
1928	A. Windaus	Chemistry	Study of sterols and vitamins	Showed relationship between vitamins and sterols
1929	A. Harden and H. von Eulerchelpin	Chemistry	Study on sugar fermentation and enzymes	Gave impetus to pathway studies of carbohydrates
1930	H. Fischer	Chemistry	Work on porphyrins	Showed relationship between heme and chlorophyll
1931	O. Warburg	Physiology	Respiration studies	Contributed greatly to studies of enzymes involved in respiration
1932	I. Langmuir	Chemistry	Surface chemistry	Studies on surface phenomena applicable to enzymes
1932	C. Sherrington and E. D. Adrian	Physiology	Function of neuron	Description of functional aspect of single cell
1933	T. H. Morgan	Physiology	Chromosomes as hereditary units	Opened up field of genetics and cytogenetics
1936	P. J. W. Debye	Chemistry	Studies on molecular structure, dipole movements, and x-ray diffraction	Work applicable to many areas
1936	H. H. Dale and O. Loewi	Physiology	Discoveries on chemical transmission of nerve impulses	Work demonstrated that nerve impulses not only electric phenomena
1937	W. N. Haworth	Chemistry	Work on carbohydrates and vitamin C	Showed three-dimensional configuration of sugars

Continued.

Table 3-1. Nobel Prizewinners who have contributed to the field of cell physiology, cont'd

Year	Nobel recipient	Field	Cited contribution	Importance to cell physiology
1937	P. Karrer	Chemistry	Work on vitamins	Worked out structure of vitamins and showed requirement of cells for them
1937	A. Szent-Györgyi	Physiology	Discoveries on oxidations in tissues; discovered fumaric acid	Work led to many exciting discoveries in many areas
1943	G. von Hevesy	Chemistry	Use of isotopes as chemical indicators	Added to radiobiological techniques
1944	J. Erlanger and H. S. Gasser	Physiology	Work on different functions of a single nerve fiber	Added to knowledge of nerve physiology
1946	J. B. Sumner	Chemistry	Crystallization of enzymes	Classical work done in 1927 on crystallization of urease
1946	J. H. Northrup and W. M. Stanley	Chemistry	Preparation of enzymes in pure form and crystallization of viruses	Showed that proteins could be crystallized and still maintain activity
1946	H. J. Muller	Physiology	Discovered that x-rays can produce mutations	Opened up wide field of genetic research
1947	C. F. Cori and G. Cori	Physiology	Discovered action of insulin on sugar metabolism	Proof of external factors affecting metabolism of cells
1948	A. Tiselius	Chemistry	Biochemical discoveries	Gave many techniques to field
1952	A. J. P. Martin and R. L. M. Synge	Chemistry	Identification and separation of chemicals by chromatography	Gave invaluable tool to field
1953	F. Zernike	Physics	Phase-contrast microscope	Great tool for cytological studies
1953	H. Staudinger	Chemistry	Studies on large molecules	Techniques applicable to biological molecules
1953	F. Lipmann and H. A. Krebs	Physiology	Work in biosynthesis	Invaluable work on Krebs cycle and importance of phosphates (Lipmann)
1954	L. C. Pauling	Chemistry	Basic research on structure of protein	First to appreciate secondary and tertiary structure of protein
1955	A. du Vigneaud	Chemistry	Synthesis of hormones	Synthesis of biologically active protein
1958	F. Sanger	Chemistry	Determined sequence of amino acids in insulin	Showed that chemical techniques can give precise structure of proteins

Table 3-1. Nobel Prizewinners who have contributed to the field of cell physiology, cont'd

Year	Nobel recipient	Field	Cited contribution	Importance to cell physiology
1958	G. W. Beadle, E. L. Tatum, and J. Lederberg	Physiology	Contributions to genetics	Cytogenetics and biochemical genetics
1959	S. Ochoa and A. Kornberg	Physiology	Synthesis of nucleic acids	Gave impetus to molecular genetics
1961	M. Calvin	Chemistry	Work in photosynthesis	Showed relationship of carbon compounds of photosynthesis and those of common pathways
1962	M. F. Perutz and J. C. Kendrew	Chemistry	Structures of globular protein	Opened door to correlation between molecular structures and function
1962	J. Watson, F. Crick, and M. Wilkins	Physiology	Structure of DNA	Classical work; basis for many areas of investigation
1963	A. L. Hodgkin, A. F. Huxley, and J. C. Eccles	Physiology	Worked on nerve impulses and synapses	Structure-function at subcellular level
1964	C. Block and F. Lynen	Physiology	Cholesterol and fatty acid metabolism	Further elucidation of specific metabolic pathways
1965	A. Lwoff, J. Monad, and F. Jacob	Physiology	Studies on control of bacterial enzyme synthesis	Great impact on developmental biology

ment was introduced. The lower limits of the light microscope became the upper limits of the electron microscope. Once limited to describing the larger subcellular particles, cytologists were now able to look at macromolecules. The phrase "fine structure of the cell" began to mean just that. Morphological studies progressed from the excitement of being able to see a cell to the delight of describing deoxyribonucleic acid (DNA) molecules and aggregates of enzymes. The time span has been short, but the cytologists were just waiting for the tools with which to work.

Biochemical studies

The biochemical studies of the cell parallel the development of the interest in respiration. The requirement of oxygen for living things had been established for some time before the cell was used as a tool to investigate the ramifications of this need. Discovery of the many compounds having an effect on the metabolism of the cell was one facet of study. Isolation and determination of the structure of cytochromes and other molecular components had great impact. Coupling of respiration to the production of the ubiquitous high-energy compound adenosine triphosphate (ATP) was another breakthrough in understanding of the processes of the cell. Elucidation of common pathways, their steps and energetics, opened another door for investigation. Early hints concerning the mechanism of photosynthesis from studies on bacteria led to uncovering of the carbon pathway and some theories on the mechanism of transfer from light to chemical energy. All of these avenues, and many more, converged toward the heart of cell physiology today—corollation of structure and function.

THE PRESENT

Cell physiology today still investigates along morphological and biochemical lines, but the new challenge, that of synthesizing these bodies of knowledge into a unified approach to the study of the cell, is being met. The realization that in vivo biochemical reactions may be different from in vitro reactions emphasizes the importance which structure has to the cell. Isolation studies are necessary to find out what kinds of reactions occur, but the discovery of how they occur depends on the structural aspects of the cell. Paradoxically, to understand how the cell works at the level of the whole cell it is necessary to understand its function at the molecular level. Investigations are progressing in two directions. On the one hand is the intense search for the molecular and macromolecular configurations of the functional elements in the cell. The concept of molecular biology incorporates these investigations into the study of the phenomena at the molecular level. At the other extreme is the attempt to reconstruct the structure and function of the intact cell. Extrapolation of the results to the whole cell can be made only when there is knowledge in depth of the molecular mechanisms.

THE FUTURE

To predict the roads that the study of cell physiology will take in the next few decades is difficult indeed. A new technological advance may open up avenues not even considered at the present. When we look back at the impact made by the electron microscope, radioisotopes, and the ultracentrifuge, it is apparent that techniques determine to a great extent the ways that investigative processes follow. However, some generalizations are possible. The present trend in which the cell is put back together from pieces of biochemical and morphological data will continue. After determining what behaviors an individual intact cell undergoes, scientists will want to find out what forces, biological and nonbiological, modify its activity. A precise cellular ecological approach may result, shifting back to biological emphasis but endowed with past biochemical and biophysical knowledge. This may be far in the future, because there are still many areas of uncertainty at the molecular level. But the field is progressing rapidly, and ten years from now the approach to the study of cell physiology may not be "The Cell—chemistry and function."

General references

Annual review of physiology. 1950-1965. Annual Reviews, Inc., Palo Alto, Calif. Vol. 12-27.
Franklin, K. J. 1949. A short history of physiology. Staples Press, Ltd., London.
Singer, C. 1950. A history of biology. Henry Schuman, Inc., Publishers, New York.

Section **II**

Biochemistry of the cell constituents

While studying the protozoans of the *Sarcodina* and *Foraminifera,* the famous French biologist DuJardin once described the contents of the cell as a "perfectly homogeneous, elastic, contractile, diaphanous, gelatinous substance, insoluble in water and without traces of organization." An elemental acquaintance with the constituents of the cell led to this misconception. The increasing realization that the cell is composed of individual molecular constituents which have precise functions has provided the basis for modern concepts of the contents of the cell.

When a group of elements and compounds are so arranged as to have the attributes of life, the resulting mixture may be called protoplasm. Even this panacean protoplasmic theory falls short of giving full appreciation of the complexity and importance of the individual molecular constituents of the cell.

The characteristics and basic chemistry of the primary cell constituents are given in this section. Carbohydrates, lipids, proteins, purines, pyrimidines, nucleic acids, porphyrins, quinones, and several miscellaneous compounds are discussed in that order. These components of the cell provide the chemical framework in which the biological processes occur.

4

Carbohydrates

INTRODUCTION

The carbohydrates are an important class of compounds for the cell because they offer not only the major source of energy for the metabolic pathways, but also a structural unit for some of the cell organelles. The traditional reasons for considering the carbohydrates first are that their chemistry is relatively easy to understand and that some basic ideas which will be helpful in the study of the other organic compounds are presented. The intricate involvement of carbohydrates in the metabolism of the cell provides additional motivation for study.

Carbohydrates can be defined as polyhydroxylic aldehydes and ketones including those compounds which are derivatives or polymers of these two forms. The basic nomenclature of the carbohydrates is both confusing and overlapping. The three general criteria upon which classification is based are as follows:

1. The number of single units in the molecule
2. The number of carbon atoms in the compound
3. The potential or actual presence of either an aldehyde or a ketone group

For example, a carbohydrate which is a single sugar unit is known as a monosaccharide. As we add more sugar units, the compounds are known as either oligosaccharides or polysaccharides. The etymology of *oligo-* (a few) and *poly-* (many) indicates the relative complexity of these groups. To apply the second criterion, we can say that if the monosaccharide unit has three carbon atoms it is called a triose; four, a tetrose; five, a pentose; and six, a hexose. Further complexities in nomenclature will be pointed out as we consider in some detail the structure of the individual carbohydrates.

MONOSACCHARIDES

The empirical formula for the monosaccharides is $C_nH_{2n}O_n$. Although formaldehyde, acetic acid, and hydroxyacetaldehyde conform to this empirical formula,

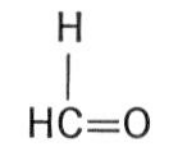

$$
\begin{array}{ccc}
& & H\ \ O \\
& & |\ \ \| \\
H & & HC\text{—}COH \\
| & & | \\
HC\text{=}O & & H
\end{array}
\qquad
\begin{array}{c}
H \\
| \\
C\text{=}O \\
| \\
CH_2OH
\end{array}
$$

Formaldehyde 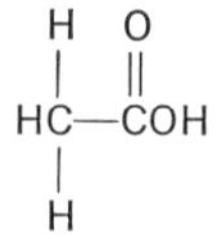   Acetic acid 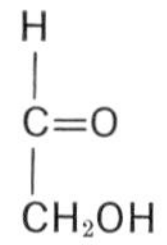   Hydroxyacetaldehyde

the smallest molecules designated as true carbohydrates are glyceraldehyde and dihydroxyacetone.

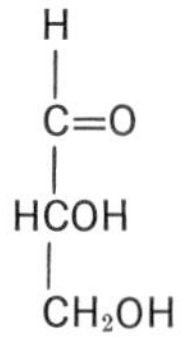

$$
\begin{array}{c}
H \\
| \\
C\text{=}O \\
| \\
HCOH \\
| \\
CH_2OH
\end{array}
\qquad\qquad
\begin{array}{c}
CH_2OH \\
| \\
C\text{=}O \\
| \\
CH_2OH
\end{array}
$$

Glyceraldehyde 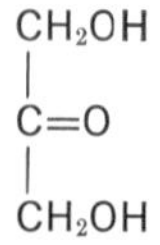   Dihydroxyacetone

Note that the two sugars depicted are the only possible trioses, as the carbonyl group must be either ketonic, as on the second carbon, or aldehydic, as on either end carbon.

If these trioses are considered typical saccharides, certain characteristics of the whole group are revealed. First, the carbon skeleton is unbranched. This is the most typical situation since very few deviate from this linear arrangement of the carbon atoms. Second, each carbon has a hydroxyl group, with the exception of one, in which the remaining carbon atom bears a carbonyl oxygen. This carbonyl oxygen may be on the terminal carbon, giving an aldehyde, or it may be on a central carbon, giving a ketone. Most commonly, the ketone arrangement is found on the penultimate, or next to the end, carbon.

Glucose, the common hexose monosaccharide, will be considered in discussion of structure and reactions of this group of carbohydrates. This aldehydic hexose is probably the most important physiological sugar. Its chemistry not only serves as a model for the other saccharides, but also reflects the versatility of this particular compound. With a molecular formula of $C_6H_{12}O_6$, the structural formula may be written in a straight chain configuration, as shown below.

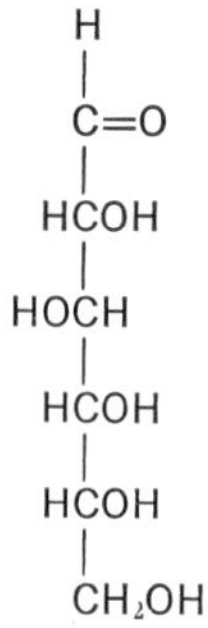

$$
\begin{array}{c}
H \\
| \\
C\text{=}O \\
| \\
HCOH \\
| \\
HOCH \\
| \\
HCOH \\
| \\
HCOH \\
| \\
CH_2OH
\end{array}
$$

Glucose

Two facts are particularly striking when this structure is examined. First, it can be noted that in the case of the four central carbon atoms a different group is attached to each of the four bonds on the carbon; that is, the carbons are asymmetrical. Second, since the exact placement of the hydroxyl groups is an important characteristic of individual saccharides, there must be many compounds with the molecular formula of $C_6H_{12}O_6$. These two observations are the basis for the study of isomerism, a physiochemical or configurational difference that turns out to make a definite biological difference.

Isomerism

Isomerism, by definition, is the condition of having identical molecular composition but different chemical or physical properties, and the compounds having these properties are known as isomers. It is the presence of these asymmetric carbon atoms in a compound which makes possible the formation of isomers of that same compound. Since the molecules are three-dimensional, the four bonds around these centers of asymmetry project into space at different angles. The groups on these bonds may be arranged potentially to give similar compounds, but simple experimentation with modeling clay and sticks shows that they are in fact not identical, but are mirror images of each other; that is, there exists left and right compounds (Fig. 4-1). Such compounds which have the same molecular weight but a different structural or spatial configuration are called stereoisomers, geometric isomers, and enantiomorphs.

Stereoisomerism

The number of possible stereoisomers of a compound depends on the number of asymmetric carbon atoms. According to the rule of "n" as described by van't Hoff, if n represents the number of asymmetric carbons, then the number 2^n equals the total number of isomers. Thus, glucose, with four asymmetric carbon atoms, would have sixteen possible isomers, eight of which belong to the so-called D series (for dextro, right) and eight belonging to the L series (levo,

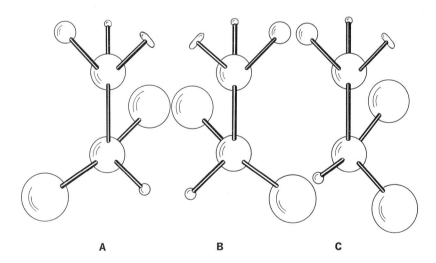

A   B   C

Fig. 4-1. Diagrammatic representation of three different geometric isomers. Notice that **A** and **B** are mirror images of each other; thus, they are not superimposable.

left). In effect, we have both a right-hand and a left-hand series since the rule for telling a D-sugar from an L-sugar is that the center of asymmetry most remote from the aldehyde end of the molecule, which in hexoses is carbon 5, determines the configuration. For example, D-glucose and L-glucose are written as follows:

<pre>
        H   H
        | |
        C=O   C=O
        | |
       HCOH   HOCH
        | |
       HOCH   HCOH
        | |
       HCOH   HOCH
        | |
       HCOH   HOCH
        | |
       CH₂OH   CH₂OH
     D-Glucose   L-Glucose
</pre>

When the —OH of the compound is on the right of this center of asymmetry, the sugar is one of the D series; when it is on the left, it is a member of the L series. Notice that if just the fifth carbon hydroxyl and hydrogen were shifted the compound is no longer glucose but becomes one of the eight stereoisomers of glucose, in this case L-idose.

Of the sixteen possible stereoisomers of glucose, very few occur naturally in the cell. Most biological systems discriminate against the L-sugars and show a preference for the D forms. Those occurring most frequently in addition to D-glucose are D-mannose and D-galactose.

Optical isomerism

The presence of asymmetric carbon atoms also confers optical isomerism on the compound. Optical isomerism is that peculiar effect which solutions of such an isomer have on polarized light. If a beam of polarized light, which has electromagnetic waves vibrating in only one plane, is passed through a solution which shows optical isomerism, the beam will be rotated to the right or left in accordance with the type of compound present. An isomeric compound which causes rotation of polarized light to the right is said to be dextrorotatory and a plus (+) sign is used to designate members of this group. Rotation of the beam to the left, called levorotatory action, is designated by a minus (−) sign.

When equal amounts of the dextrorotatory and levorotatory isomers are present, the resulting compound has no optical activity and is said to be racemic. All synthetically produced compounds are racemic since the opportunity to form both classes is equal. However, biological systems again discriminate in both the use and formation of optical isomers. Some organisms use the levorotatory forms and others use the dextrorotatory isomers. Since individual biological systems show this preference for one form or the other, it is necessary to resolve these synthetic racemic mixtures if the cells are to be exposed to an artificial medium of only one isomer. Although there are now many techniques of separation, one of the most interesting methods of resolving racemic mixtures is to expose the compound to a microorganism that can metabolize only the $(+)$ or $(-)$ form, not both. The material that remains will then be optically active.

There is some confusion in the nomenclature of isomers. In the literature d and l are sometimes used to indicate dextrorotation and levorotation. However, it has become standard practice to use plus and minus signs for optical isomerism and D and L to indicate configurational relationships among the sugars. It should be pointed out here that the two types of isomerism, stereoisomerism and optical isomerism, are independent properties. That is, a compound may be a D-sugar configurationally and still show a minus type of optical isomerism.

The cell exerts fairly careful control of the classes of isomers which get into the internal medium. Abnormal isomers do occasionally penetrate, but the presence of these is not usually damaging. An accumulation of the wrong isomers, however, could influence the production of abnormal structures. This condition would be damaging!

Because abnormal isomers such as D-amino acids or L-sugars can inflict damage to the cell and its metabolic processes, many such isomers are found as functional components of antibiotics.

Configurations

Although the phenomenon of isomerism is a very real thing, writing of the structural and configurational formulas of the sugars is in part arbitrary. Various degrees of shorthand are used to depict those characteristics of the molecule which seem to be important to the particular context in which they are being used. In Figs. 4-2 and 4-3, the aldose and ketose sugars are represented by the straight chain structure.

At one time this straight chain structure *did* show all that was known about these sugars. The precise structural configurations were predicted and elucidated in these sugars by reactions with the very reactive hydroxyl groups. However, when two different species of D-glucose were prepared, each with a different optical rotation, it was apparent that some additional asymmetry was placed on the molecule. The locus of this asymmetry was found to be at the 1, or aldehyde, carbon. Here, then, were two isomers of D-glucose, both dextrorotatory, but with different optical properties. These two forms, designated alpha (α) D-glucose and beta (β) D-glucose, were due to a cyclic structure of the sugar. Alpha and beta D-glucose could then be written as follows:

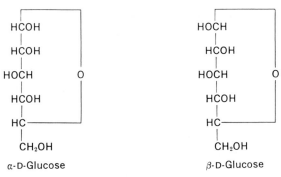

α-D-Glucose   β-D-Glucose

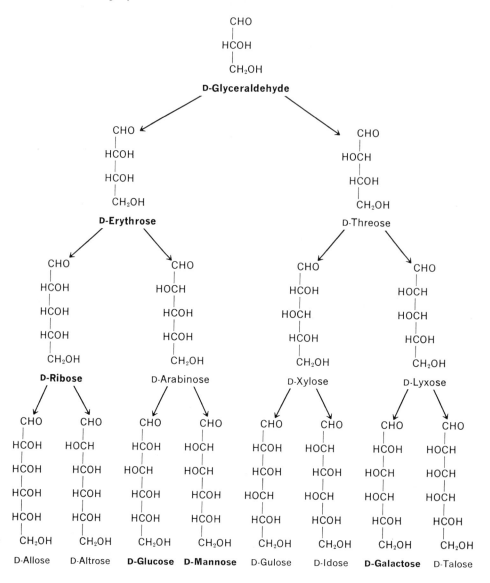

Fig. 4-2. Aldose sugars depicted in the D-configuration. Those of greatest physiological importance are set in boldface Roman type.

Further experimentation indicated that these two distinct stereoisomeric modifications of D-glucose could be interconverted in aqueous solution. This phenomenon, known as mutorotation, is a general phenomenon of sugars and has been observed in almost all forms. The oxygen bridge between the first and fifth carbon atoms results in two modifications of our original straight chain representation of glucose. First, there is now a fifth center of asymmetry, yielding 32 possible isomers of glucose. Second, the molecule now contains a six-membered ring which is pyranlike, and sugars containing this ring are called pyranoses.

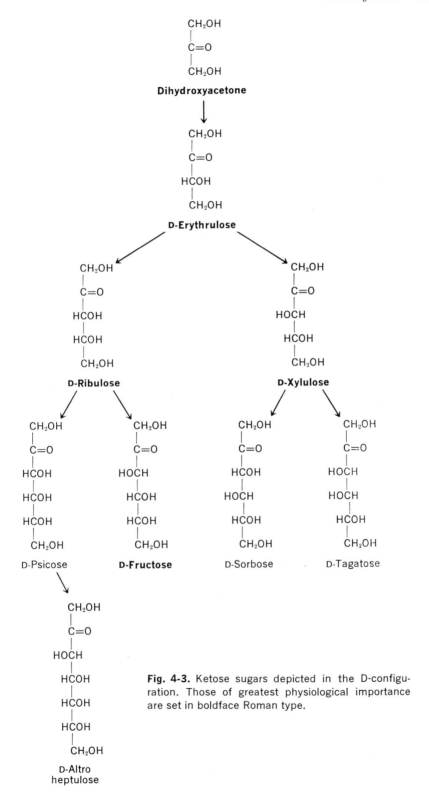

Fig. 4-3. Ketose sugars depicted in the D-configuration. Those of greatest physiological importance are set in boldface Roman type.

Because of all the reactive hydroxyl groups on these monosaccharides, there are theoretically many different types of ring structures, but the six-membered pyran ring and five-membered furan ring are the ones normally found. Fructose, because of the carbonyl oxygen in the ketone form, can occur as both a pyranose and a furanose.

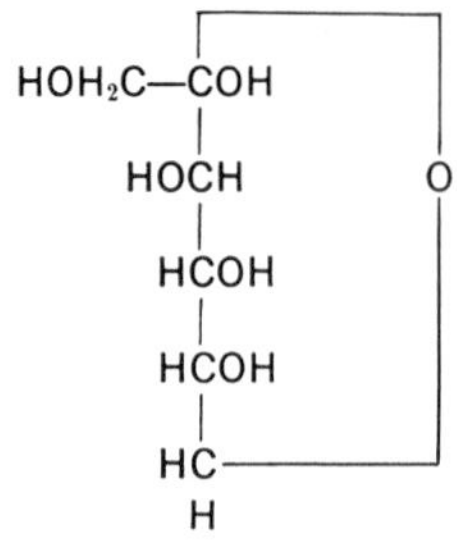

HOH$_2$C—COH
|
HOCH   O
|
HCOH
|
HCOH
|
HC
|
H

α-D-Fructopyranose

HOH$_2$C—COH
|
HOCH   O
|
HCOH
|
HC
|
CH$_2$OH

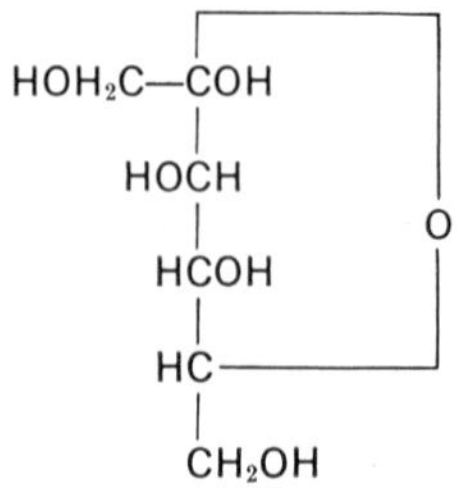

α-D-Fructofuranose

It is not possible to depict a three-dimensional molecule in two dimensions completely. The representation of the sugar molecules by a hexagon for the pyran ring and a pentagon for the furan ring does have the advantage of showing the relationships between the groups more accurately.

Alpha-D-glucopyranose and beta-D-fructofuranose may be written in the Haworth formulation as follows:

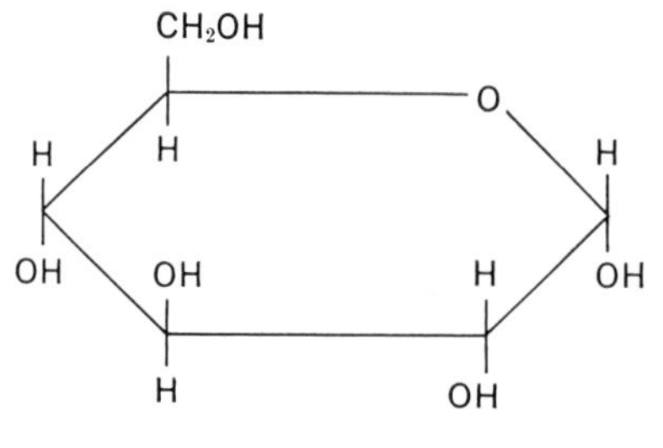

CH$_2$OH

H   H   O   H

OH   OH   H   OH

H   OH

α-D-Glucopyranose

O

HOH$_2$C   OH

H   H   OH   CH$_2$OH

OH   H

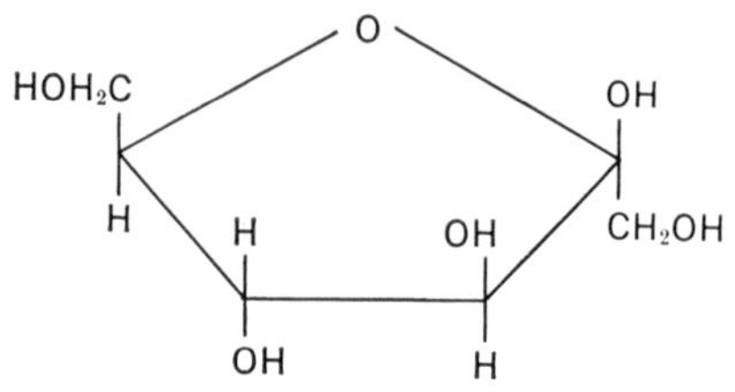

β-D-Fructofuranose

According to the scheme set up by Haworth, the components of the pyran or furan ring are imagined in one plane at right angles to the plane of the paper. The hydrogens and hydroxyls project either above or below this plane. In the standard situation, the bonds directed upward or above the plane correspond to left in the straight chain formula, and those directed downward or below the plane correspond to right in the straight chain formula. In addition, on a plane between the first and fourth carbon there is a bend, so that if the model were cut out from the paper and creased on a line connecting the first and fourth carbons, a clearer three-dimensional picture could be obtained. The molecular structure of the monosaccharides is best represented by these Haworth models, or by the "chair" or "boat" models, but the other representations are still used interchangeably.

Basic reactions

Concerning the reactions of these sugars, all the models plainly show the presence of many reactive hydroxyl groups. In addition, there is the carbonyl oxygen which is highly active, whether it is in the aldehyde form or involved in the oxygen bridge. As a result, many derivatives can be made of these monosaccharides by simple oxidation or reduction of these groups. If the aldehyde group of an aldose is oxidized to a carboxyl group, the result is a glyconic acid. If the primary hydroxyl group at the other end is oxidized to the carboxyl group, another acid derivative, glycuronic acid, results. If both ends are oxidized, a dicarboxylic acid is formed, and the members of this group are called saccharic acids. On the other hand, the reduction of the aldehyde group to alcohol yields

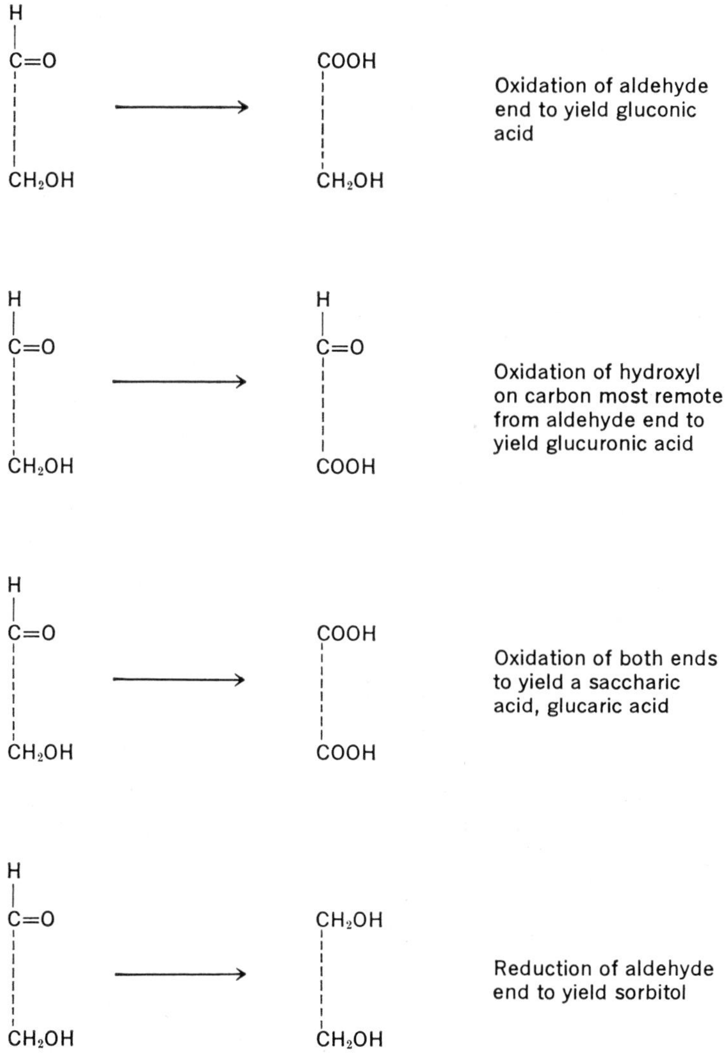

H
|
C=O   COOH
| | Oxidation of aldehyde
| ⟶ | end to yield gluconic
| | acid
| |
CH₂OH   CH₂OH

H   H
| |
C=O   C=O
| | Oxidation of hydroxyl
| ⟶ | on carbon most remote
| | from aldehyde end to
| | yield glucuronic acid
CH₂OH   COOH

H
|
C=O   COOH
| | Oxidation of both ends
| ⟶ | to yield a saccharic
| | acid, glucaric acid
| |
CH₂OH   COOH

H
|
C=O   CH₂OH
| | Reduction of aldehyde
| ⟶ | end to yield sorbitol
| |
| |
CH₂OH   CH₂OH

Fig. 4-4. Several reactions of aldehyde sugars, showing only the 1- and 6-carbons of glucose.

a polyhydric alcohol derivative of the sugar (Fig. 4-4). Changes on internal carbons also yield derivatives of the monosaccharides. For example, if one of the hydroxyl groups is replaced by an —NH_2 group, the result is an amine sugar. Other radicals may replace or add on also, but the group most commonly added is the amine.

The glycoside bond

When structures, bonds, and reactions of the monosaccharides are discussed, linkage must be considered. The glycoside bond is so important biologically that it is worthwhile to give it separate consideration.

If one considers just the aldehyde end of a sugar, it is apparent that it could potentially form two hydroxyl groups by the addition of water across the double bond. If one hydroxyl group is substituted, such as in the pyran and furan ring formation, a structure called a hemiacetal is formed, leaving one hydroxyl group unsubstituted. When a substitution is made with a compound outside of the structure itself, an acetal structure or glycosidic linkage results.

$$
\begin{array}{ccc}
\begin{array}{c}
\text{H} \\
| \\
\text{C=O} \\
| \\
\text{HCOH} \\
| \\
| \\
|
\end{array}
+\text{H}_2\text{O} \longrightarrow
\begin{array}{c}
\text{OH} \\
| \\
\text{HCOH} \\
| \\
\text{HCOH} \\
| \\
| \\
|
\end{array}
\longrightarrow
\begin{array}{c}
\text{HCOH} \\
| \\
\text{HCOH} \quad \text{O} \\
| \\
| \\
|
\end{array}
\end{array}
$$

Hemiacetal

For example, if a methyl group substitutes in this remaining hydroxyl, a glycosidic linkage is formed to give the compound methyl α-D-glucoside if glucose is the sugar involved.

$$
\begin{array}{c}
\text{HCOCH}_3 \\
| \\
\text{HCOH} \\
| \\
\text{HOCH} \quad \text{O} \\
| \\
\text{HCOH} \\
| \\
\text{HC} \\
| \\
\text{CH}_2\text{OH}
\end{array}
$$

Methyl α-D-glucoside (an acetal)

Glycoside linkage has biological importance for two reasons. Primarily, the polymers of the monosaccharides are formed through this linkage to yield the oligosaccharides and polysaccharides. The addition compound, however, does not have to be another sugar, but may be some nonsugar organic compound, to which, in this context, the term *aglycone* is applied. Many of the glycosides are important in physiology, particularly when the aglycone is a steroid. An example would be the plant derivative digitalis, a cardiac stimulant of vertebrates.

Enolization

One more important reaction deserves mention here. It is the interconversion of saccharides through enolization. In Fig. 4-5, it is seen that glucose is easily interconvertible with mannose and fructose by forming an intermediate structure known as the endiol form. This endiol form has obvious biological importance because it offers a simple mechanism for converting from one metabolic inter- mediate to another. Although enolization may involve epimers such as mannose and glucose, which differ only in the arrangement of the hydroxyl around one carbon, it also permits a shift from an aldehyde to a ketone, such as the conver- sion from glucose to fructose.

Many other carbohydrate reactions have biological importance. One is the phosphoric acid ester formation which occurs particularly on the end hydroxyl group. However, these specific reactions will be considered in more detail in the section on metabolism, where such esters have great importance.

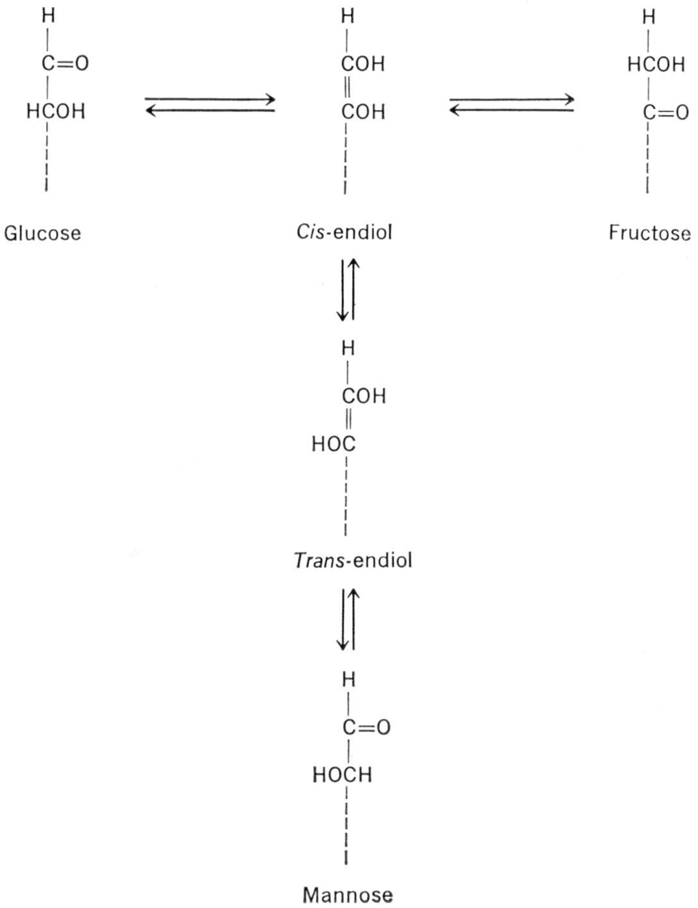

Fig. 4-5. Interconversion through enolization. Glucose and mannose are epimers in that they differ only in arrangement of groups around a single carbon, in this case carbon 2.

OLIGOSACCHARIDES

The oligosaccharides are those polymers of the monosaccharides which contain two to ten residues. The most commonly occurring oligosaccharides are the disaccharides which form the building blocks for the polysaccharides that occur in nature.

As it has been pointed out, the glycosidic bond is the linkage that joins one sugar fragment with another. Methylation and other similar techniques afford a complete blueprint of the structure of carbohydrates. Since the only specification of this glycoside bond is that one side of the linkage must come off from the carbonyl carbon as alpha or beta linkage, the other half of the linkage may be on any carbon of the second sugar. Potentially, then, there are many disaccharides.

The commercial sugar sucrose, which is made up of a glucose and a fructose, demonstrates glycoside linkage in the disaccharides.

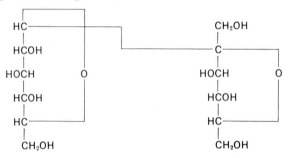

α-D-Glucopyranosyl – β-D-Fructofuranoside

It can be seen that the oxygen bridge of the glycoside goes from carbon 1 in the glucose to carbon 2 of the fructose, involving both carbonyls. Notice that there are no active carbonyl groups, and thus this sugar is known as a non-reducing sugar and cannot be tested for by the usual Benedict and Fehling tests.

Two disaccharides with great biological importance are maltose, or α-D-glucopyranosyl–1,4-α(or β)-D-glucopyranoside, the repeating unit in starch, and cellobiose, or β-D-glucopyranosyl–1,4-β-D-glucopyranoside, the repeating unit in cellulose.

Maltose

Notice the very subtle difference between these two disaccharides. Cellobiose, however, is nonmetabolizable in animals, where maltose, of course, is a major energy source. This gives an idea of the extreme specificity of the enzymes which are inherent in any one group of animals or plants.

Cellobiose

Other disaccharides of lesser importance include the following:
1. Lactose, or β-ᴅ-galactopyranosyl—1,4-β-ᴅ-glucopyranoside
2. Isomaltose, or α-ᴅ-glucopyranosyl—1,6-α-ᴅ-glucopyranoside
3. Gentioboise, or β-ᴅ-glucopyranosyl—1,6-β-ᴅ-glucopyranoside
4. Trehalose, a 1,1-α-glucosyl, glucose

POLYSACCHARIDES

Since polysaccharides are more complex and larger substances than oligosac-charides, they lend themselves better to be structural components of the cell. Since they are polymers of the smaller sugars, they range in size from relatively small molecules to molecules as large as those found in colloids. The polysac-charides are characterized by whether they yield one or more than one compound on hydrolysis—that is, whether they are homopolysaccharides or heteropolysac-charides. Animal starch, or glycogen, and cellulose yield only glucose upon hydrolysis, and chitin has glucosamine as the repeating unit. On the other hand, hyaluronic acid contains N-acetyl glucosamine and glucaric acid as repeating units. In addition to their large size, the polysaccharides are more complex than the oligosaccharides in that they may be linear, cyclic, or branched. For example, starch has two distinct forms—the straight chain starch amylose and the branched chain starch amylopectin. The glucose-glucose attachment is both 1,4 and 1,6 in the latter.

Classification of the polysaccharides is at best arbitrary. They are normally named according to the predominate type of monosaccharide unit. If they are mostly 5 carbon fragments, they are called pentosans; they are called hexosans if the repeating fragment is a 6 carbon sugar. Or, they are named more spe-cifically as glucosans if the repeating unit is glucose and fructosans if the repeating unit is fructose, and so on. The nitrogenous heteropolysaccharides are also known as mucopolysaccharides. These are substances which have the hexosamines as the component portion or parts of their molecules.

Biochemical characterization of polysaccharides was limited in the past by lack of techniques which could be applied to these higher weight molecules. Chromatographic procedures are now being used to separate these carbo-hydrates. Molecules from the size of monosaccharides through the poly-saccharides can be separated on exchange resins, and special eluting agents have been designed to take these polysaccharides off of the columns. For example, diethylamino ethyl (DEAE) cellulose is used to elute the neutral polysaccharides, and hyaluronic acid, chondroitin, and heparin can be separated on epichlorohydrintriethanolamine (ECTEOLA) cellulose.

PHYSIOLOGICAL IMPORTANCE
Monosaccharides

In addition to being the units from which the oligosaccharides and polysaccharides are built, the monosaccharides are important to the cell in their own right. Their role is reflected not only in intermediary metabolism, but also in overall physiology.

Enough cannot be said about the role of glucose in the cell. It is directly involved in many of the major metabolic pathways; it is a source of immediate energy since it penetrates the membranes quicker than all of the other sugars. And it and its derivatives easily polymerize to provide structural molecules as well as those with physiological importance. For example, glucosamine polymerizes to form chitin and is also a part of hyaluronic acid, an intercellular component. The other hexoses, although important, do not play as large a role as does glucose. In fact, the major significance of mannose and fructose is that they are easily converted to glucose. Galactose is seldom found free in nature but appears mostly in combination in both plant and animal cells.

The pentose sugars were at one time considered to be of trivial importance to the cell. However, with breakthroughs in genetics and photosynthesis, the role of these sugars became quite prominent. The fixation of carbon dioxide through the photosynthetic mechanism results in formation of a series of possible products, not the least important of which is the five carbon sugar ribulose. This monosaccharide can then yield energy to the cell by being fed into some of the major metabolic pathways. The overall picture of this function should become clear when we discuss intermediary metabolism in detail.

The terms *deoxyribose* and *ribose* have become so common that little needs to be said about these compounds at this point. The fact that they are the sugar component of deoxyribonucleic acid and ribonucleic acid is knowledge shared by both biologists and nonbiologists.

Collectively, the phosphate esters of the monosaccharides are also compounds of great physiological importance. They contribute to, and are involved in, the major anaerobic pathway in the cell, the glycolytic cycle. In addition to this energy-yielding function, these phosphate esters of the monosaccharides are the forms in which most of these sugars are transported in a multicellular system.

Sialic acids, derivatives of a deoxyamino sugar called neuraminic acid, are ubiquitously distributed in nature. These acids are normally found in all types of mucoproteins with a high carbohydrate content. A very good review of the occurrence of these sialic acids, and their chemistry and biology, is given by Gottschalk.[2]

Oligosaccharides

The oligosaccharides have little physiological importance per se, but occur mainly as breakdown products of the larger polysaccharides. This is particularly true of maltose, the breakdown product of animal starch, and cellobiose, the basic unit of cellulose. Sucrose, the commercial extraction from cane and beet, seems to have little importance in the overall function of the cell. Lactose, a disaccharide of mammalian origin exclusively, is the secretion product of the milk-producing cells of the mammary glands. Although this sugar is broken down into galactose and glucose before assimilation in multicellular forms, some single-celled organisms are capable of direct utilization. For example, certain bacteria such as *Lactobacillus acidophilus, Bacillus aerogenes,* and many others can convert this lactose into lactic acid.

The literature indicates that other oligosaccharides occur naturally, particularly in plants, but the physiological importance of these compounds has not yet been described.

Polysaccharides

The polysaccharides are second only to the proteins in importance as structural units of cells or cell products. The great numbers of these compounds and their importance are too overwhelming to present here. Representative examples are given to indicate their versatility and ubiquity.

As structural units, the polysaccharides attain their greatest importance in the plant kingdom. In fact, at least 50 percent of all the carbon in vegetation is in the form of cellulose, making this polysaccharide the most abundant organic compound in the world. This compound, however, is not the only polysaccharide used structurally in plants. The teichoic acids are polymers of glycerophosphate and ribitolphosphate which occur in the cells and walls of some of the gram-positive bacteria. In addition, the pectins, lignins, and many of the filler compounds of the cell walls of plants are polysaccharide in nature. The common material agar extracted from seaweed is a polysaccharide which is for the most part a galactan. An interesting sideline to the physiological importance of the polysaccharides of plants is that these sugar polymers may be elaborated by microorganisms. These by-products of the metabolism of bacteria in many cases act as pyrogens, or fever-producing compounds, most of which are stable polysaccarides containing significant amounts of nitrogen. Among the first polysaccharides of bacterial origin to be considered antigen-like were those of the pneumonial organism *Diplococcus pneumoniae.* Although there are several of these polysaccharides, all of them have not been biochemically analyzed. Roberts, Buchanan, and Baddiley[3] have described one of these specific substances from *Diplococcus* as being a pentasaccharide repeating unit of three galactoses, one glucose, and one ribitol molecule.

Some of the polysaccharides which occur in the animal kingdom have already been mentioned. Chondroitin and hyaluronic acid are both intercellular materials. Polysaccharides found within the cells include two located in corneal cells and those polysaccharides found on human blood cells. The latter are nitrogen-containing heteropolysaccharides related to the mucopolysaccharides in that they contain the hexose sugar N-acetyl-D-glucosamine. The mucopolysaccharides are a family of related sugar polymers which contain alternating hexuronic acid and hexosamine residues. The system of nomenclature for these glycosamino-glycuronoglycans has recently been revised by Jeanloz.[4]

The polysaccharides, then, have a variety of functions in the cell. (1) They may act as a food storage compound, such as glycogen in animal cells and starch in plant cells. (2) They may act as structural units as in the case of cellulose. (3) They may be by-products of the metabolism of one cell which affects the physiology of another. (4) They may characterize the intercellular material of the tissues. (5) They may be associated with the protein of the cell in order to perform a specific physiological function.

SUMMARY

As a major energy source, the carbohydrates have an important role in the cell. The building blocks of all of the carbohydrates are the monosaccharides, of which glucose is the common example. Insofar as the simple sugars are repeating units of the oligosaccharides and polysaccharides, their reactions reflect the basic chemistry of the entire group.

The monosaccharides demonstrate an important property of many biological compounds: isomerism. The subtle differences among molecules of the same chemical formula are enough to impart biological specificity to the various molecules.

The polymerization of the monosaccharides into larger compounds makes use of the glycosidic bond. Ten or less sugar residues in a molecule define an oligosaccharide; polysaccharides have ten or more. The most common members of the latter group are starch and glycogen.

Literature cited

1. Ultricht, T. L. V. 1962. Optical asymmetry of metabolites, vol. 4, pp.1-21. In Florkin, M., and H. Mason (editors): Comparative biochemistry. Academic Press, Inc., New York.
2. Gottschalk, A. 1960. The chemistry and biology of sialic acids and related substances Cambridge University Press, London.
3. Roberts. W. K., J. G. Buchanan, and J. Baddiley. 1963. The specific substance from Pneumococcus type 34 (41). The structure of a phosphorus-free repeating unit. Biochem. J. 88:1-7.
4. Jeanloz, R. W. 1960. The nomenclature of mucopolysaccharides. Arthritis & Rheumat. 3:233.

General references

Annual review of biochemistry (yearly). Annual Reviews, Inc., Palo Alto, California.
Baker, J. J. W., and G. E. Allen. 1965. Matter, energy, and life. Addison-Wesley Publishing Co., Inc., Palo Alto, Calif.
Bell, D. J. 1962. Natural monosaccharides and oligosaccharides: Their structure and occurrence, vol. 3, part A, pp. 288-354. In Florkin, M., and H. S. Mason (editors): Comparative biochemistry. Academic Press, Inc., New York.
Florkin, M., and E. Stotz (editors). 1963. Comprehensive biochemistry, vol. 5, sect. 2. Carbohydrates. Elsevier Publishing Co., New York.
Jeanloz, R. W. 1963. Recent developments in the biochemistry of the amino sugars. Advance. Enzymol. 25:433-456.
Karlson, P. 1963. Introduction to modern biochemistry. Academic Press, Inc., New York.

Kleiner, I. S. and J. M. Orten. 1962. Biochemistry. 6th ed. The C. V. Mosby Co., St. Louis.

Pigman, W. W. (editor). 1957. The carbohydrates: Chemistry, biochemistry, and physiology. Academic Press, Inc., New York.

Whistler, R. L., and C. L. Smart. 1953. Polysaccharide chemistry. Academic Press, Inc., New York.

White, A., P. Handler, and E. L. Smith. 1964. Principles of biochemistry. 3rd ed. McGraw-Hill Book Co., New York.

5

Lipids

T **INTRODUCTION**

The term *lipids* is a general name for a group of organic substances of fatty nature which are insoluble in water, soluble in fat solvents such as ether, chloroform, and benzene, related to the fatty acids as esters, and utilizable in metabolism. From this definition, it can be seen that in contrast to carbohydrate classification, lipid classification is not based on structure, but on function. This heterogeneous, poorly defined group, however, contains many members with biological importance. Some of these are the neutral fats, phospholipids, alcohols, waxes, terpenes, steroids, and a variety of derived lipids.

FATTY ACIDS

Before we can discuss the various groups of lipids, it is necessary to consider the fatty acids in order to better appreciate the physical and chemical properties of many of the lipids. These fatty acids rarely occur free, but are usually found in some ester linkage. They are obtained quantitatively from the lipids when the latter are hydrolyzed. Despite the many potential varieties of fatty acids, those encountered in a biological system have certain properties which allow generalizations to be drawn.

First, the acids are normally monocarboxylic and unbranched. Second, the naturally occurring acids for the most part have an even number of carbon atoms, although occasionally a species of odd-numbered acid has been found. Finally, these acids may be saturated or unsaturated. When they are unsaturated, the double bond rarely occurs in the portion of the molecule between the ninth carbon and the carboxyl group, and in most cases the initial point of unsaturation is between the ninth and tenth carbon in the fatty acids with longer chains.

When the simplest fatty acid, acetic acid, CH_3COOH, and the empirical formula of $C_nH_{2n+1}COOH$, are considered, it can be seen that a series of saturated fatty acids can be built. Examples of some of these common saturated fatty acids are given in Table 5-1.

Of the saturated series, the 16 and 18 carbon acids, palmitic acid and stearic

Table 5-1. The saturated fatty acids, 2 to 20 carbons

Number of carbons	Common name	Source of isolation*
2	Acetic	Vinegar
3	Propionic	Milk products
4	Butyric	Butterfat
5	Pentanoic	Various oils
6	Caproic	Butterfat and palm oils
7	Heptylic	Violet-leaf oil
8	Caprylic	Butterfat
9	Nonanoic	Butterfat and hair fat
10	Capric	Butterfat
11	Undecylic	Hair fat
12	Lauric	Oils of *Lauraceae* family
13	Tridecylic	Hair fat
14	Myristic	Fats of *Myristicaceae* family
15	Pentadecylic	Mutton, hair, and milk fats
16	Palmitic	Animal fat and palm oil
17	Margaric	Hair and mutton fats
18	Stearic	Animal fat
19	Nonadecylic	Ox fat
20	Arachidic	Peanut oil

*Data from Altman, P. L., and D. S. Dittmer (editors). 1964. Biology data book. Federation of American Societies for Experimental Biology, Washington, D. C.

acid, are those most commonly found in the lipids. Acetic acid and propionic acid, although true fatty acids, are more often found in situations other than in combination with lipoid materials. Butyric, caproic, and the caprylic or octanoic acids are involved in certain metabolic pathways.

The unsaturated fatty acids, containing one or more double bonds, may be subdivided as to degree of saturation. The first group consists of the oleic series, in which the fatty acids contain one double bond. The general formula for these acids, $C_nH_{2n-1}COOH$, should allow construction of a series similar to the saturated series. However, the most common singly unsaturated fatty acids are only three in number. Included in this group are crotonic acid, palmitoleic acid, and oleic acid. The characteristics of these acids are seen in Table 5-2. Notice that the double bond is in the 9, 10 position. This, of course, does not occur in crotonic acid which is involved more in the synthetic pathways than in the structure of lipids.

The multiunsaturated fatty acids contain only two structurally important

Table 5-2. Some common unsaturated fatty acids

Number of carbons	Common name	Number of unsaturated bonds	Location of bonds
4	Crotonic	1	2:3
16	Palmitoleic	1	9:10
18	Oleic	1	Cis 9:10
18	Elaidic	1	Trans 9:10
18	Linoleic	2	Cis 9:10; cis 12:13
18	α- Linolenic	3	Cis 9:10; cis 12:13; cis 15:16
20	Arachnidonic	4	5:6, 8:9, 11:12, 14:15
24	Nervonic	1	15:16

members. These are the double unsaturated linoleic acid and the triply unsaturated linolenic acid, the characteristics of which are also depicted in Table 5-2.

The presence of double bonds in these unsaturated series poses the possibility of isomerism. This particular type is called *cis-trans* isomerism because the four valence bonds arising from the ethylene lie in one plane and are not free to rotate. The 18 carbon singly unsaturated acid, oleic, could be written in either of the following ways:

$$HC(CH_2)_7CH_3 \qquad\qquad HC(CH_2)_7CH_3$$
$$\| \qquad\qquad\qquad \|$$
$$HC(CH_2)_7COOH \qquad HOOC(CH_2)_7CH$$

Oleic acid   Elaidic acid
(*cis* form)   (*trans* form)

The formula on the left is for oleic acid, the *cis* form, and the one on the right is for elaidic acid, the *trans* form, which is a nonmetabolizable form of the fatty acid. It is quite useful in tracing the path of oleic acid since elaidic acid would occur where oleic acid normally does but is not turned over as the naturally occurring acid. In general, the *cis* configuration is found in nature.

Many fatty acids do not precisely fit into one of these classifications. Some of them are mentioned later in this chapter in the discussion of the physiological importance of lipids.

The properties and chemical reactions of these fatty acids determine many of the characteristics of the fats themselves. Some general properties will be discussed before the results of a very important property of fatty acids, esterification, are demonstrated.

As indicated by their name, fatty acids are all acidic in nature, and as a result they undergo dissociation in aqueous medium.

$$RCOOH \quad \leftrightarrows \quad RCOO^- + H^+$$

This dissociative ability lends to fairly high reactivity in that the hydrogen ion is readily replaced by a series of substances. The cations such as sodium and potassuim comprise one such group which reacts with these acids to give the so-called soaps. Soaps, which occur much more in nature than would be expected, are extremely important in the maintenance of biological colloids. In addition, all the fatty acids exhibit high polarity. The carboxyl end, whether substituted or nonsubstituted, is very hydrophilic, whereas the hydrocarbon, or paraffin, end is more soluble in oils and fats and thus is the hydrophobic portion of the molecule. The polarity tends to orient the molecules, making them ideal for the surfaces involved in the biocolloids.

A final point of reactivity is the double bond. In a biological system the integrity of these double bonds is maintained better than in nonbiological situations.

NEUTRAL FATS

As was pointed out, structurally the lipids are esters. If glycerol, a trihydroxy alcohol, is the compound which is esterified with fatty acids, the resulting substance is a neutral fat. If the esters are not of glycerol, the compound is not a neutral fat but belongs to some other class such as the waxes.

Glycerol can be represented as follows:

$$CH_2OH$$
$$|$$
$$CHOH$$
$$|$$
$$CH_2OH$$

The general form of a neutral fat might be represented thus

$$CH_2OOCR$$
$$|$$
$$CHOOCR'$$
$$|$$
$$CH_2OOCR''$$

where the R groups are the fatty acids. In most cells, the R groups are almost exclusively palmitic, stearic, or oleic acid. If just one of these acids is represented on the molecule, the nomenclature is simple. The fat would be called tripalmitic, tristearin, or trioleic, respectively. However, mixed triglycerides occur more frequently, and because of the three sites of attachment, several permutations exist. If we consider two acids, stearic and palmitic, as being represented, there are two possible arrangements.

Notice that the α,β-distearopalmitic is asymmetrical both positionally and optically since the center carbon shows asymmetry.

Neutral fats may undergo several reactions in the cell. Certainly the most prevalent is substitution of one of the fatty acids for another during the dynamic turnover which occurs continually. The most important reaction from the stand-point of assimilation and dissimilation, however, is hydrolysis of the fat into its components, glycerol and three molecules of fatty acids. This reaction is enzymatically controlled by a group of enzymes called esterases or lipases. In the laboratory, however, hydrolysis is not easily carried out as such. It is more convenient, and certainly easier, to decompose the fats in the presence of an alkali rather than in water. The products of the reaction, termed saponifi-cation, are glycerol and the sodium or potassium derivatives of the fatty acids. The fact that this is carried out in the laboratory does not preclude the possi-bility that the reaction also occurs in the cell. In fact, the presence of a certain amount of these "soaps" is necessary for the integrity of many components of the cell.

Alteration of the fat, both deliberate and accidental, also occurs. One of the best known alterations is hydrogenation of liquid fats and oils to yield solid fats.

PHOSPHOLIPIDS

Biologically, the phospholipids are extremely important because they tend to aggregate at surface interfaces and thus appear as constituents of the cell membrane system. This group is generally characterized by yielding phosphoric acid, a nitrogenous compound, fatty acids, and glycerol, inositol, or sphingosine upon hydrolysis. These compounds are ubiquitous in the cell, occurring in both animals and plants. Some phosphatides are specifically located, whereas others seem to be dispersed throughout many kinds of cells. For example, the cephalins and sphingomyelins are quite prevalent in nerve cells. Lecithin, on the other hand, occurs in most types of cells. Structurally, however, they are all related in that all three are derivatives of phosphatidic acid.

$$\begin{array}{l} CH_2OOCR \\ | \\ CHOOCR \\ | \\ CH_2OPO_3H_2 \end{array}$$

This phosphatidic acid does occur free in nature, but most often it is found with the phosphate group in an ester link.

Lecithin and cephalins are direct derivatives in that the phosphoric acid is bound in an ester linkage with one of three compounds—choline, β-ethanolamine, or serine.

If choline is added, the result is lecithin.

$$\begin{array}{l} CH_2OOCR \\ | \\ CHOOCR \\ \quad\quad O^- \\ \quad\quad | \\ CH_2O-P-O-CH_2CH_2-N\!\!\equiv\!\!(CH_3)_3 \\ \quad\quad \| \\ \quad\quad O \end{array}$$

The high charge and high basicity attributed to quaternary nitrogen is characteristic of choline compounds and is important as far as the function of lecithin is concerned.

When either β-ethanolamine or serine is added, the compound is a cephalin.

$$\begin{array}{l} CH_2OOCR \\ | \\ CHOOCR \\ \quad\quad O^- \\ \quad\quad | \\ CH_2O-P-OCH_2CH_2NH_3 \\ \quad\quad \| \\ \quad\quad O \end{array}$$
$$\begin{array}{l} CH_2OOCR \\ | \\ CHOOCR \\ \quad\quad O^- \\ \quad\quad | \\ CH_2O-P-OCH_2-CHCOO^- \\ \quad\quad \| \qquad\quad | \\ \quad\quad O \qquad\quad NH_3 \\ \qquad\qquad\qquad + \end{array}$$

In the above compounds, the ratio of nitrogen to phosphorus is equal to 1. There are some phospholipids in which this is not the case. Sphingomyelin is a case in point. This compound yields fatty acid, choline, phosphoric acid, and sphingosine or dihydrosphingosine on hydrolysis. Note that glycerol is not a breakdown product here.

The structure of a typical sphingomyelin may be represented as follows:

$$CH_3(CH_2)_{12}CH=CH-CH-CH-CH_2O-\overset{\overset{\displaystyle O}{\parallel}}{P}-O-CH_2CH_2\overset{+}{N}\equiv(CH_3)_3$$

with OH, NH groups below, O^- below P, and RC=O below NH.

There are several other categories of phospholipids in nature. They are mostly specialized compounds, and we will not dwell on them at this point.

The *plasmologens* are widely distributed phospholipids in which a higher fatty aldehyde is substituted for the fatty acids, possibly in an acetal structure.

The *cardiolipins* are, as the name suggests, found in heart tissue. They are rather large molecules in which a chain of several phosphatidic acids and glycerols are linked together, with a variety of fatty acids projecting from the chain.

The *malignolipins* are a special group of phospholipids present in human malignant tumors. They are not found in normal tissue, although one of the components, spermine, does occur abundantly in human sperm.

GLYCOLIPIDS

Yet another class of lipids are the glycolipids, or cerebrosides. These compounds occur in the myelin sheaths of nerves, in brain tissue, and in certain ectopic areas in various disease states.

The individual cerebrosides are differentiated by the particular fatty acid in the molecule. For example, the three glycolipids from brain tissue—kerasin, phrenosin, and nervon—contain lignoceric, hydroxylignoceric, and oxynervonic acid, respectively, as the characteristic fatty acid.

In addition to the fatty acid, hydrolysis yields the compound psychosin which is composed of sphingosine and a hexose sugar, usually galactose, linked through the aldehyde group. The basic formula would then be

$$CH_3(CH_2)_{12}-CH=CH-CH-CH-CH_2O-CH-$$

with OH, NH below; RC=O below NH; and the hexose ring HCOH, HOCH, HOCH, HC—, CH_2OH with O.

LIPOMIMETIC COMPOUNDS

The remaining lipids which we will discuss are those biologically important compounds that are not truly related to the fatty acids but that are nonetheless classified as lipids because of their solubility properties and chemical reactions.

Table 5-3. Several common terpenes

Compound	Importance
Phytol	Alcoholic fragment of chlorophyll
α-, β-, and γ-carotene	Plant pigments; precursor to vitamin A
	H_2O
Vitamin A	Carotene $\longrightarrow$ 2 vitamin A
Vitamin E (tocopherol)	Antioxidant

Terpenes

The structure of most of the terpenes is fairly complex, and we will not dwell on the details here. Basically, they are all related in that they contain somewhere in their structure a series of isoprene-like fragments. These compounds occur most frequently as natural constituents of many plant cells. A look at Table 5-3, however, indicates that they are important in the animal kingdom as well.

Steroids

The steroids are a group of complex compounds many of which are physiologically very active. The cells which produce these compounds apparently have specialized metabolic paths for the genesis of the steroids, which then exert their influence most markedly on a multicellular system.

Because of the complexity, we again will avoid discussion of the detailed structure. They are all related in that all bear the same base compound which is perhydrocyclopentanophenanthrene.

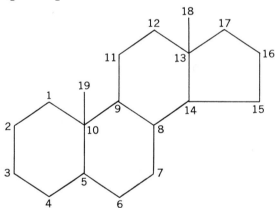

Eighteen and nineteen are angular methyl groups that extend from positions 10 and 13. Usually there is an oxygen or oxygen substitution compound on carbon 3, and side chain attachments to carbon 17 are common. A list of some of these compounds and their physiological importance are given in Table 5-4.

PHYSIOLOGICAL IMPORTANCE

Lipids as a class blend the biological importance of both carbohydrates and proteins. Like the sugars, lipids represent a source of energy in which the

Table 5-4. Representative steroids

Compound	Importance
Cholesterol	In blood and bile of vertebrates
Ergosterol	Precursor to vitamin D
Cholic acid	Major bile acid; usually coupled with glycine or taurine to form glycocholic or taurocholic acid; acts as a biological detergent
Progesterone	Hormone from cells of corpus luteum
Corticosterone	Hormone from cells of adrenal cortex
Androgens	Hormone from cells of testes and adrenal cortex
Estrogens	Hormone from cells of ovarian follicle

neutral fats potentially yield large amounts of ATP upon breakdown. Like the proteins, however, the lipids are an integral part of the structural framework of the cell, particularly the membrane systems.

The free fatty acids participate in few physiological processes other than the metabolic pathways in which they are directly involved. Most naturally occurring acids have straight chain structures. There are notable exceptions, such as chaulmoogric acid, an alicyclic compound which may possibly compete with the normal fatty acids of the tubercle bacillus organism that causes leprosy.

The fatty acids, whether free or in combination with other organic molecules, contribute to the hydrogen ion and buffering system of the cell. The dissociative ability of these acids makes them quite reactive and capable of trapping available cations.

The neutral fats seem to have as their prime function storage of energy. The enzyme systems of the cell combine excess fatty acids with glycerol as a reserve supply of both fatty acids when they are needed and potential energy when metabolism dictates an extra input of high-energy compounds.

The phospholipids as a group probably have the most ubiquitous distribution of any class of lipids. Integrity and function of the membranes of the cell depend on a particular assortment of these compounds being present. Active transport of molecules and ions may be mediated by phospholipids; diffusion of such compounds as CO_2 is facilitated by these lipids. Finally, quaternary nitrogen is exploited by the cell to impart a charge which may be involved in propagation of electrical impulses along the membrane. Some phospholipids, as well as glycolipids, seem to serve as structural spacers in the various membranes.

The terpenes and steroids, although not true lipids, were considered in this chapter because of their lipomimetic properties. Their functions are quite specialized, and they participate primarily as vitamins and hormones.

SUMMARY

The fatty acids are the reactive components of the lipids. These acids, both saturated and unsaturated, undergo a series of important reactions which characterize the lipid in which they occur. In neutral fats, the base compound is glycerol to which three molecules of fatty acids attach.

The phospholipids are highly charged, polar molecules whose properties are ideally suited for membrane structure. As lecithin, cephalins, and sphingo-myelin, they compose a large portion of the lipoid fraction of the membranes of the cell. The glycolipids, a related group, appear in the membranes of nerve cells and their accessory structures.

Lipomimetic compounds such as the terpenes and steroids are not true lipids, but they share many properties with the lipids. The terpenes and steroids are compounds which have specialized functions.

General references

Annual review of biochemistry (yearly). Annual Reviews, Inc., Palo Alto, Calif.

Baker, J. J. W., and G. E. Allen. 1965. Matter, energy and life. Addison-Wesley Publishing Co., Inc., Palo Alto, Calif.

Deuel, H. J., Jr. 1951. The lipids: Their chemistry and biochemistry, vol. 1. Interscience Publishers, Inc., New York.

Florkin, M., and H. S. Mason (editors). 1962. Comparative biochemistry, vol. 3, part A, chaps. 1-5, and 10; vol. 4, part B, chap. 14. Academic Press, Inc., New York.

Gunstone, F. D. 1958. An introduction to the chemistry of fats and fatty acids. John Wiley & Sons, Inc., New York.

Karlson, P. 1963. Introduction to modern biochemistry. Academic Press, Inc., New York.

Kleiner, I. S., and J. M. Orten. 1962. Biochemistry. 6th ed. The C. V. Mosby Co., St. Louis.

Lovern, J. A. 1955. The chemistry of lipids of biochemical significance. Methuen & Co., Ltd.. London.

White, A., P. Handler, and E. L. Smith. 1964. Principles of biochemistry. 3rd ed. McGraw-Hill Book Co., New York.

6

Proteins

INTRODUCTION

The proteins are undoubtedly the most complex components of the cell—even more so than the nucleic acids DNA and RNA. Their importance to cell function is so great that a detailed consideration of them should be attempted.

Proteins are important to animal cells because they play two significant roles. First, and of lesser importance, they are an energy source. Second, and of prime importance, they constitute the major portion of the structural framework of the cell and thus are the enzymes on whose surfaces the reactions of the cell proceed. Understanding of the basic phenomena associated with proteins is of paramount importance as groundwork for delving into the functional aspects of the cell.

A classical, and rather prosaic, definition of proteins is that they are organic substances of high molecular weight formed by a number of amino acids united by a peptide bond. This later was appended to include the statement that, although amino acids form the skeleton of proteins, nonprotein moieties may also be present. This definition does not even hint at the complexities and intricacies of proteins as coordinators of biological activity, but it does give us a sound chemical basis to approach their study.

THE AMINO ACIDS

Hydrolysis of any protein will give crystalline alpha amino acids. The general formula for these acids is as follows:

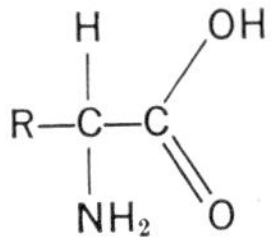

$$R-\underset{\underset{NH_2}{|}}{\overset{\overset{H}{|}}{C}}-C\underset{O}{\overset{OH}{\diagup}}$$

With few exceptions, the amine group is as pictured above, on the alpha carbon.

Table 6-1. The α-amino acids—structure, characteristics, and importance

Amino acid	Structure	Reactive groups* and biochemical characteristics	Biological importance
Neutral monoamino; monocarboxylic			
Glycine	CH₂COOH | NH₂	No optical isomerism; non-polar; hydrophobic	Acts as a spacer in interior of protein molecule; van der Waals attraction; used in synthetic pathways
Alanine	H₃CCHCOOH | NH₂	Nonpolar; hydrophobic	Acts as a spacer; van der Waals; used in synthetic pathways
Valine	H₃CCH—CHCOOH | | CH₃ NH₂	Hydrophobic	Acts as spacer; van der Waals
Leucine	H₃CCHCH₂CHCOOH | | CH₃ NH₂	Hydrophobic	Acts as spacer; van der Waals
Isoleucine	H₃CCH₂CH—CHCOOH | | CH₃ NH₂	Hydrophobic	Acts as spacer; van der Waals
Serine	HOCH₂CHCOOH | NH₂	Aliphatic hydroxyl; hydrophilic; nonionizable	Hydrogen bonding; often involved in "active site" of enzyme; phosphate carrier
Threonine	H₃CCH—CHCOOH | | OH NH₂	Aliphatic hydroxyl; hydrophilic; nonionizable	Hydrogen bonding; offers point of attachment on enzymes
Acidic—monoamino; dicarboxylic			
Aspartic	HOOCCH₂CHCOOH | NH₂	β-carboxyl; ionizable	Contributes ionic attraction
Glutamic	HOOCCH₂CH₂CHCOOH | NH₂	γ-carboxyl; ionizable	Contributes ionic attraction
Basic—two or more amines			
Histidine	HC=CCH₂CHCOOH | | | HN N NH₂ \\ // C H	Imidazole ring; ionizable	Links to nonprotein moieties; hydrogen bonding
Arginine	H₂NCNHCH₂CH₂CH₂CHCOOH || | NH NH₂	Guanidine group; ionizable	Contributes ionic attraction
Lysine	H₂NCH₂CH₂CH₂CH₂CHCOOH | NH₂	ε-amino; ionizable	Contributes ionic attraction

*Other than α-carboxyl and amine.

Table 6-1. The α-amino acids—structure, characteristics, and importance, cont'd

Amino acid	Structure	Reactive groups* and biochemical characteristics	Biological importance
		Aromatic	
Phenylalanine	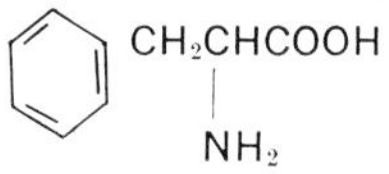 CH₂CHCOOH NH₂	Hydrophobic	van der Waals; gives spectral characteristics to protein
Tryptophan	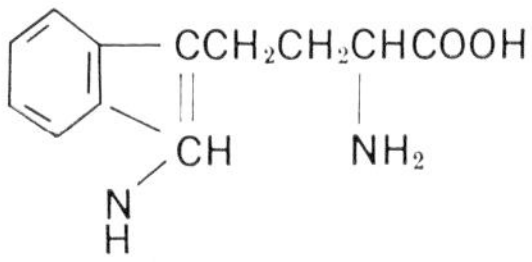 CCH₂CH₂CHCOOH CH NH₂ N H	Indole ring; hydrophobic	Hydrogen bonding; gives spectral characteristics to protein
Tyrosine	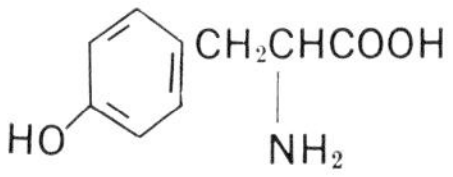 CH₂CHCOOH HO NH₂	Phenolic group; ionizable	Hydrogen bonding; gives spectral characteristics to protein
		Sulfur-containing	
Cysteine	CH₂CHCOOH SH NH₂	Sulfhydryl; hydrophobic; ionizable	Hydrogen bonding
Cystine	CH₂CHCOOH S NH₂ S CH₂CHCOOH NH₂	Disulfide bridge	Inner strand linkage
Methionine	H₃CSCH₂CH₂CHCOOH NH₂	Thio ether; hydrophobic	Hydrogen bonding
		Secondary—nitrogen ring-bound	
Proline	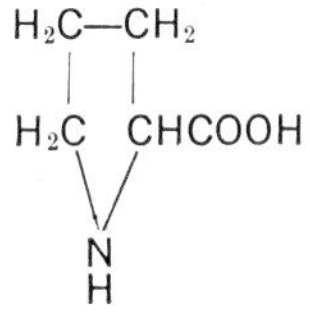 H₂C—CH₂ H₂C CHCOOH N H	Hydrophobic	van der Waals
Hydroxyproline	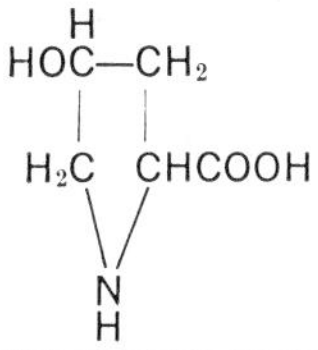 H HOC—CH₂ H₂C CHCOOH N H	Hydroxyl; hydrophilic; non-ionizable	Hydrogen bonding

The R group similarly attached to the carbon may take twenty-five to thirty various forms, but only twenty or twenty-one normally occur in proteins. All naturally occurring amino acids, with the exception of one, show some optical isomerism because of the asymmetry around the alpha carbon. Also, almost all naturally occurring amino acids belong to the L-configuration because of their relationship structurally to L-glyceraldehyde.

$$\begin{array}{cc}
\text{CHO} & \text{COOH} \\
| & | \\
\text{HOCH} & \text{H}_2\text{NCH} \\
| & | \\
\text{CH}_2\text{OH} & \text{R} \\
\\
\text{L-Glyceraldehyde} & \text{L-Amino acid}
\end{array}$$

Only the L-enantiomorph occurs in proteins; the D-form has been found only in peptides of some microorganisms. You should recall from the discussion of carbohydrates that the L-configurational representation does not preclude dextrorotary optical isomerism.

Amino acids are classified chemically according to the number of basic amine and acid carboxyl groups, presence of aliphatic or aromatic groups, and reactive groups, as well as according to their biological importance. They are listed for you, along with their structural formulas, in Table 6-1. Biological importance here does not connote metabolic involvement.

Certain physiochemical properties are also used to characterize amino acids. They will be discussed later and will not be elaborated on at this time.

Effects of dissociation

We have written all of the amino acids in an undissociated form with the carboxyl and amine groups un-ionized. In the physiological state, however, they occur not as depicted but as amphoteric, dipolar ions called zwitterions, or ampholytes.

$$\begin{array}{c}
^+\text{H}_3\text{NCHCOO}^- \\
| \\
\text{R}
\end{array}$$

This means that at any pH, there will be a degree of ionization of either or both of these primary reactive groups of amino acids; that is, each acid and each base group has a definite dissociation constant which changes as the pH changes. Although this will be discussed in more detail in the section on physiochemical phenomena, we must touch on the subject a little here in order to talk about certain properties of amino acids and proteins.

Henderson-Hasselbalch equation

If we consider K_a to be the dissociation constant of the carboxyl group and K_b as the dissociation constant of the amine group, we can define two new terms:

$$-\log K_a = \text{p}Ka$$

and

$$-\log K_b = \text{p}Kb$$

This now places the dissociation of these groups in the same context as hydrogen ion concentration and its relationship to pH:

$$-\log H^+ = pH$$

Using the Henderson-Hasselbalch equation, we can relate the pH and the pKa and the amount of ionized (acid form) and nonionized (salt) forms of the amino acid.

$$pH = pKa + \log \frac{[salt]}{[acid]}$$

We are not ignoring the pKb; however, since the pKa and the pKb relationship is implicit in the acid-base concept, we will not dwell on how to convert from one to the other.

The Henderson-Hasselbalch equation points out very clearly that the degree of dissociation of an acid or base group is dependent upon the pH. Simple mathematical substitution shows that the pKa equals the pH when one half of the acid present exists as its salt. At lower pH, because of an excess of hydrogen ions, the base end would be more dissociated (as NH_3^+); conversely, in an alkaline medium, the acid end would be more dissociated.

Isoelectric point

Since each amino acid has at least one acid and one base group, one would expect to find some pH at which the positive charges equal the negative charges. This hydrogen ion concentration is defined as the isoelectric point, pI. It is easy to predict that the dicarboxylic acids would have an isoelectric point on the acid side and the diamino acids on the basic side, but on the

Table 6-2. Isoelectric points of some amino acids*

Amino acid	pI
Alanine	6.11
Arginine	10.76
Aspartic acid	2.98
Cysteine	5.07
Glutamic acid	3.22
Glycine	6.20
Histidine	7.64
Isoleucine	6.04
Leucine	6.04
Lysine	9.47
Methionine	5.74
Phenylalanine	5.91
Proline	6.30
Serine	5.68
Threonine	5.59
Tryptophan	5.88
Tyrosine	5.63
Valine	6.00

*Data from Altman, P. L., and D. S. Dittmer (editors). 1964. Biology data book. Federation of American Societies for Experimental Biology, Washington, D. C.

surface one would not expect the "neutral" amino acids to have such a range of isoelectric points. The intramolecular forces, then, affect the dissociation of these groups, and these neutral amino acids thus do not show electric equality at the expected pH 7. Table 6-2 lists the isoelectric points of several amino acids to indicate the range of pH where charge neutrality exists.

The concept of the isoelectric point is applicable not only to individual amino acids, but also to whole proteins. It can be used as a characterizing trait, and as we shall see later, it is involved in some of the separation techniques of both amino acids and proteins.

The peptide bond

It has been inferred that the amino acids are linked together in some fashion to build up the various proteins. This linkage, called the peptide bond, is considered to be the primary structure of the protein molecule. Peptide linkage was first postulated by Fischer and Hofmeister independently in 1902. Their postulate, which later works verified, was that the amino acids are joined together by a carboxyl-to-amino group linkage, with splitting off of a water molecule. That is, the carboxyl group of one amino acid is attached to the amine group of another in an amide substitution.

There are several things to note about this bonding. First is the fact that the linkage is not uniplanar. Second, the skeleton of the protein chain is made up only of the alpha carbon, the carboxyl carbon, and the nitrogen. The R groups project as side chains from the skeleton, which has two related effects. The reactive and characteristic groups of amino acids are not involved in the primary structure, and this provides variation not only in arrangement of the R's along the chain, but also in potential interaction among the different R groups.

It is presumed, then, that the number and kinds of amino acids, their order in the chain, and the configuration of the skeleton itself are the controlling factors in the nature of the protein, the nature of its surface, and its physiochemical properties. The higher levels of protein structure, termed secondary, tertiary, and quaternary, will be discussed later in this chapter.

ANALYSIS OF PROTEINS

It is apparent that these characteristics present problems which are quite formidable and involve tremendous technical difficulties because of the enormous diversity and complexity of these important cell macromolecules.

The analysis of protein molecules and their eventual synthesis are the areas to which much of the work of protein chemistry is devoted. We want to discuss some of these methods of analysis and means of characterizing both amino acids and proteins.

We have mentioned that the proteins, like amino acids, behave as ampholytes. This charge on the molecule, along with other properties such as solubility and weight, is very useful in separating the various components in order to identify them. There are two valuable techniques which avail themselves of these properties—chromatography and electrophoresis.

Chromatography

In analysis of a protein, the first step often is to find out what amino acids are present, and chromatography is one of the easier methods. Acid hydrolysis will break the peptide bonds and cause re-formation of the individual amino acids from their residues in the protein by rehydration.

At any one pH, as we have inferred earlier, the pKa's of almost all of the individual amino acids are different. This difference can be exploited by allowing the acids to migrate on some surface. In paper chromatography, the migrating surface is a piece of special filter paper. This paper is placed in contact with a solution containing two "phases," a mobile phase and a stationary one. They are so distinguished by the fact that one, the mobile phase, migrates by capillary action and carries the amino acids at a faster rate than the stationary phase. The mobile phase is usually an organic acid or alcohol, but may be a number of compounds. The stationary phase, on the other hand, is often water or water mixed with base or acid.

What we have set up, then, is a multiphase system where the individual amino acids, by differential solubility between, or among, the phases will migrate proportionally to the ratio of their solubilities in the phases. The procedure is outlined in the discussion that follows.

A spot of an unknown protein which has been hydrolyzed or a mixture of unknown amino acids is placed on the left-hand corner of a large rectangular sheet of filter paper and is then dried. The edge of the filter paper is placed in contact with the chromatography solution and is allowed to remain until capillary action has moved the front, or migrating edge, the desired distance. As the solution passes over the dried spot, the individual components are separated according to their relative solubility in the different phases. At the desired time, the front is marked and the paper is removed from the airtight chamber where the procedure has taken place. At this time, the paper is dried and sprayed with a substance which gives a specific color test for amino acids, usually triketohydrindene hydrate (ninhydrin), and the spots where the amino acids are located are marked. The ratio of distance the spots moved over the distance the front moved is called the R_f. This ratio is of diagnostic value when compared to known amino acids run under identical circumstances. If separation by this one-dimensional migration is incomplete, the paper can be turned 90° and a two-dimensional chromatogram is developed (Fig. 6-1).

This technique can be refined to give quantitative results as well as qualita-

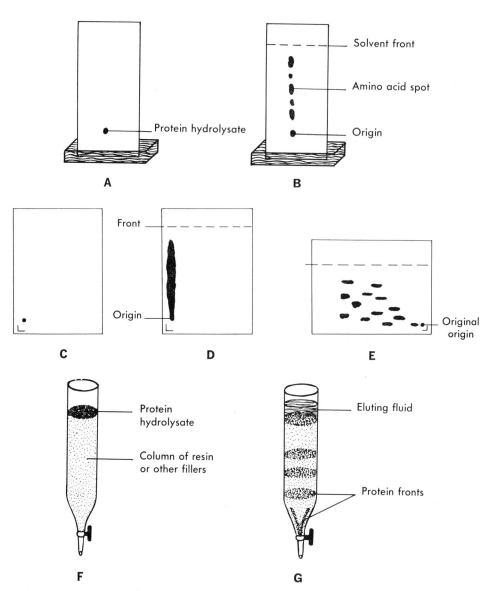

Fig. 6-1. Three basic variations of chromatography. **A** and **B,** One-dimensional chromatography. Solvent is allowed to move across the dried protein hydrolysate (**A**). After the front has moved a certain distance, the strip is dried and the amino acid spots are developed. The ratio of the movement of the front/movement of the amino acid (R_f) can be calculated. **C** to **E,** Two-dimensional chromatography. The technique is the same as for one-dimensional chromatography, except that the filter paper is turned 90° and a second solvent is allowed to move across the paper. The developed spots are more separated than they are in one-dimensional chromatography. **F** and **G,** Column chromatography. A column is prepared by drying a protein hydrolysate at the top of a column of material. An eluting fluid is then allowed to run through the column, the rate of flow being determined by the stopcock setting. The compounds are separated as in paper chromatography, but the material is collected at the bottom of the column.

tive. The individual amino acids can be eluted off the paper with an appropriate solvent and can be either titrated or determined spectrophotometrically.

Chromatography is also done by a column method. In this technique, a glass cylinder is filled with one of many classes of compounds such as a charged resin or a relatively inert substance such as powdered cellulose or silica. The separating principles are the same as in paper chromatography. The mixture to be separated is placed at the top of the column and the chromatographic solvent is poured over the dried unknown and allowed to drain through the packed cylinder. The mixture is then separated as in paper chromatography. A great advantage, however, is that the material as it is separated may be collected at the bottom of the tube in predetermined aliquots. The separated substances can then be further purified and identified. In the case of amino acid separation, the ninhydrin test can be applied to a small portion of each fraction collected. A positive test would show not only which tubes contained amino acids, but also proportionally how much as determined by depth of color development.

Although chromatography is simple and not as quantitative as more sophisticated techniques, it is still one of the best and most commonly used methods to separate organic compounds of lower molecular weight.

Electrophoresis

Whereas chromatography is best utilized to separate lower weight organic compounds, electrophoresis is best applied to separation of higher weight materials such as polypeptides and proteins. As in chromatography, purification of compounds can also be brought about by this technique. In theory, electrophoresis is based on a simple axiom: a charged substance will migrate in an ionic medium which has a current running through it. There are two types of electrophoresis in which this maxim is applied.

In paper electrophoresis, a strip of filter paper is wetted with an ionic medium and the two ends are placed in reservoirs of the solution to keep the paper moist. A positive electrode is placed in one reservoir and a negative one in the other. The mixture to be separated is placed in the center of the strip with a fine double wire. A direct current circuit is then completed by attaching the electrodes to an electrical source.

The mixture of materials will then migrate differentially, depending on degree of charge, molecular weight, and various solution-substance or substance-substance interactions. Again, as in paper chromatography, the paper is dried and sprayed to bring out colored complexes where the unknowns are located. Parameters such as distance migrated under certain voltage, depth of color, shape of colored fronts, and relative position to other fronts are used as identifying features. Automatic analyzers can be used to "read" with a photoelectric cell the depth of color and integrate under the curve obtained to give an accurate, quantitative measurement of the amount of each compound.

The most advanced electrophoresis technique, cell electrophoresis, was first designed by Tiselius. In this apparatus use is made not only of the electric field migration principle as in paper electrophoresis, but also of a special optical device for locating migrating fronts without the use of colored complexes. In addition, the cell setup is so designed as to allow the investigator to isolate these protein fronts from one another.

In theory, like many excellent experimental devices, the Tiselius apparatus is fairly simple. A U-shaped tube is filled with the conducting medium, with an electrode in each end of the U. The protein is placed at the bottom of the U where it can then migrate up either arm, depending on charge. The U, however, is constructed so that it is made of partitions which can be separated from one another by flat inserts of glass, which allows any particular migrating front to be isolated.

The method of determining where the protein fronts are in the liquid medium consists of a very ingenious device called the schlieren setup. Briefly, the method involves passing a beam of light through the medium, allowing the protein fronts, with a refractive index different from the medium, to deflect the beam. The deflection is then recorded and analyzed. A more complete explanation is given in Fig. 6-2.

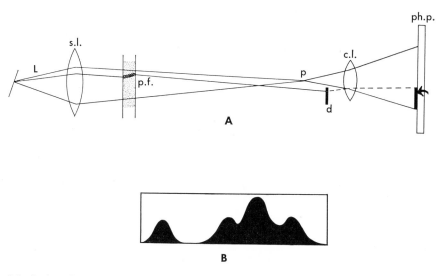

Fig. 6-2. Optics of the schlieren setup. **A,** A narrow beam of light, *L,* is passed through a concave lens, *s.l.,* which is placed near the optical glass cell. The beam of light is passed through the liquid medium and focused on point *p*. This produces a simple image, and the beam is then passed through the camera lens, *c.l.,* exposing the moving photographic plate, *ph.p.* However, if the diaphragm, *d,* of the camera is closed so that the beam of light just fills the aperture, any deflection of the beam results in only partial exposure of the photographic plate. The deflection occurs as protein fronts, *p.f.,* with refractive indices different from the medium, pass through the glass cell. The moving fronts appear as a series of shadows (schlieren) on the photographic plate. That is, because of the deflection, there were areas on the plate which were not developed. **B,** A typical electrophoretic pattern as seen with schlieren optics. Size and shape of peaks are characteristics of the protein being determined. Total unexposed area under the peak gives quantitative estimate of amount of protein present. (Modified from Gortner, R. A., and W. A. Gortner. 1953. Outlines of biochemistry. John Wiley & Sons, Inc. New York.)

The ultracentrifuge

There is another very elaborate technique which also uses the schlieren lighting system, and it is the ultracentrifuge as originally designed by Svedberg. This apparatus is one of several for determining molecular weight of large molecules.

The rate of sedimentation of suspensions under the influence of gravity had been used by early workers to estimate particle size. However, when colloidal material is dealt with as protein "solutions," the force of gravity will not cause sedimentation. Neither will normal centrifuges. The ultracentrifuge was then designed in order to obtain rotations of high speed and thus great gravitational force. To apply the schlieren system, an optical window is cut in the rotating heads containing the protein mixture. As the heads spin, the moving fronts of the proteins can be determined as in cell electrophoresis, and the rate of sedimentation under a given force can be calculated.

The apparent molecular weight of the compound may be expressed as

$$M = \frac{RTS}{D(1-\rho V)}$$

where R equals the gas constant, T the absolute temperature; S, the sedimentation constant expressed in Svedberg units where 1 Svedberg $= 1 \times 10^{-13}$ seconds; D, the diffusion constant; ρ, the density of the solvent; and V, the partial specific volume.

Other techniques

Molecular weight can also be determined by using any of the colligative properties, such as osmotic pressure. However, these methods have many drawbacks. They are fairly accurate for small molecules, but when larger molecules are present, the weight is so great that only a fraction of a mole is present. Since the colligative changes depend upon molarity, the inherent error is great if only a fraction of a mole exerts the change.

In addition to molecular weight, many other properties of proteins can be determined. For example, techniques as birefringence of flow and X-ray diffraction have added much to our knowledge of the shape and structure of molecules. The results of the application of these methods is discussed under protein structure.

PROTEIN STRUCTURE

Perutz, in his fine review of the work on proteins and nucleic acids to 1961,[1] has divided the topic of protein structure into three subcategories—primary, secondary, and tertiary. The division is not unique, but the decision as to what to include in each category is, to a degree, arbitrary. I shall use his approach here.

Primary

We have discussed how we have at our disposal a series of methods for determining *what* amino acids are present in a particular protein. *How* these residues are linked together constitutes the primary structure of proteins. The analysis of protein molecules and eventual resynthesis were the starting points for protein chemists. Resolving of the order of the amino acids requires special techniques and special fortitude.

The method used with good success is that of end group analysis. In this technique, all the free carboxyl or amino groups of the protein are blocked except those on the end amino acid(s). The terminal residue(s) is then pulled off and identified. The reverse of this, where the end amino or carboxyl groups are complexed with some compound and then identified, is also used. In either case, the process is repeated until the protein chain is completely analyzed. The possibility of multiple chains, branching, and the inordinately large number of residues make this anything but a simple technique.

The specific activity of certain proteinase enzymes such as trypsin and pepsin is also used as a tool to determine the order of the residues. The knowledge that these enzymes attack only certain linkages helps to locate the position of these bonds in the chain.

A major milestone in protein chemistry was achieved when Sanger, using chromatography and end group analysis techniques, determined the sequence of amino acids in the double chain protein insulin. In addition to establishing without doubt existence of the peptide linkage, this dedicated researcher gave great impetus to the entire field of protein chemistry by demonstrating that the primary structure of a biological macromolecule can be determined by chemical methods. Since this first breakthrough, the amino acid sequence of quite a number of proteins has been established.

One ramification of Sanger's work was establishment of the S-S linkage as a primary linkage between peptide chains. These disulfide bridges have their origin from sets of two cysteine residues. The sulfhydryl group of each amino acid is oxidized, forming this bridge between two peptide strands. In the case of insulin, for example, there are two disulfide bridges between the two peptide chains as well as one intrachain bridge connecting two cysteine residues of the alpha chain.

Secondary and tertiary

Reconstruction of a protein by knowing the amino acid sequence and the location of disulfide bridges will not necessarily result in a compound with biological activity. This primary structure alone, then, does not account for all of the specificity attributed to proteins. To resolve this, we must consider the configuration of the polypeptide chain itself, or the secondary structure, and the three-dimensional organization in the cell, or the tertiary structure.

Recall that even though twenty L-amino acids are involved as residues of the polypeptide chains, they are all linked together by the same peptide bond which acts as the skeleton structure. In essence, then, polypeptides are long-chained polymers with a repeating atomic pattern, and compounds with this model tend to have a helical, or screw, symmetry.

Spiraling of the peptide skeleton, however, is to a degree limited by the diversity of side chain projections of the acid residues. Second, the spiral, whether right-handed or left-handed, necessitates the presence of some sta-bilizing interchain or intrachain linkage. This linkage is the hydrogen bond.

To digress a bit, the hydrogen bond is biologically one of the most important linkages so far as endowing biological activity to organic compounds. This bond combines stability with flexibility in that it is thermolabile as well as pH sensitive, and, yet, when it is present, it gives necessary rigidity to the molecule. The hydrogen bond is involved not only in the secondary structure of proteins, but also directly in enzyme activity since it provides one means of creating a temporary enzyme-substrate complex.

In proteins, this hydrogen bond may be found between the polypeptide chains or as bonds within the same strand; the latter is biologically more important so far as secondary structure is concerned.

The presence of hydrogen-bonded rings in the same polypeptide strands confers a helical structure on the entire chain. The variables involved in this spiral are (1) the number of residues per 360° turn of the helix, (2) whether the helix is right-handed or left-handed, and (3) the number of atoms par-ticipating in the ring.

A typical peptide chain has 3.6 residues per turn, and in an α-helix this repeat occurs along an axial length of about 5.4 Å since each residue occupies slightly less than 1.5 Å. Most biological compounds exhibit right-handedness, and theoretically these compounds are also more stable than left-handed ones. The number of atoms involved in the ring is determined by the manner in which the amino group is attached to the carbonyl and the number of acid residues participating. However, strain energies on the helix to a certain extent dictate this number.

All of these features of secondary structure still do not explain how these long, almost two-dimensional polypeptide chains are compactly folded into the three-dimensional units as they are found in the living cell. This micro-anatomical configuration has become the focal point of protein chemistry, for herein lies the basis for both biological activity and structure.

There are a series of noncovalent bonds which participate in giving not only stability but also three-dimensional folding to the protein chains. They are illustrated in Fig. 6-3. However, the task of determining the exact tertiary structure in order to understand the basis for catalytic functions of proteins falls primarily to X-ray analysis. Painstaking work with series of isomorphous crystals, thin sectioning for determining electron dense areas, and subsequent Fourier-like resynthesis by a number of workers has given us the structures of such proteins as myoglobin, homoglobin, ribonuclease, and a few others (Fig. 6-4).

We can now summarize some of the facts that we know about proteins.

1. Proteins are large molecules with molecular weights ranging from 6000 to many millions.
2. Proteins exhibit amphoteric properties.
3. Proteins are highly reactive and very specific in their action.
4. Proteins are labile and easily modified by alteration in physical or chem-ical environment.

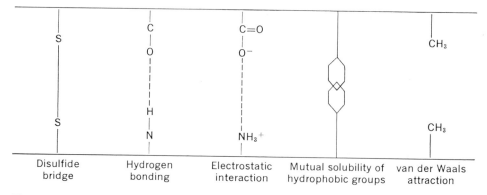

| Disulfide bridge | Hydrogen bonding | Electrostatic interaction | Mutual solubility of hydrophobic groups | van der Waals attraction |

Fig. 6-3. Various bonds involved in primary, secondary, and tertiary structures of proteins. The disulfide bridge and the hydrogen bonding are the only types involved in the primary structure.

Fig. 6-4. Diagrammatic representation of the beta chain of hemoglobin and myoglobin. The disc represents the heme moiety; the twisted tubing represents the globin portion. The three-dimensional configurations of the beta chain of hemoglobin and of the myoglobin are essentially identical.

5. The skeleton linkage is the peptide bond, but linkage between chains can be as strong as the disulfide bridge or as weak as a hydrogen bond or van der Waals attraction.

6. The three-dimensional structure has been found to take many forms—spheres, rods, spirals, or discs.

7. Individual chains usually occur as helices—the direction of turn, the number of amino acid residues per turn, and the kinds and number of atoms included in the turn being characteristic for specific chains.

8. Proteins may occur as pure amino acid polymers, or they may occur in complexes with nonprotein moieties. These complexes are known as conjugated proteins.

CLASSIFICATION

When we consider how much we know about proteins, the classification system is highly arbitrary. Many of the proteins may fit into more than one taxon, but as in all classification systems, convenience of reference is an important criterion. Since the classification of proteins is difficult on purely chemical structure, solubility reactions serve as a means both of classification and of separating the various proteins.

A. *Simple proteins.* Only α-amino acids or their derivatives
1. *Albumins.* Soluble in water; denatured by heat: for example, egg albumin and serum albumin
2. *Globulins.* Slightly soluble in water; soluble in dilute salt solutions: for example, serum globulins
3. *Glutelins.* Soluble in acids and alkalies but not neutral solvents: for example, many grain proteins
4. *Prolamines.* Insoluble in water or absolute alcohol; soluble in 70% alcohol
5. *Albuminoids, or scleroproteins.* Fibrous, insoluble animal proteins; highly resistant to proteolysis
   a. Collagen
   b. Elastin
   c. Keratin
6. *Histones.* Soluble in water and dilute acids; basic proteins; found combined with nucleic acids
7. *Protamines.* Strongly basic; found principally combined with nucleic acids; found in sperm cells
B. *Conjugated proteins.* United to some nonprotein moiety, the prosthetic group, by other than salt linkage
1. Nucleoprotein
2. Mucoids, or mucoproteins (more than 4% of hexosamine)
3. Glycoprotein (less than 4% hexosamine)
4. Lipoprotein
5. Chromoprotein
6. Metalloprotein
7. Phosphoprotein

PHYSIOLOGICAL IMPORTANCE

It is impossible to discuss, or even to list, the physiological importance of proteins in the functioning cell. They, for the most part, *are* the functioning cell. Even the elaborate system by which the cell ensures itself of a constant and correct supply of the right kinds of protein (Chapter 27) gives further evidence of the important role these compounds play in a dynamic biological system.

SUMMARY

The proteins, composed of α-amino acids linked together by peptide bonds, are of unique importance to the cell. They are the workers, the enzymes whose properties are used to regulate the activities of the cell. Hydrolysis of proteins yields a mixture of α-amino acids. These acids are highly reactive. As a result of their dissociation at physiological pH, they form the ionized zwitterions. The individual properties of the amino acids add to the property of the intact protein.

Analysis of protein structure begins with determination of both the overt characteristics of the protein and which amino acids are present and in what order they are linked together in the protein chain. Various techniques for characterizing both the amino acids and proteins are chromatography, electrophoresis, high-speed centrifugation for determining molecular weight of protein, and a series of special techniques for determining shape and other basic properties.

The primary structure of proteins is not a complete description of how the chain orients itself in the cell. The secondary and tertiary structures describe this three-dimensional structure. Only when a protein is in its normal tertiary structure does it seem to have biological activity.

Literature cited

1. Perutz, M.F. 1962. Proteins and nucleic acids. Elsevier Publishing Co., New York.

General references

Anfinsen, C. B. Jr., M. L. Anson, K. Bailey, and J. T. Edsall, (editors). Advances in protein chemistry. Academic Press, Inc., New York. (An annual series beginning with vol. 1 in 1944.)

Annual review of biochemistry (yearly). Annual Reviews, Inc., Palo Alto, Calif.

Baker, J. J. W., and G. E. Allen. 1965. Matter, energy and life. Addison-Wesley Publishing Co., Inc., Palo Alto, Calif.

Edsall, J. T., and J. Wyman. 1958. Biophysical chemistry, vol. 1. Academic Press, Inc., New York.

Greenstein, J. P., and M. Winitz. 1961. Chemistry of the amino acids. John Wiley & Sons, Inc., New York. 3 vol.

Karlson, P. 1963. Introduction to modern biochemistry. Academic Press, Inc., New York.

Kendrew, J. C., and M. F. Perutz. 1957. X-ray studies of compounds of biological interest. Ann. Rev. Biochem. 26:327.

Kleiner, I. S., and J. M. Orten. 1962. Biochemistry. 6th ed., The C. V. Mosby Co., St. Louis.

Linderstrom-Lang, K. U., and J. A. Schellman. 1959. Protein structure and enzyme activity, vol. 1, pp. 443-510. In P. D. Boyer, H. Lardy, and K. Myrbäck (editors): The enzymes. Academic Press, Inc., New York.

Ling, G. N. 1962. A physical theory of the living state: The association-induction hypothesis. Blaisdell Publishing Co., New York.

Martin, R. B. 1964. Introduction to biophysical chemistry. McGraw-Hill Book Co., New York.

Meister, A. 1957. Biochemistry of the amino acids. Academic Press, Inc., New York.

Neuberger, A. (editor). 1958. Symposium on protein structure. Methuen & Co., Ltd., London.

Neurath, H. (editor). The proteins: Composition, structure and function, 2nd ed. Vol. 1, 1963; vol. 2, 1964. Academic Press, Inc., New York.

Rich, A., and D. W. Green. 1961. X-ray studies of compounds of biochemical interest. Ann. Rev. Biochem. 30:93.

Springall, H. D. 1954. The structural chemistry of proteins. Academic Press, Inc., New York.

Tanford, C. 1961. Physical chemistry of macromolecules. John Wiley & Sons, Inc., New York.

White, A., P. Handler, and E. L. Smith. 1964. Principles of biochemistry, 3rd ed. McGraw-Hill Book Co., New York.

7

Purines, pyrimidines, and nucleic acids

N INTRODUCTION

No consideration of the chemistry of the cell would be complete without including some discussion of the nucleic acids and the components of which they are composed. The controlling device for determining which of the other chemical compounds are to be synthesized and where and how this synthesis will occur lies in these nucleic acids. As the hereditary information of the cell is inherent in these molecules, these important high-weight substances form the blueprint and template of cellular activity, properties which have been fairly exploited in both popular and scientific literature.

The specific roles of both deoxyribonucleic acid (DNA) and ribonucleic acid (RNA) in the overall picture of the functioning cell will be discussed in some detail in Chapter 26. Here, we wish to consider the DNA and RNA molecules and the units that make up these nucleic acids primarily from a chemical standpoint as some of the biochemical constituents of the cell.

HYDROLYTIC PRODUCTS OF NUCLEIC ACIDS

The various nucleic acids are surprisingly quite similar chemically. Complete acid hydrolysis of both DNA and RNA yields a 5 carbon sugar (*ribose* in RNA and *deoxyribose* in DNA), phosphoric acid, and a mixture of basic substances called purines and pyrimidines. It is the subtle differences among these building blocks and their arrangement that determines the individual character of each nucleic acid molecule.

The products obtained by successive hydrolytic degradation of nucleoproteins are listed in the flow chart on the following page.

We will consider some of the properties of each of these components, starting with the basic units and synthesizing up to the macromolecule, nucleoprotein.

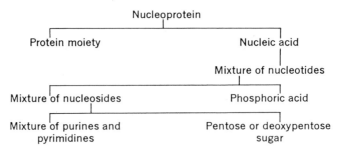

The sugar moiety has been discussed in Chapter 4 (Carbohydrates). The important difference to keep in mind is the absence of the hydroxyl group on carbon 2 of the deoxy sugar.

PURINES AND PYRIMIDINES

Both the purines and pyrimidines are ring compounds; the purine ring is nine-membered and the pyrimidine ring has 6 atoms comprising it. The close relationship between these rings is seen below, where the structure and numbering system of the atoms are depicted.

Pyrimidine

Purine

The pyrimidines which are normally found in nucleic acids are uracil, thymine, cytosine, and methylcytosine.

Uracil
(2,6-dioxypyrimidine)

Thymine
(5-methyl, 2,6-dioxypyrimidine)

Cytosine
(2-oxy, 6-aminopyrimidine)

Methylcytosine
(5-methyl, 2-oxy, 6-aminopyrimidine)

As can be seen from these naturally occurring pyrimidines, a plethora of derivatives is possible. However, with a few exceptions, only these four are incorporated into DNA and RNA. The importance of a limited number of bases being in these nucleic acids will become apparent when we better understand the concepts involved in the control of cellular activity.

Chemically, the pyrimidines all exhibit the lactim–lactam tautomerism. This fluctuation of the double bond yields a dual property to the ring in that an oxygen may occur as a part of a carbonyl group or as a hydroxyl group which is easily substituted.

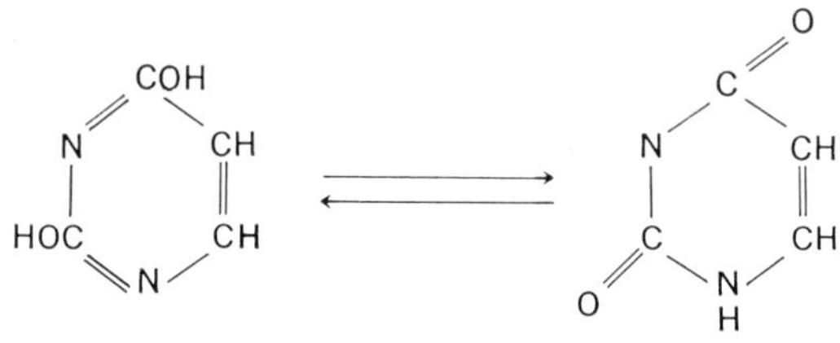

Lactim   Lactam

Although we initially think of the pyrimidine bases as being associated with nucleic acids, the biological importance of these compounds is not restricted to this. Vitamin B_1 (thiamine), for example, is an important pyrimidine derivative, being involved as a cofactor in many metabolic processes, as so many of the vitamins are. Uridine diphosphate glucose (UDPG) is an example of a coenzyme with a pyrimidine base.

The purines contain the six-membered pyrimidine ring and the five-membered imidazole ring, with carbons 4 and 5 shared by both rings. Only two derivatives have been found to normally occur in nucleic acids—adenine and guanine.

Adenine
(6-aminopurine)

Guanine
(2-amino, 6-oxypurine)

A large number of other important purines, however, has been found to occur. There is a series of derivatives of adenine (and guanine) which are among the compounds containing high-energy bonds. Most well-known of these are adenosine triphosphate (ATP) and adenosine diphosphate (ADP). In addition, adenine is complexed with other moieties to participate in other cellular reactions. Examples are coenzyme A, nicotinamide *adenine* dinucleotide (NAD), and flavin *adenine* dinucleotide (FAD). The latter two are hydrogen and electron acceptors in the metabolic pathways.

The hydroxyl addition derivative series of hypoxanthine, xanthine, and uric acid occurs throughout nature. The compounds—the 6-hydroxy, 2,6-dihydroxy, and 2,6,8-trihydroxy derivatives, respectfully—are metabolic products of adenine and guanine. Further substitution of xanthine in particular yields other compounds found in plant cells and cell products such as caffeine, theophylline, and theobromine.

NUCLEOSIDES

The nucleosides are a combination of pentose or deoxypentose and a purine or pyrimidine base. The purine nucleosides are conjugated in an α-glycosidic-like linkage from carbon 1′ of the sugar to the nitrogen in position 9 of the purine. Similarly, the bond in pyrimidine nucleosides is between the 1′ of the sugar and the nitrogen in position 3 of the six-membered ring. The nomenclature of the nucleosides simply involves the addition of an -*ine* suffix to the root of the base. For examples, the adenine nucleoside is adenosine, guanine is guanosine, and thymine is thymidine.

NUCLEOTIDES

The nucleotides, because they are phosphoric esters of the nucleosides, are strong acids. The nomenclature thus includes adenylic acid, guanylic acid, and thymidylic acid as the respective nucleotides of the nucleosides just mentioned. Unfortunately, however, there is a dual system of nomenclature for these compounds. For example, adenylic acid may also be called adenosine monophosphate. The latter is more consistent with naming of the multiphosphorylated derivatives which are high-energy compounds (adenosine diphosphate and adenosine triphosphate).

The attachment of the phosphate group in an ester linkage is limited to the sugar moiety. Furthermore, group substitution is possible only at the 3′ and 5′ carbons if the sugar is deoxypentose and only at the 2′, 3′, and 5′ carbons if ribose is the sugar. You will recall that these locations are the only carbons with a free hydroxyl group.

NUCLEIC ACIDS

The determination of the structure of nucleic acids was a combination of physical and chemical techniques and biological intuition. The *a priori* assump-

```
                 |
                 O
                 |
          O=P—O—Sugar—Base
                 |         |
                 O⁻        O
                           |
                    O=P—O—Sugar—Base
                           |         |
                           O⁻        O
                                     |
                              O=P—O—Sugar—Base
                                     |         |
                                     O⁻        O
                                               |
                                        O=P—
                                               |
                                               O⁻
```

tion that these high-molecular weight acids were polymers of nucleotides was
borne out by early investigations. The phosphate residues of each nucleotide was
found to act as a bridge thus forming diesters.

Deoxyribonucleic acid

In the case of *deoxyribo*nucleic acid, the linkage between the sugars by the
phosphoric acid is a 3′-5′ straight chain link. This linkage must be made in
this manner in that the 3′ and 5′ carbons are the only positions in the sugar containing reactive hydroxyls. The base side chain is one of four purines and
pyrimidines: adenine, guanine, thymine, or cytosine. Our chemical information
about this molecule, fortunately, does not end here. Chromatography and
ultracentrifugation in cesium chloride ($CsCl_2$) indicate that the amounts of
the nucleotides of DNA may vary from species to species but the ratio of
adenine to thymine and guanine is cytosine approximates 1. That is

$$\frac{\text{Adenine}}{\text{Thymine}} = 1 \text{ but } \frac{\text{Adenine}}{\text{Guanine}} \neq 1$$

In April of 1953, J. D. Watson and F. H. C. Crick of Cambridge, England,
published their classic short article entitled simply, *Molecular Structure of
Nucleic Acids: A Structure for Deoxyribose Nucleic Acid.*[1] Their work, inspired
in part by the X-ray studies carried out by Wilkins and associates, proposed the
first workable model of DNA. Although some minor modifications and refine-
ments have since been made,[2,3] their basic premises were found to be sound.

In addition to those mentioned above, some of the data from which they
made their proposal is summarized as follows:
1. The molecule is long, thin, unbranched, and relatively straight.
2. X-ray patterns of DNA from different species are uniquely similar despite
   the fact that the amounts of individual bases may vary.
3. The distance from one phosphate group to the next cannot be more
   than 7 Å.
4. The molecule, however, repeats crystallographically every 28 Å.

The discrepancy between the chemical repeat units and the crystallographic
repeat units were explained by Watson and Crick as being due to an α-helix
of the phosphate-sugar backbone. Furthermore, this helix is made up of two
chains which run in opposite directions, yielding a double helical structure
(Fig. 7-1).

The atomic distances between the two chains is such that neither the two
purines nor the two pyrimidines can oppose each other. One purine must be
linked to one pyrimidine and the base ratio data suggest that adenine is always
attached to thymine and the guanine of one chain is opposite the cytosine of
the other chain. The linkage between base partners is that of a hydrogen bond.
The significance of this specific base pairing and the weak hydrogen linkage
will become apparent when the duplication of DNA is discussed.

The arrangement of all of these units, the sugar, phosphate, and bases, is
that of an open spiral staircase where the flat purines and pyrimidines are the

Fig. 7-1. Helical structure of DNA. The purine and pyrimidine bases are omitted to emphasize the twisting framework.

individual steps, with the sugar phosphate esters forming the vertical supporting framework (Fig. 7-2).

The flat sides of the bases are hydrophobic and do not easily bind water molecules. This sets up an attraction between the bases when the DNA is in an aqueous medium. The bonding due to mutual solubility, or mutual repulsion of the medium, lends stability, and this force, along with the hydrogen bonding of the opposing base pairs, helps to maintain the integrity of the molecule.

Several configurations of the DNA chain have been found, but only one apparently occurs in vivo. The A form of DNA was the first crystalline form to be observed. In this particular helix, the base pairs are tilted 70° from the vertical axis of the spiral—that is, 20° from a horizontal perpendicular plane. The B configuration is found in vivo and the bases here are on a plane perpendicular to the long axis of the molecule. Finally, the C configuration is an artifact of preparation.

Although most native DNA occurs in the typical double helix, there have been found some single-stranded DNA in some viruses. Exceptions to the fact that the nucleic acid is complexed with protein are found in the viruses and bacteria.

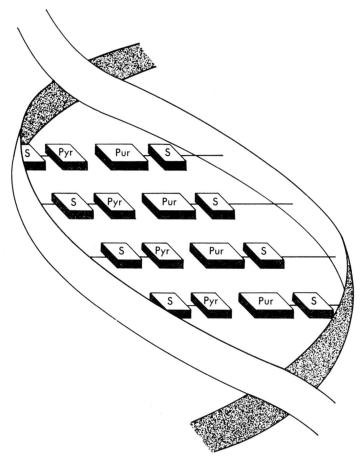

Fig. 7-2. Enlarged view of the α-helix of DNA diagrammatically that shows the location of the purine and pyrimidine bases in relation to the helical structure. A portion of the sugar moiety also projects into the center of the spiral. *Pur.,* Purine; *Pyr.,* pyrimidine; S, sugar.

Deoxyribonucleic acid is found in the nucleus of all living cells, except those such as erythrocytes which are anucleate. The occurrence of this acid is not restricted to the nucleus, though. The presence of DNA in bacteria which have no apparent nucleus, in the cytoplasm of most cells, and in the chloroplasts of the plant cells has been well established. What has not been determined, however, is the significance of this traditionally nuclear constituent in these seemingly ectopic areas.

The nucleic acids exhibit a fairly high acidity, and, as a result, they are normally found complexed in the cell with basic proteins. Those which are the most common generic classes of proteins are the histones and the protamines.

Ribonucleic acid

Ribonucleic acid is a branched, irregular molecule that has the same backbone of phosphates and sugars with the projecting side groups as does DNA.

The sugar involved, however, is the pentose sugar ribose, with the unsubstituted hydroxyl in the 2 position. It is at this —OH that the branching of the molecule may occur. Another difference is the kind of bases present. As in deoxyribonucleic acid, RNA contains adenine, guanine, and cytosine (or methyl cytosine), but thymine is replaced by uracil.

Methylated purines have been found in RNA. The presence of 6-methyl aminopurine was reported by Adler,[4] and Littlefield and Dunn[5] report the occurrence of 6-methyl adenine purine and 6-dimethyl aminopurine in certain forms of ribonucleic acid.

The study of RNA is compounded by the fact that there is more than one species of this nucleic acid. Transfer RNA, messenger RNA, and ribosomal RNA are the three members of the genus. However, it has been found that the RNA chain is very similar to the A configuration of DNA; that is to say, there is a helical structure with tilted base pairs occurring along the spiral.

Ribonucleic acid is primarily localized in association with the ribosome particles on the endoplasmic reticulum. RNA does occur in other areas—for instance, in the nucleus. The transfer RNA and the messenger RNA are not bound to proteins and, as a result, are more free to move around the cell.

PHYSIOLOGICAL IMPORTANCE

The physiological importance of the nucleic acids will not be dealt with here. We must appreciate that as biochemical constituents of the cell the nucleic acids present a patterned molecule whose structure and function involve all the physiological activity of the cell. But this is another story.

SUMMARY

The purines and pyrimidines are among the more important biochemical constituents of the cell. Although their role primarily involves that of the macromolecules ribonucleic and deoxyribonucleic acids, they have some accessory functions which are of value to the cell. Examples of purines and pyrimidines which are not nucleic acid components are thiamine (B_1), coenzyme A, NAD, FAD, and ATP.

Literature cited

1. Watson, J. D., and F. H. C. Crick, 1953. Molecular structure of nucleic acids: A structure for deoxyribose nucleic acid. Nature 171:737.
2. Langridge, R., H. R. Wilson, C. W. Hooper, M. H. F. Wilkins, and L. D. Hamilton, 1960. The molecular configuration of deoxyribonucleic acid. I. X-ray diffraction study of a crystalline form of the lithium salt. J. Molec. Biol. 2:19.
3. Langridge, R., D. A. Marvin, W. E. Seeds, H. R. Wilson, C. W. Hooper, M. H. F. Wilkins, and L. D. Hamilton, 1960. The molecular configuration of deoxyribonucleic acid. II. Molecular models and their fourier transform. J. Molec. Biol. 2:38.
4. Adler, M., B. Weissmann, and A. B. Gutman, 1958. Occurrence of methylated purine bases in yeast ribonucleic acid. J. Biol. Chem. 230:717.
5. Littlefield, J. W., and D. B. Dunn, 1958. The occurrence and distribution of thymine and three methylated-adenine bases in ribonucleic acids from several sources. Biochem. J. 70:642.

General references

Annual review of biochemistry (yearly). Annual Reviews, Inc., Palo Alto, California.

Baker, J. J. W., and G. E. Allen. 1965. Matter, energy and life. Addison-Wesley Publishing Company, Inc., Palo Alto, Calif.

Chargaff, E., and J. N. Davidson (editors). The nucleic acids. Chemistry and biology, vols. 1 and 2, 1955; vol. 3, 1960. Academic Press, Inc., New York.

Davidson, J. N. 1960. The biochemistry of the nucleic acids. 4th ed. John Wiley & Sons, Inc., New York.

Karlson, P. 1963. Introduction to modern biochemistry. Academic Press, Inc., New York.

Kleiner, I. S., and J. M. Orten. 1962. Biochemistry. 6th ed. The C. V. Mosby Co., St. Louis.

Perutz, M. F. 1962. Proteins and nucleic acids. Elsevier Publishing Co., Amsterdam.

White, A., P. Handler, and E. L. Smith. 1964. Principles of biochemistry, 3rd ed. McGraw-Hill Book Co., New York.

Wilkins, M. H. F. 1963. Molecular configuration of nucleic acids. Science 140:941.

8

Porphyrins, quinones, and other organic constituents

INTRODUCTION

It would be impossible in a short chapter to discuss in any depth the chemistry and physiology of all of the organic constituents of the cell not mentioned in the previous chapters. However, several classes of these compounds will be discussed superficially not only because of academic interest but also because the ones chosen are so directly involved in physiological phenomena of the cell. Such excellent series as Florkin and Mason's *Comparative Biochemistry* or the *Annual Review of Physiology* should be consulted for a concentrated study of these compounds.

PORPHYRINS

The first group of compounds is one found ubiquitously in nature, occurring in forms from the bacteria through the cells of vertebrates and angiosperms. Their involvement in such activities as oxidation, photosynthesis, and electron transport necessitates at least a cursory examination of their chemical properties and biological functions.

Chemistry

Porphin

The porphyrins are derivatives of the macrocyclic porphin ring. This structure contains four unsubstituted pyrrole rings which are linked by methene bridges.

In nature, this form rarely occurs in that the internal hydrogens are usually replaced by metallic ions and the peripheral hydrogens by organic groups. Placing of the double bonds in the structural formula is arbitrary because of the high degree of resonance occurring in the molecule.

The chemical nomenclature of the porphyrins is determined by the number of dissimilar groups replacing the peripheral hydrogen. For example, if there are two dissimilar groups such as CH_3 and C_2H_5, the general class of porphyrins are known as etioporphyrins. Since there are four possible isomeric arrangements of these two groups, the resulting compounds are known as etioporphyrins I, II, III, and IV, respectively.

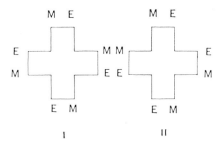

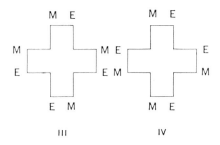

Etioporphyrins

Substitution of methyl and propionate yields four coproporphyrins, and four uroporphyrins result from isomeric arrangements of the acetate and propionate groups. The characteristics of the porphyrins, then, are determined by these addition groups and the complexing ion, if any, in the center of the porphin ring.

The most prevalent group of porphyrins, the protoporphyrins, contains three dissimilar groups—four methyl, two vinyl, and two propionate residues. Of the fifteen possible isomers of protoporphyrins, the arrangement known as protoporphyrin IX has the greatest biological significance.

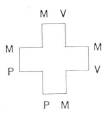

Protoporphyrin IX

Because of their ability to form complexes with metal ions, rarely do the porphyrins found in biological systems occur free. Iron is often the ion with which the porphyrin is complexed. The ferro-to-ferri shift allows the porphyrin to have more than one species of charge, a characteristic which is important to many compounds. Copper and magnesium are also found in the porphyrins as the complexing ion. These metalloporphyrin complexes are usually colored, and when in combination with a protein moiety, they are capable of unique physiological processes.

Traditionally, the heme portion of hemoglobin is dissected chemically and functionally as an example of a metalloporphyrin, and we will not digress from this.

As in most metal–porphyrin complexes, this combination in the heme portion of hemoglobin is not a true salt. Here the divalent iron atom replaces the two dissociable hydrogen atoms of the pyrrole rings of protoporphyrin IX and simultaneously binds to the remaining rings by coordinate valences. The bonds are in resonance, as are the double bonds in the porphin nucleus.

The resultant ferroprotoporphyrin, or heme, is the prosthetic group of hemo-globins, occurring in a ratio of 4:1 with the protein moiety, the globin. Only the latter seems to be species specific in that the ferroprotoporphyrin moiety is identical in all mammals studied. The attachment of the hemes to the globin is such that the valency does not change when oxygen is added to the molecule. Since the coordination number of ferrous iron is 6, and since four of the bonds are involved in the metallocomplex, the remaining two available bonds are believed to be involved with the attachment of the ferroprotoporphyrin to the globin. All evidence points to the nitrogens of imidazole residues as being the locus of bonding (Fig. 8-1), and it is across this bond that the oxygen is believed to be added.

The ferroprotoporphyrin IX serves as the prosthetic group of several enzymes in addition to being an integral part of heme and its derivatives. These compounds and their occurrence are summarized in Table 8-1.

Physiological importance

The porphyrins have physiological functions which span both the animal and plant kingdoms. In addition to the familiar role as oxygen carriers in hemoglobin, myoglobin, chlorocruorin, and erythrocruorin, this class of compounds is directly involved in such activities as photosynthesis and intra-

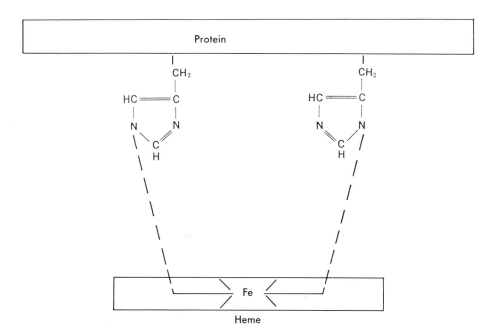

Fig. 8-1. Diagrammatic representation of imidazole linkage between heme and globin. The nitrogens of the imidazole residues of histidine form the fifth and sixth linkages to the iron of the porphyrin.

Table 8-1. Some important derivatives of iron and protoporphyrin IX*

Class of compound	Compound	Occurrence and remarks
Heme	Hematin	Oxidation product of heme; present in red blood cells of organisms with malaria; certain poisonings and other pathological conditions
	Heme	Prosthetic group of hemoglobins
Respiratory carriers	Chlorocruorin	Found in some annelids, particularly in polychaetes
	Erythrocruorin	Found in most invertebrates which contain a respiratory pigment: e.g., insects, nematodes, oligochaetes, crustaceans, molluscs, and echinoderms
	Hemoglobin	Four hemes plus globin with iron in ferro^{++} state; found in red blood cells of all vertebrates
	Myohemoglobin	Found in muscle cells of higher vertebrates
Enzymes	Catalase	Present in aerobic cells and a few anaerobes; destroys H_2O_2
	Cytochromes	Electron transport carriers in most animal and plant cells
	Peroxidase	Occurs in plant and animal cells; probably functions similar to catalase

*Data compiled from Spector, W. S. (editor), Handbook of biological data. 1956. W. B. Saunders Co., Philadelphia.

cellular oxidation and electron transport. The terminal oxidation in aerobic cells is totally dependent upon the presence of the cytochrome system, and both the cytochromes and the enzyme oxidizing them, cytochrome oxidase, are ferro-protoporphyrins. In plant cells, the photosynthetic phenomenon is, of course, the role of the chlorophylls, a magnesium complex of a porphyrin derivative.

The province of the porphyrins in the cell, then, is that of storing oxygen and/or utilizing this oxygen to complete basic physiological functions. It is no surprise to find these compounds occurring in each and every cell type in both kingdoms.

QUINONES

The quinones have only recently come to the fore as a group of important chemicals in the cell. Their significance was at one time thought to be limited to that of being natural pigments. These colored compounds do occur in many phyla, particularly flowering plants, fungi, arthropods, echinoderms, and bacteria. However, there are many other areas in which the quinones serve the cell. The only facet which will be discussed is their involvement in the electron transport system of both animals and plants.

Chemistry

The quinones are unsaturated ring structures having two carbonyl groups in *para* position. The parent, or base, structure may contain 1, 2, 3, or 5 rings, but there are still only two oxygens present.

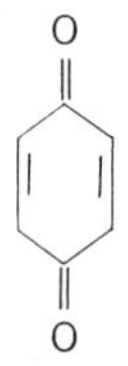

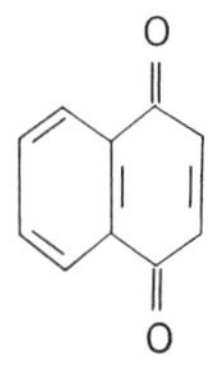

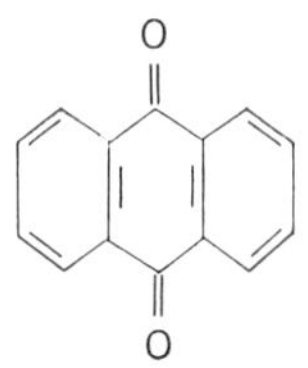

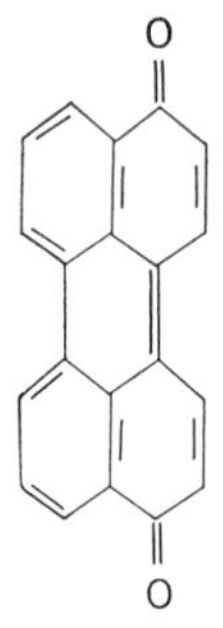

Physiological importance

A series of benzoquinones known as the ubiquinones (coenzyme Q) is involved as a group in respiratory electron transport and possible oxidative

Table 8-2. The vitamins*

Vitamin	Chemical nature	Function
A	Terpene	Maintains integrity of epithelial cells; precursor to visual pigments; may be involved in synthesis of chondroitin sulfate
Ascorbic acid	Hexalactone	Integrity of mesenchymal cell functions; may act synergistically with folic acid; involved in iron exchange; may participate, with its oxidized form, in redox reactions
Biotin	Fatty acid derivative	Prosthetic group of enzymes involved in CO_2 fixation and synthesis of fatty acids
Choline	(β-hydroxyethyl)- trimethyl ammonium hydroxide	Integral part of membrane phospholipids; methyl group transfer
Cobalamin (B_{12})	Porphyrin derivative	Participates in interconversion of some Krebs cycle intermediates; methylation reactions
D	Sterol	Promotes intestinal uptake of calcium and phosphorus reabsorption in renal tubule
E (α-tocopherol)	Terpene	Necessary for sperm motility; integrity of epithelium of renal tubule and germinal epithelium; inhibits auto-oxidation of fatty acids; i.e., acts as an antioxidant
Folic acid (pteroyl glutamic)	Pterin derivative	Carrier of 1 carbon groups (hydroxymethyl and formyl); involved in purine and thymine synthesis
Inositol	Cyclohexane	May be lipotropic; alternate functions doubtful
K	Quinone	Involved in synthesis of prothrombin; may be involved in redox reactions
Nicotinic acid (niacin)	Pyridine derivative	Participates as NAD and NADP in electron transport
Pantothenic acid	Pantoyl β-alanine	Helps maintain integrity of adrenal cortical cells; component of CoA
Pyridoxine (B_6)	Pyridine derivative	Transamination and amino acid interconversion; may be involved in active transport of amino acids
Riboflavin (B_2)	Isoalloxazine derivative	Participates in electron transfer as FAD and FMN
Thiamine (B_1)	Pyrimidine derivative	Participates in many reactions yielding CO_2 as a product; i.e., acts as cocarboxylase

*Data compiled from Spector, W. S. (editor). Handbook of biological data. 1956. W. B. Saunders Co., Philadelphia; and Altman, P. L., and D. S. Dittmer (editors). Biology data book. 1964. Federation of American Societies for Experimental Biology, Washington, D. C.

phosphorylation. Coenzyme Q is located in the mitochondria and participates in the electron transport chain by being located possibly between other electron or hydrogen carriers and the cytochromes. The role of coenzyme Q in the electron transport chain is uncertain, although some very feasible postulates have been presented (Chapter 21). Plastoquinone, on the other hand, is the chloroplast pigment involved in photosynthetic electron transport.

OTHER ORGANIC CONSTITUENTS

In addition to the previously mentioned groups, there is an array of secondary chemical constituents of the cell whose functions remain somewhat in obscurity in that the exact biological reactions of the compounds are not completely understood. The pteridines, of which folic acid is a representative, the flavinoids, and the terpenoids are a few of these minor groups. Their value to the functioning cell is not always clear, but what is clear is their widespread occurrence. This latter infers an integral function in the overall physiology of the cellular system. At this time, there is no clear picture as to what these duties may be. Some of these constituents do occur as vitamins, however, and knowledge about their function is more advanced. These data are summarized on Table 8-2.

SUMMARY

The biochemistry and characteristics of some of the minor organic constituents of the cell are considered. These substances are minor in degree of prevalence in the cell, but their functions are not necessarily secondary. The porphyrins are active ring structures, being involved in such physiological processes as electron transport and photosynthesis. The quinones are also believed to participate in electron transport. Other organic constituents, particularly the vitamins, are critical to the dynamics of the cell.

General references

Annual review of biochemistry (yearly). Annual Reviews, Inc., Palo Alto, Calif.

Karlson, P. 1963. Introduction to modern biochemistry. Academic Press, Inc., New York.

Kleiner, I. S., and J. M. Orten. 1962. Biochemistry. 6th ed. The C. V. Mosby Co., St. Louis.

Rimington, C., and G. Y. Kennedy. 1962. Porphyrins: Structure, distribution, and metabolism, vol. 4, pp. 558-607. In Florkin M., and H. S. Mason (editors): Comparative biochemistry. Academic Press, Inc., New York.

Thomson, R. H. 1962. Quinones: Structure and distribution, vol. 3, pp. 631-713. In Florkin M., and H. S. Mason (editors): Comparative biochemistry. Academic Press, Inc., New York.

White, A., P. Handler, and E. L. Smith. 1964. Principles of biochemistry. 3rd ed. McGraw-Hill Book Co., Inc., New York.

The physiochemical environment

No biological activity at the cellular level is apart from being influenced by the environment in which the cell exists. Neither can these activities occur as they do in biosystems without a certain finite set of physiochemical prerequisites being met. The external fluctuation of such parameters as temperature, atmospheric and osmotic pressures, incident radiation, and pH affects the coordinated functioning of the cell. In addition, the peculiar colloid state of the protoplasm dictates a series of physiochemical phenomena modifying these effects and introducing supplementary ones which, together, help control the internal environment of the cell.

This section deals with the cell environment—both external and internal—and that physiochemical state peculiar to the integrity of a functioning cell, the colloid. The discussion of biocolloids (Chapter 9) is followed by an investigation of the roles of electrolytes, temperature effects, and radiation effects on the functioning cell.

9

Biocolloids

INTRODUCTION

No discussion of cellular phenomena could be complete without developing some feeling for the physical state which facilitates, if not dictates, many of these phenomena. In the final analysis, the study of the colloid helps to explain and predict the behavior of the molecular components of the cell, but it must be kept in mind during this study that a colloid is a state of matter and not a kind of matter.

CHARACTERISTICS OF THE COLLOIDAL STATE

The definition of the colloidal state—that system which exhibits colloidal properties—is totally unrevealing. Some enlightenment can be gained by describing such a state. The colloid is a two-phase state whereby one phase, the dispersed phase, is suspended in the second phase, the dispersal phase. This two-phase system, however, generally involves size limitations on the particle or molecule making up the dispersed phase. Arbitrarily, the limit normally imposed is that the dimensions of one of the components must be between 10 and 1000 Å. Because of these arbitrary limits, there is no sharp line of demarcation between the colloidal and the noncolloidal state, and therefore, the most important single criterion is that the two-phase mixture must behave like a true colloid.

The true colloid has a series of properties which in themselves are not unique, but they are consistently present in this colloidal state. Three such properties might be mentioned. First, the colloids show higher viscosity than normally would be expected for the amount of material in the system, second, chemical activity is generally quite high, and, third, colloids do not seem to conform to the expected behavior of observed phenomena associated with colligative properties. Colloids have other peculiar, and very salient, properties which will be developed as the discussion progresses.

Table 9-1. Classification of colloids

Class	Dispersed phase	Dispersal phase	Example
1	Liquid	Solid	Pearl; organic liquids in rocks
2	Liquid	Liquid	Any emulsion
3	Liquid	Gas	Aerosols; fog
4	Solid	Solid	Ruby glass
5	Solid	Gas	Smoke
6	Gas	Liquid	Foam
7	Gas	Solid	Some minerals
8	Solid	Liquid	Biological systems (proteins in aqueous medium)

The three states of matter can be combined as a colloidal state into eight permutations (Table 9-1). The ninth possibility, gas in gas, does not occur since gas molecules uniformly disperse and do not aggregate into groups large enough to exhibit colloidal properties.

Class 8, solid in liquid, is biologically the most important in that the individual constituents of the cell often exist in this form. In light of this, our discussion will be focused on this class.

LYOPHILIC, LYOPHOBIC, AND ASSOCIATIVE COLLOIDS

Three distinct categories of solid in liquid colloids exist: lyophobic, lyophilic, and the associative or complex colloid, which is a combination of the first two.

Characteristics

The distinction between the lyophilic and the lyophobic colloids is the degree of affinity for the solvent in which the particle or molecule is dispersed. A strong attraction between the two phases as exists in the lyophilic colloids yields a system which is thermodynamically stable and is, in most senses, a true solution. On the other hand, a system in which there is little attraction between the solvent and the particles (lyophobic) is thermodynamically unstable and depends on a series of forces to maintain its integrity as a colloid. Mysels[1] has sophisticated the stability terminology by using *diuturnal* to describe a relatively stable system and *caducous* to describe an unstable system.

The associative or complex colloids consist of aggregates of smaller molecules which may have both lyophilic and lyophobic components.

Forces involved in stability

Apart from the unique surface events which occur in colloids, there are a series of forces which are involved in the maintenance of the stability of the colloidal state. The degree to which each is involved depends upon the property of the particular colloid.

We might list the forces as follows:

1. Kinetic energy—the molecules of the dispersing phase bombard the particles to give brownian movement.

2. Mutual solubility of two phases—primarily occurs in lyophilic colloids.
3. Electrostatic forces—attraction between charged groups allows orientation and could increase stability; conversely, this attraction could lower the stability; repulsion could enhance stability.
4. van der Waals forces—attractions between noncharged groups could support the electrostatic forces to promote aggregation.

These forces interact to give a certain stability to the colloid. As was pointed out earlier, however, the prime factor determining stability is the degree of affinity of the particle for the solvent—that is, whether the colloid is lyophilic or lyophobic.

Biological importance

The lyophilic colloids are biologically important to the cell in that many of the enzymic and enzymatic-like reactions occur on the surface of their thermodynamically stable particles. The proteins, and the nucleic acids, are prominent members of this category. The fact that the macromolecules of the cell fall mainly into the lyophilic grouping is not surprising. The uncertainties involved in the stability of lyophobic colloids would be a strong deterrent factor. In discussing properties of lyophilic colloids, it should be reemphasized that they are very close to being true solutions. The subtle differences will be brought out later.

The lyophobic colloids, although predictably unstable, still have their role in biological systems. Not all the metabolites of the cell are water soluble, and even some of those which are exist in greater concentration than one can physically put into solution in a test tube.

The associative, or complex, colloid blends the properties of both its lyophilic and lyophobic counterparts. The particles which participate in the associative colloid are stable aggregates of substances having both lyophobic and lyophilic components. These large aggregates, called micelles,* are quite stable due to the orientation of the soluble and the nonsoluble parts.

The line separating these three categories of colloids in biological systems is gray, and the nomenclature is mainly as a point of reference. Clearly there are colloids which behave purely as one kind or another, but when they are placed together in a dynamically functioning cell, the distinction is sometimes lost. These three do share, however, a series of special phenomena peculiar to the colloidal state.

SURFACE PHENOMENA

The very core of colloidal activity is the surface phenomena that accompany these systems. The critical surface-to-volume ratio of the suspended particles or micelles yields a tremendous surface area upon which many of the reactions of the cell occur. The classical example to demonstrate the surface area potential is given by comparing the surface of a cube 1 cm on a side (6 cm^2 area) to the same cube if cut into bits 0.1 μ on a side (600,000 cm^2). A finite limit is

---

*The term *micelle* is used by some authors to denote any colloidal particle of large size.

reached, however, where the surface of each particle is too small to allow for the various surface phenomenon associated with colloids to occur. It is at this point that the system is called a crystalloid.

Assuming this very large surface area in the colloid, one can see that an interface is established between the particles and the solvent and that the characteristics of this interface vary, depending on the degree of affinity between the two phases. In either case, the active forces at this interface are proportional to the surface area.

Surface energy

There are two distinct forces at work in a colloidal system—the kinetic energy which is dependent upon the characteristics of the particle and the surface energy which is dependent upon the interface. This surface energy is the product of two factors. The intensity factor, which is the surface or interfacial tension, and the capacity factor, which is the extent of surface area, both contribute to the overall surface energy.

Surface, or interfacial, tension, which occurs due to the imbalance of particles at the interface (Fig. 9-1), is of prime importance in biological systems. The very fact that the enzyme-substrate interactions are, in part, a surface phenomenon suggests the role of surface tension in these processes. The physics of this force will not be dealt with; however, it should be mentioned that the unit of measurement is dynes per centimeter, or force per unit area. To the biologist, the concept of surface tension must be understood. This active, interfacial force can participate in many cellular phenomena—enzyme reactions, pinocytosis, and

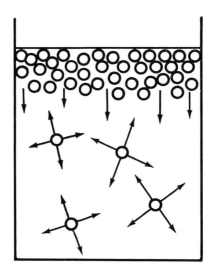

Fig. 9-1. Molecular interaction in surface tension. The vectors on molecules in the center of the liquid are balanced, with no net force in any direction. The molecules on the surface have unbalanced vectors, yielding a net force downward. The result is closer packing of molecules at the surface.

active transport being only a few. Surface tension, and thus surface energy, is an active form of energy and is readily converted into work or other forms of energy. This high energy is necessary in a cellular environment where large amounts of energy are needed in a small area.

Adsorption

Colloids owe many of their properties to the surface phenomena, of which surface energy is only one. A property directly related to surface tension is that of adsorption. Adsorption is the concentration of material at the interface where the two phases of the colloid are in contact. This accumulation, which is generally nonstoichiometric (Fig. 9-2), is dependent upon the total surface area available for adsorption, the nature of the interface, and the properties of the adsorbed material.

Again, the use of a classical example illustrates the principle quite easily. If one liquid is placed on another, the added liquid will either form a series of droplets or will spread over the surface of the second fluid. If the resultant surface tension of the two combined liquids is greater than either one separately, the droplets will form. On the other hand, if the surface tension of either liquid alone is greater than the sum of the surface tension after addition, a spreading will occur. This lowering of the interfacial tension facilitates the adsorption process.

Take, for example, oil and water. If a small amount of oil is placed on a pure water surface, a droplet will form. To cause it to spread, one merely has

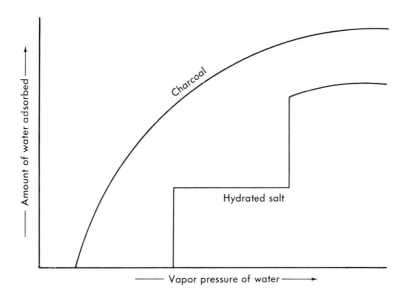

Fig. 9-2. Comparison of stoichiometric and nonstoichiometric uptake of water. As the vapor pressure is increased, the adsorption, or nonstoichiometric uptake, of water by charcoal shows a smooth curve. Stoichiometric uptake, as illustrated by hydration of a salt, is a stepwise process.

to add some third substance, alcohol for instance, which will accumulate at the interface of the two fluids. The addition of alcohol causes the oil to spread and the alcohol to be sandwiched between the two immiscible liquids with its polar end oriented toward the water layer and the nonpolar end toward the oil. The overall effect is to reduce surface tension. A molecule need not be polar to lower the surface tension and thus be adsorbed, but in biological systems with their many lipoid-aqueous and lipoid-protein interfaces, polarity plays an important role.

Electrokinetic phenomenon

Like many similar phenomena (Gibbs-Donnan, for example) the electrokinetic properties associated with colloidal particles cannot truly be measured without a series of assumptions and approximations. Accepting these terms, one can develop some theories and models which imply more than prove; however, these discussions are very useful in that they mimic the kinds of physiochemical phenomena which can be quantitatively measured at higher levels.

The fact has been established that any particular surface has the tendency to adsorb particles at the interface. Thus, either as a result of the adsorption phenomena or the conditions in the solution, there may be a layer of ions along the surface which can impart an overall charge to an otherwise noncharged micelle.

This first adsorbed layer is generally monomolecular and fairly stabilized

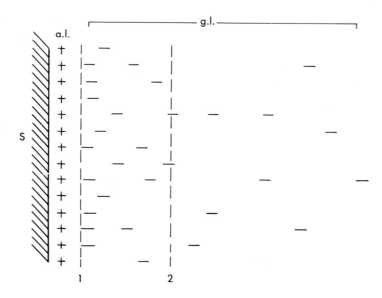

Fig. 9-3. The electrokinetic phenomenon. A surface, *S*, adsorbs a monomolecular layer of ions of one charge, *a.l.* This adsorption causes attraction of ions of opposite sign, the gegen ions, *g.l.* Calculation of the electrokinetic potential is carried out by treating the diffuse gegen ion layer as a plate condenser, with one plate being at the innermost layer of ions, *1,* and the second plate being at the center of gravity of the gegen ions, *2.*

at the interface (Fig. 9-3). As a result of this layer of charged ions, there is an orientation of the ions of opposite charge, called gegen ions or counterions around this now charged micelle. This second layer, which is diffuse in contrast to the unimolecular first layer, yields an electrokinetic potential which is called the zeta potential. If this potential could be accurately measured, it would be determined by thermodynamically treating the system as a plate condenser, with one plate being the innermost layer of counterions and the other plate being the center of gravity of these gegen ions.

$$\zeta = \frac{4\,\pi\,\delta\,\sigma}{\epsilon}$$

where δ is the distance between plates, σ the charge density, and ϵ the dielectric constant. In theory, however, it can be established that this aura of ions does have electrokinetic properties. In the lyophobic colloids, a high zeta potential would give more stability to the system; even the lyophilic colloids, containing proteins, may have areas along the micelle where ion orientation occurs. It should be pointed out here that in the aqueous biological system the polar water molecules may act as the adsorbed ions, yielding a layer of hydration.

PARTICLE STATES

Particles in aqueous colloidal states can take one of four forms (Fig. 9-4).
A. Uncharged and unhydrated (lyophobic)
B. Charged and unhydrated (lyophobic)
C. Uncharged and hydrated (lyophilic)
D. Charged and hydrated (lyophilic)
In states B and D the charge may be due to either the net charge of the molecule or the charge imparted by adsorbed ions. In states A and C, the zeta potential has collapsed, although C has a layer of hydration. These are the least stable systems. The collapse of the potential is very nicely accomplished by the addition of salts which disrupt this zeta potential. This technique has practical

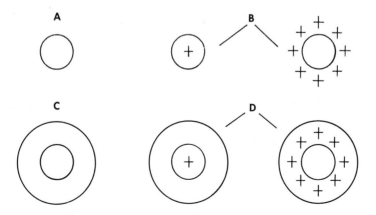

Fig. 9-4. Various forms which particles in an aqueous colloid can take. (See text.)

application in the "salting out" of proteins from a colloidal suspension in that the salt first collapses the zeta potential and, on higher concentrations, strips the layer of hydration. Either, or both, causes the individual protein molecules to aggregate.

SOL-GEL STATES

In biological systems, the physical state of the colloid is extremely important. Whether it acts as a solution (the sol state) or as a semirigid structure (the gel state) is critical to the functioning of the cell. In a dynamic situation, the cell is capable, under special circumstances, of bringing about reversible conversion between the sol and the gel. Thus the same colloid may be either a sol or a gel, depending on prevailing conditions.

In a gel, the micelles are relatively immobile in relation to each other and therefore form an elastic system through which the suspending fluid can freely traverse. To form such a structural framework, some of the micelles must be fibrous since fibers cover the greatest area with the smallest amount of material. In the cell, the protein chains are well suited for this purpose. An additional prerequisite, that the fibers be lyophilic, is also met by the proteins.

For stability, these fibrous compounds must be linked together in some manner as to give enough rigidity to form the characteristic gel and yet be weak enough since the transformation into the sol is reversible (Fig. 9-5).

There are several possibilities of linkage which could fit into a biological system, and these are enumerated below:

1. Hydrogen bonding
2. Mutual solubility
3. Electrostatic interaction
4. van der Waals force

Notice that these are exactly the forces which also impart tertiary structure to proteins.

WATER PHENOMENA

The solvent phase of the colloid undergoes some characteristic behaviors which are unique to the colloid state.

Imbibition

In an aqueous medium, the uptake of water by the colloidal system is called imbibition. This can be an extremely strong force, depending on how lyophilic the colloid is. In cell development and in embryological growth and differentiation, imbibition plays an important role.

Water retention and bound water

The corollary to imbibition in a lyophilic system is the water retentive properties of colloids. The ability of colloids to hold on to their water is evidenced by the different "dry weights" obtained under different conditions (Fig. 9-6). From this figure, it can be seen that it is very difficult to remove all the water

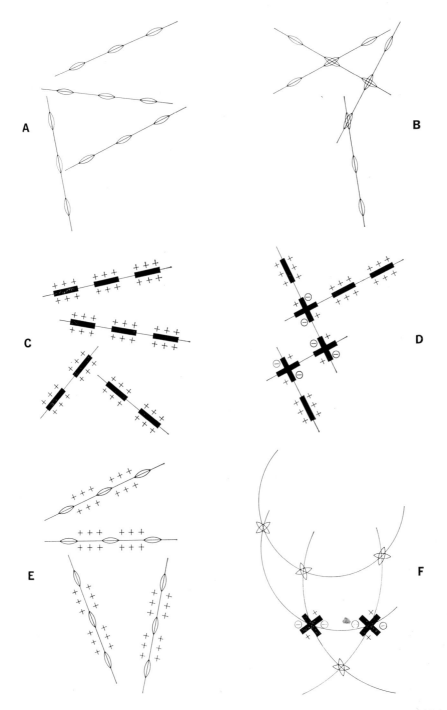

Fig. 9-5. Sol-to-gel conversion in thermogels and ionogels. In the first conversion, which is typical of thermogels, the protein fibers have areas on them which are mutually soluble due to layers of solvation. In **A**, thermal agitation keeps the micelles from aggregating. In **B**, a lower temperature reduces the thermal agitation, and the particles cling together at these areas of mutual solubility. In ionogels, the particles are stabilized by electrokinetic charges which keep the micelles apart (**C**). However, if these charges are stripped, or modified to bring about an attraction, the gel will form (**D**). Most biological systems are stabilized by both charges and regions of solvation. Conversion from the sol (**E**) to the gel (**F**) involves both of these phenomena.

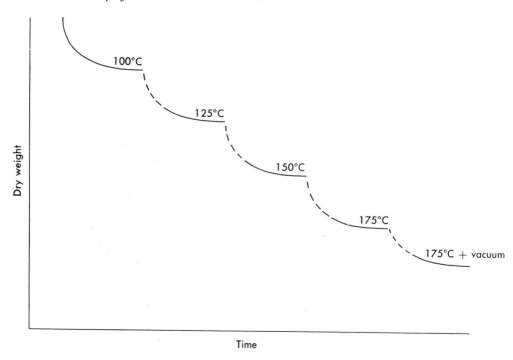

Fig. 9-6. The effect of increased temperature on the dry weight of a colloid, illustrating retention of water in the system.

from a colloid. Because of this fact, some workers differentiate between bound and free water. Bound water is defined as that water which is so tied up that it is not available for reactivity. The free water, conversely, is that which can participate in the normal activities of the cell. The difference would seem to be an adsorption effect, with the "bound" water being that which is more tightly adsorbed to the colloidal particles.

Hysteresis and syneresis

Two phenomena which involve the amount of water retention and/or the percent of "bound" water are hysteresis and syneresis.

In vitro, it has been found that the ability of a colloid to take up water may depend on previous treatment of the colloidal system. Alternate heating and cooling and shift in pH are two physiochemical changes that may affect this uptake. To what extent this occurs in a living cell is not certain. In theory, hysteresis may be used to partially explain other phenomena, but again the extent is obscure at this point.

Spontaneous loss of water from a colloidal system is called syneresis. This process seems to involve two separate, but interrelated, factors. Increased binding among the fibrillar micelles from an increased number of cross-links both decreases the sites for water adsorption and more tightly binds the system. Second, the fibrillar micelles may undergo changes which make them less hydrophilic. Both factors are important in cell aging, where water retention is significantly decreased.

SUMMARY

Colloidal phenomena are an integral part of the properties of the dynamic cell.

The reactions and the interactions in the cell are surface events and, thus, *colloidal* events. This sketchy résumé of the peculiarities of this physical state was provided in hopes that better understanding of and insight into the biological reactions will be gained.

Literature cited

1. Mysels, K. J. 1959. Introduction to colloid chemistry. Interscience Publishers, Inc., New York.

General references

Bayliss, L. E. 1959. Principles of general physiology. 5th ed. John Wiley & Sons, Inc., New York.

Gortner, R. A., Jr., and W. A. Gortner. 1949. Outlines of biochemistry. 3rd ed. John Wiley & Sons, Inc., New York.

Hansen, R. S., and C. A. Smolders. 1962. Colloid and surface chemistry in the mainstream of modern chemistry. J. Chem. Education 39:167.

Kruyt, H. R., and J. Th. G. Overbeek. 1962. An introduction to physical chemistry for biologists and medical students with special reference to colloid chemistry. Holt, Rinehart & Winston, Inc., New York.

Ling, G. N. 1962. A physical theory of the living state: The association-induction hypothesis. Blaisdell Publishing Co., New York.

Symposium on biocolloids. 1956. Gatlinburg, Tennessee. Sponsored by the Biology Division, Oak Ridge National Laboratory. Reprinted in J. Cell. & Comp. Physiol. 1957. 49: supp. 1.

Vold, M. J., and R. D. Vold. 1964. Colloid chemistry. Reinhold Publishing Corp., New York.

West, E. S. 1963. Textbook of biophysical chemistry. 3rd ed. The Macmillan Co., New York.

10

The role of electrolytes

INTRODUCTION

The role of electrolytes in the cell is not only maintenance of local pH and ionic strength but also participation in many physiological processes. Mediation of the enzyme-substrate complex, contraction, selective activity of the membranes, irritability, and integrity of the colloidal state are but a few of the activities of the cell in which electrolytes are involved. It is important, then, that the concepts of acid-base chemistry be understood, and, in particular, it is necessary to grasp the biological ramifications of these concepts—the phenomena of buffering and dissociation. Although all of the ions or electrolytes do not directly contribute to the buffering systems of the cell, the fact that they are ions indicates that the effect of their charge is exerted upon the buffers themselves.

BUFFERING

Very rarely in a biological system are the strong acids and bases encountered. Among the notable exceptions are certain sulfur bacteria and the cells producing hydrochloric acid in the stomach of vertebrates. Therefore, attention must be directed toward a discussion of the weak acids and bases which exhibit those properties which make them ideal for biological application. The peculiarities of reversible dissociation and the nonlinear relationship between pH and available hydrogen and hydroxyl ions as seen in buffering are fully exploited in cellular systems.

The pH concept

The concept of pH, as pioneered by such workers as Sørenson and Brønsted, reduces to simplest form the hydrogen ion concentration. The fact that this ion concentration can be expressed in logarithmic form, $pH = -\log [H^+]$ or $\log 1/[H^+]$, yields values to which one can more easily attach significance. The pH scale of 0 to 14 with 0 to 7 connoting an acidic solution, 7 a neutral solution, and 7 to 14 an alkaline solution can be used with some ease. However, the convenience of this scale offers some areas of misinterpretation. It may not be obvious, for instance, that a solution with pH 4.7 has twice the hydrogen ion concentration of a solution with pH 5. Simple arithmetic bears this out in that the solution of pH 4.7 must have an ion concentration of 2×10^{-5} N, whereas, the solution of pH 5 has a $[H^+]$ of 1×10^{-5} N. Pursuing this same argument, it must be remembered that an increase or decrease of 1 pH unit is the equivalent of a tenfold increase or decrease in hydrogen ion concentration.

The basis of buffering

It must be assumed that the concepts of basic chemistry such as the mass action law, milliequivalents, conjugate acids and bases, titration, and dissociation are well assimilated before appreciating the biological aspects of acid-base chemistry and buffering. If certain areas are unclear, the excellent self-teaching manual on pH and dissociation by Christensen[1] should be consulted. The specific examples presented here are abstracted from his book.

Recall that the Henderson-Hasselbalch equation.

$$pH = pKa + \log \frac{[salt]}{[acid]} \, ,$$

is used to determine the degree of dissociation of a weak acid at a certain hydro-

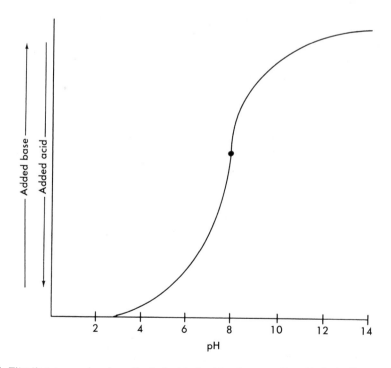

Fig. 10-1. Titration curve showing effect of added acid or base on the pH of a buffered solution.

gen ion concentration. From this equation, the amounts of the salt form, or conjugate base, and its weak acid can be determined. What is also implicit is that when the conjugate base and the weak acid are in a ratio of 1:1, the pH equals the pKa. Since this ratio provides the most effective buffering, or resistance to pH change, the best buffer system would seem to be made up of a conjugate base and weak acid whose pKa is near the desired pH. In Fig. 10-1 is shown the flattening of the curve at the pK, which indicates a small pH change during added acid or base.

Ideally a buffer system would be more effective if the molecule were capable of more than one dissociation, giving strong buffering at each pK value. The very dominant phosphate buffer system in the cell does, in fact, exhibit this multiple dissociation. With the three ion species of $PO_4^{\equiv}$, $HPO_4^{=}$, and $H_2PO_4^{-}$, one would expect three distinct flat areas of the sigmoid titration curve. This is well illustrated in Fig. 10-2.

In addition to the phosphate system, the carbonate system also contributes to the buffering ability of the cell. Here, there are two pKa's, 6.34 and 10.25, at 25° C.

The fact that free amino acids and proteins occur as zwitterions or ampholytes in the cell allows these compounds to participate in the overall buffering

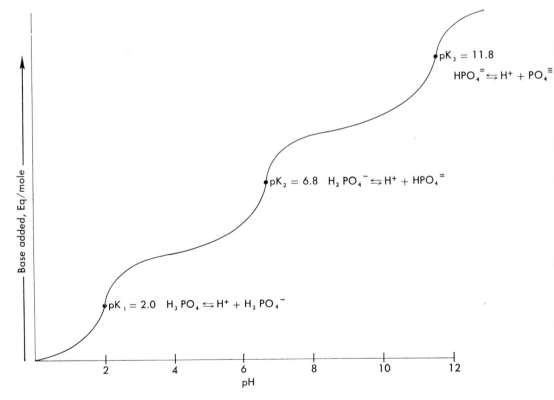

Fig. 10-2. Titration curve of phosphoric acid. Notice the three distinct flattened areas corresponding to the pK values.

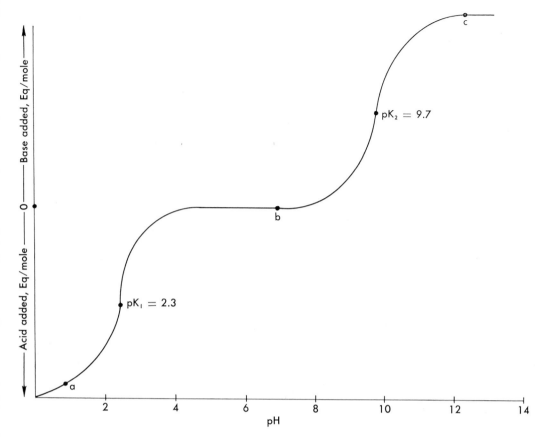

Fig. 10-3. Titration curve of glycine. The two pK values are indicated. At point *a* the glycine would be in the form $^+H_3NCH_2COOH$. At point *b* the charges would be balanced, and the ionic species would be $^+H_3NCH_2COO$. This is the isoelectric point. Point *c* indicates the pH at which the glycine would be in the form $H_3NCH_2COO^-$.

system. Taking, for example, the simplest monoamino, monocarboxylic acid, glycine, it can be seen that a cation form, $^+H_3NCH_2COOH$, is predominant at lower pH's and an anion form, $NH_2CH_2COO^-$, is present at higher pH's. At the lower pH values there is an excess of hydrogen ions. This represses the dissociation of the carboxyl groups and facilitates the formulation of the $-NH_3^+$ group. Conversely, at higher pH values, there is a deficiency of hydrogen which effectively forces the ionization of the carboxyl, yielding the $-COO^-$ group. This hydrogen ion deficiency also pulls the extra hydrogen from the amine, leading to the non-ionized $-NH_2$ group. Because of the two dissociating groups, there are two pK's—one at 2.3 and one at 9.7. There are, then, three interacting forms of glycine in solution—the cation, the anion, and the balanced zwitterion. The titration curve of glycine (Fig. 10-3) illustrates at which points each of these is the predominant species.

Thus, each free amino acid in the cell has its own individual pK's—all with at least two of these values and some with more. At any given pH, those amino

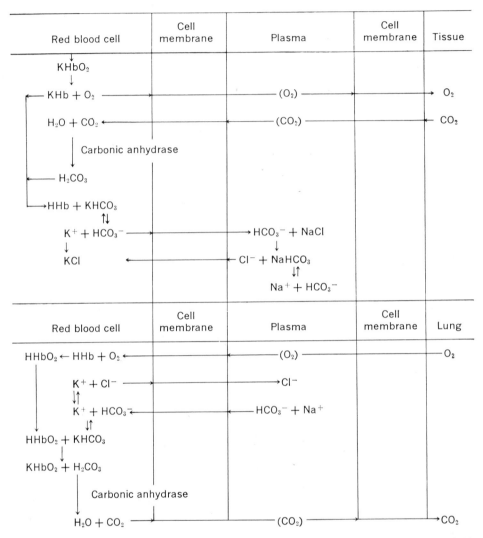

Fig. 10-4. The blood buffer system. This system is predicated on the fact that oxyhemoglobin (HHbO$_2$) is a stronger acid than reduced hemoglobin (HHb). Thus, at any given pH, there will be a greater tendency for the potassium to combine with HHbO$_2$ than with HHb. In this figure, at the tissue site the oxygen is carried by the KHb as KHbO$_2$. Under diffusion pressure, the oxygen is pulled off into the tissue cells. Concomitantly, CO$_2$ is released by the tissue cells and diffuses into the RBC, where, under the influence of carbonic anhydrase, it combines with water to form the carbonic acid, H$_2$CO$_3$. There is a release of the potassium from the reduced hemoglobin which buffers the system by forming KHCO$_3$. Some of the bicarbonate ion exchanges with chloride ion (chloride shift) to increase the buffering capacity of the plasma by forming NaHCO$_3$. At the lung, essentially the reverse occurs, with oxygen moving into the erythrocyte and forming the acid oxyhemoglobin. This requires buffering, and as a result, the bicarbonate moves from the plasma in exchange for chloride. This allows formation of the potassium oxyhemoglobin and the carbonic acid. The latter separates into water and CO$_2$, which diffuses into the lung alveoli for expulsion.

acids with a pK near the pH value will contribute to the buffering ability of the cell. By the same token, at any pH some amino acids will be less soluble; that is, they will be near the iso-electric point (Table 6-2).

In native proteins, the acid-base effect and buffering do not reside so much in the terminal –NH₂ and –COOH groups as in the free amines and carboxyls which are part of the amino acid residues of the protein. In the example given by Christensen,[1] a peptide of 100 alanyl residues with a molecular weight of 7118 theoretically has no more buffering or pH effect than a single alanine molecule of 89 molecular weight. The characteristic pH and buffering traits of the proteins, then, reside in the dicarboxylic and diamino acids as well as in those with groups which are nucleophilic or active.

Specific buffering systems

One buffer system which has been worked out in fine detail is the hemoglobin buffer system of the red blood cell and its complement, the bicarbonate system of the plasma. This combined system provides over 75 percent of the buffering capacity of the blood; the phosphate system is next in importance. The interrelationships in the hemoglobin–bicarbonate system are seen in Fig. 10-4.

There are many individual buffering systems within the cell. The phosphate system is the most important because of its three dissociation plateaus and the fact that it is prevalent in the cell. Many organic molecules, particularly the proteins, also contribute to the buffering capacity.

IONS

It would be impossible to enumerate all the involvements of the various ions in cell processes. The mere fact that cells take such precautions to ensure a constant level of their own flora of ions (Chapter 24) is indication enough of the importance that ions, and their specific intracellular concentrations, have.

In general, all ions contribute to the isosmotic control of the cell, with some being more specifically involved in the various buffer systems. Finally, all ions in theory could affect the membrane potentials which arise from deliberate ionic imbalances. Although some cations or anions are primarily responsible (Chapter 24), the remaining species cannot be without some effect.

The alkali metals

Of all of the generic groupings of ions, the alkali metals have perhaps been investigated the most. This was not a series of fortuitous probes but, instead, was an attempt to answer some questions about certain ions which are important both teleologically and functionally.

Macallum proposed sometime ago that the levels of K⁺ and Na⁺ reflect the degree of evolutionary advance, and as animals evolved, the intracellular K⁺ level has remained fairly constant, whereas the Na⁺ level varies quite a bit. In fact, two distinct potassium-concentrating mechanisms occur in nature, that of active binding and that in response to an electromotive force.

Steinbach[2] has indicated that the alkali metals participate in physiological processes of the cells as follows:

1. Influencing the structural patterns of the bulk water of protoplasm.
2. Acting as chelating agents with other cellular constituents.
3. Altering secondary or tertiary structure of proteins by electrostatic or covalent binding.
4. Altering activity of some macromolecules. The example stated was that K^+ is able to fit in the adsorbed water lattice without disrupting the structure. The same does not apply to Na^+.

In addition to these generalized statements, it is known that some of the alkali metals exert specific enhancing effects on certain enzymes. Lubin[3] has compiled from various sources a list of some twenty-three enzymes which are strongly activated by the potassium ion. Moreover, some ATPase systems may be affected by Na^+ as well as by Mg^{++}. Steinbach[2] suggests that all growing cells have a specific requirement for K^+ and that no exceptions have as yet been found.

Other ionic constituents

A cursory review of the effects of other major ionic constituents on some of the phenomena and processes of the cell is all that space will allow. This discussion is not meant to be inclusive, but it should give an idea of the variety and scope of participation of the ions in the functioning cell.

The calcium ion has had a tumultuous history as far as its physiological importance is concerned. A great proponent of the ubiquitous involvement of this ion in many cellular processes was L. V. Heilbrunn, who felt that Ca^{++} was critically necessary for the integrity of the cell. Although his ideas were railed by some, veracity of many of his original proposals has been borne out by more recent work.

There seems little doubt now that calcium is involved in both muscle contraction and propagation of the nerve impulse. In addition, more specific functions have been attributed to this ion. Lehninger and associates[4] suggest that the calcium is necessary for mitochondrial phosphate uptake, a process so necessary for ATP production. Furthermore, several enzymes are calcium-dependent or calcium-requiring.

The divalent ions Mg^{++} and Mn^{++} are involved in many reactions. They can substitute for each other in many of these reactions. Generally, magnesium is essential for the kinase reactions where there is phosphorylation. Manganese, on the other hand, is bound to other enzymes such as phosphoglucomutase, choline esterase, and muscle ATPase. Their action is apparently facilitation of the formation of the enzyme-substrate complex.

Copper and zinc also are bound to, or are integral parts of, various enzymes. Tyrosinase and cytochrome oxidase have copper as a component; zinc appears in carbonic anhydrase, lactic acid dehydrogenase, and glutamic dehydrogenase.

The anion picture is even hazier than that of the cations. The phosphate radical, for example, participates in a great number of critical reactions of the cell. Not only does this group supply the primary high energy bond, but it also is a major anion of the cell buffer system. Sulfur is involved in a variety of roles in the cell in that it, too, can supply a high-energy bond. But, as was previously pointed out, its very critical role is to offer bonds which help characterize primary and secondary structures of macromolecules. The complete role of chloride is still uncertain. It may participate in membrane potential phenomena, and it is known to be necessary for maintenance of the normal buffer capacity of the erythrocyte. The plant cell has a series of trace elements for which it has specific requirements. Boron, chlorine, copper, manganese, molybdenum, and zinc are required for integrity and functioning of the plant, although other minerals are also important for a normal, functioning cell.

SUMMARY

The ecology of the cell depends to a very large extent on the ionic content of its external and internal environments. The pH effects, of course, have a very strong influence, but, with the exception of the unicellular forms, most cells experience rather limited hydrogen ion concentration range during their life-span. What variation does occur is normally handled by the inorganic and organic buffer systems of the cell. The physiology of the cell is so dependent on certain ions that elaborate, and often energy-requiring, mechanisms have been devised to ensure constancy of the various electrolytes. These precise schemes are an indication of the great role ions play in the functioning cell.

Literature cited

1. Christensen, H. N. 1963. pH and dissociation. W. B. Saunders Co., Philadelphia.
2. Steinbach, H. B. 1962. Comparative biochemistry of the alkali metals, vol. 4, p. 677. In Florkin, M., and Mason, H. S. (editors): Comparative biochemistry, Academic Press, Inc., New York.
3. Lubin, M. 1964. Cell potassium and the regulation of protein synthesis, p. 193. In Hoffman, J. F. (editor): The cellular functions of membrane transport, Prentice-Hall, Englewood Cliffs, N. J.
4. Lehninger, A. L., C. S. Rossi and J. W. Greenawalt. 1963. Respiration-dependent accumulation of inorganic phosphate and Ca^{++} by rat liver mitochondria. Biochem. Biophys. Res. Commun. 10:444.

General references

Baker, J. J. W., and G. E. Allen. 1965. Matter, energy, and life. Addison-Wesley Publishing Co., Inc., Palo Alto, Calif.
Bayliss, L. E. 1960. Principles of general physiology, vol. 2. 5th ed. John Wiley & Sons, Inc., New York.
Christensen, H. N. 1963. pH and dissociation. W. B. Saunders Co., Philadelphia.
Davson, H. 1959. A textbook of general physiology. 2nd ed. Little, Brown & Company, Boston.
Edsall, J. T., and J. Wyman. vol. 1. 1958. Biophysical chemistry. Academic Press, Inc., New York.
Giese, A. C. 1962. Cell physiology. 2nd ed. W. B. Saunders Co., Philadelphia.
West, E. S. 1963. Textbook of biophysical chemistry. 3rd ed. The Macmillan Co., New York.

11

Temperature effects

INTRODUCTION

The existence of all cell types depends upon the availability and control of a supply of thermal energy, but the temperature range in which most cells must operate is extremely narrow. This stenothermal situation, then, places a physiological burden on most cells—a burden which cannot adequately be coped with in many cases. Because of this combined need for thermal energy and the narrow increment in which it can be obtained, temperature and its effects play an important role in the ecology of the cell.

BIOKINETIC ZONE

That range of temperature in which life can exist is defined as the biokinetic zone. Often this zone is more specifically defined as that temperature range wherein occur most physiological processes (that is, 10° to 45° C.), but this does not seem an inclusive enough term. Hence, the first definition will take precedence here. Because of the variations of survival and preferential existence shown by single cells as well as by whole organisms, this zone has its own set of nomenclature to further characterize life within it.

Although most cell types are stenothermal, that is, tolerate a narrow range of temperature, there are some which can survive and develop over a wide temperature range. These are referred to as eurythermal.

A majority of cells carry on the normal physiological processes in a rather narrow, moderate range of temperatures and are thus termed *mesophilic*. The upper and lower limits of this range are arbitrary and vary somewhat with the author. Consensus is that the more stringent temperature limits of the biokinetic zone, 10° to 45° C., also define the mesophilic range, although there are some authors who give even narrower limit to this range. Nevertheless, the physiology of most cells runs rather smoothly in these moderate temperatures.

The thermophilic cells, on the other hand, are both those which can live at temperatures far exceeding the upper limit of the mesophilic range or those which can tolerate this higher zone. Some algae and bacteria, for example,

Table 11-1. Temperature tolerance range of some representative organisms*

Organism	Tolerance range (°C.)	
Bacteria		
Achromobacter ichthyodermis	—2 to 30	FC
Bacillus thermodiastaticus	50 to 75	OT
Diplococcus pneumoniae	18 to 42	M
Lactobacillus casei	10 to 40	M
Lactobacillus thermophilus	30 to 65	FT
Pasteurella pestis	0 to 45	FC
Algae		
Chlamydomonas nivalis	—36 to 0	OC
Fucus vesiculosus	—18 to 30	FC
Oscillatoria filiformis	59 to 85	OT

FT, facultative thermophile; OT, obligatory thermophile; M, mesophile; FC, facultative cryophile; OC, obligatory cryophile.
*Data from Spector, W. S. (editor). 1956. Handbook of biological data. W. B. Saunders Co., Philadelphia.

normally live in hot springs where temperatures may rise to 75° to 85° C. They are the true, or obligatory, stenothermal thermophiles in that many of these same cells are incapable of surviving at temperatures near the lower end of the mesophilic range. Other cells, however, are capable of withstanding high temperatures, but they normally live in the more moderate mesophilic range. They are the facultative thermophiles. Several illustrations of the various tolerance ranges of organisms are given in Table 11-1.

Conversely, the cryophilic or psychrophilic cells are those cells which can either live at or tolerate temperatures below the lower mesophilic limit. An extreme example would be those bacteria that grow in ice cream at −10° C., although some multicellular forms are known to live at even lower temperatures. The distinction between obligatory and facultative cryophiles parallels that of thermophiles.

The physiology of thermophily and cryophily can best be appreciated after digression into the consequences that temperature has on kinetics and reaction rates and the factors that affect and effect these consequences.

The rate of reactions in a cell generally increases with an increase in the temperature up to a maximum, at which point the rate may again decline. To compare the various reactions and processes of the cell, it is necessary to quantitatively characterize the rates at any given increment or interval of temperature. In giving a quantitative term to a process or a reaction one must keep in mind that it refers only to a particular process or reaction and may not characterize the total physiological rate of the cell. A temperature which is favorable for one process may not be optimal for others. As in all chemical reactions which proceed in series, however, if the rate-limiting step is characterized, the entire pathway or process may follow suit.

QUANTITATIVE CHARACTERIZATION OF TEMPERATURE EFFECTS ON REACTION RATES

The best way to appreciate the effect which temperature or temperature change has on a physiological process is to characterize this effect by giving it a quantitative treatment. The measurement of the effect is often difficult and may involve approximations, but the concepts developed from studying isolated reactions are applicable, with some modification, to in vivo extrapolation.

Q_{10}

In giving quantitative treatment to a biological reaction it is tempting to use the epistemic approach of an operational definition rather than use a physical definition. The Q_{10}, which is the ratio of the rate of a reaction at a given temperature to the rate of the same reaction occurring at a temperature 10° C. lower, conforms to the operational approach. This concept of Q_{10}, also called the *temperature coefficient*, can be modified by use of the van't Hoff equation to apply to any temperature increment.

For a 10-degree differential, the equation

$$Q_{10} = \frac{K_{t+10}}{K_t}$$

would apply, where K_t is the rate of the reaction at one temperature and K_{t+10} is the rate at 10° C. higher. In experimentation, however, rarely are reactions compared at precisely 10° C. apart. The van't Hoff modification allows the calculation of Q_{10} at temperature intervals of greater or less than 10° C. This modification merely compares the two reaction rates taken to the power (10 divided by the degree difference). That is

$$Q_{10} = \left(\frac{K_2}{K_1}\right)^{\left(\frac{10}{t_2 - t_1}\right)}$$

or

$$\log Q_{10} = \left(\frac{10}{t_2 - t_1}\right) \log \left(\frac{K_2}{K_1}\right)$$

The temperature coefficient for many chemical reactions is about 2; that is, the reaction rate approximately doubles for each 10-degree rise in temperature. Most physical processes, on the other hand, show a Q_{10} much lower than 2. The Q_{10} for simple diffusion of both electrolytes and nonelectrolytes is less than 1.5, for example. In fact, it approaches 1 under certain conditions. By contrast, reactions peculiar to biological systems such as enzyme denaturation may show Q_{10}'s of several thousand! Representative Q_{10} values for a biological process are seen in Table 11-2.

Critical thermal increment or temperature characteristic

The dependence of reaction rates on temperature is merely an extension of the kinetic theory of matter. In any given population of molecules, different energy levels are represented. Only certain molecules, then, contain enough energy to freely participate in a reaction. As thermal energy is increased, thereby increasing the electron spin, the concentration of molecules with this higher

Table 11-2. Q_{10} values for protoplasmic streaming of several organisms at various temperatures*

Organism	Temperature range (C.)	Q_{10}
Nitella sp.		
	5° to 15°	1.95
	10° to 20°	1.75
	15° to 25°	1.72
	20° to 30°	1.60
	25° to 35°	1.38
Elodea canadensis		
	5° to 15°	1.83
	10° to 20°	1.36
	15° to 25°	1.31
	20° to 30°	1.26
	25° to 35°	1.45
Vallisneria spiralis		
	5° to 15°	3.43
	10° to 20°	2.29
	15° to 25°	1.74
	20° to 30°	1.56
	25° to 35°	1.50

*Data on protoplasmic streaming from Altman, P. L., and D. S. Dittmer (editors). 1964. Biology data book. Federation of American Societies for Experimental Biology, Washington, D. C.
*Calculation of Q_{10} values by Trumbore.

level of energy rises. That is, there are more molecules with an *energy of activation*. This increase in turn accelerates the overall rate of reaction.

Arrhenius and others derived mathematical formulas for expressing the energy of activation. Arrhenius correctly predicted that the increase of energy-rich molecules was exponential with the increase in the temperature. An exponential curve is often made a straight line using a log plot, and Arrhenius proposed a plot of the natural log, *ln*, of the reaction rate, *K*, versus the reciprocal of the absolute temperature, $\frac{1}{T}$. This resulted in a straight line of the form

$$\ln K = -m \frac{1}{T} + b$$

where m is the slope and b the intercept of the reciprocal. The first derivative with respect to the temperature gives the rate of change of the reaction rate with the temperature and results in

$$\frac{d \ln K}{dT} = \frac{m}{T^2}$$

Here Arrhenius made the assumption that the rate of a reaction is dependent upon the number of molecules possessing the heat of activation ΔH_a. Since the slope, m, is a rate term, he proposed substituting $\frac{\Delta H_a}{R}$ for m where R is the Boltzman gas constant.

The resulting equation now reads

$$\frac{d \ln K}{dT} = \frac{\Delta H_a}{RT^2}$$

Finally, integrating between two limits of temperature T_2 and T_1, with the respective rates of reaction K_2 and K_1, the equation reads

$$ln\left(\frac{K_2}{K_1}\right) = \frac{\Delta H_a}{R}\left(\frac{1}{T_1} - \frac{1}{T_2}\right)$$

or more simply

$$log\left(\frac{K_2}{K_1}\right) = \frac{\Delta H_a}{2.303\ R}\left(\frac{T_2 - T_1}{T_2 T_1}\right)$$

It does not take complete understanding of the derivation of this equation to appreciate the fact that the heat of activation, ΔH_a, is the most critical term and which term can be determined by merely measuring the two reaction rates and the two temperatures. The ΔH_a, sometimes referred to as μ, is called the critical thermal increment or temperature characteristic, and it is a direct indication of how much energy, thermal or otherwise, must be added to a molecule to have it reach a reactive state. This concept will be helpful later in explaining the necessity of the enzyme-substrate complex and the high-energy bonds.

GENERAL TEMPERATURE EFFECTS

No physiochemical factor in the environment of the cell can exert its influence without being affected by the other elements in the milieu. Temperature effects are susceptible to modification by several factors and conditions.

Water structure

Tanford[1] has indicated that there are at least three structures which water may take in a biological system. He enumerated these as follows:
1. The structure of pure water
2. That structure which water forms in the vicinity of nonpolar solute molecules or near the nonpolar portion of proteins and other semipolar solutes
3. The structure of water oriented about an ion

As temperature effects depend to a large extent on the thermal stability of the materials, the water structure may play an important role. In the order of *decreasing* thermal stability, the above three states are rated as follows:
1. Structure around ions
2. Structure of pure water
3. Structure around nonpolar areas such as protein

This infers, then, that the system which would be most affected by a thermal change is the biological system where proteins are the integral part of the functioning cell. This further implies that any modification of the normal mesophilic increment must involve some change in this protein-water relationship.

Physiological state

The resistance to temperature effects in part depends upon the physiological state of the cell. The rate of metabolism, the pathways being employed, the degree of hydrogen-bonding on the proteins, and the functional integrity of the membranes all seem to have some part in determining the temperature effect. Some of these factors will be included in the discussion of the physiology of thermophily and cryophily.

Environmental medium

The precise medium in which an organism is living when exposed to thermal change can increase or ameliorate the temperature effect. Hypertonic solutions have been found to yield some protection from extreme temperature fluctuation, whereas other investigators have found that some salts and organic acids decrease this resistance. The availability of adequate nutrients cannot be without some effect as well.

SPECIFIC TEMPERATURE EFFECTS
Biochemical effects

Apart from the predicted Q_{10} effect on physiological processes, it is possible to get more specific when discussing temperature effects on the biochemistry of the cell. As would be expected, some enzyme reactions increase their overall rate with an increase in the temperature, following the normal positive correlation with Q_{10}. However, it has also been found that imposing of cold on cells or organisms may also significantly increase the activity of certain enzymes. Stoner[2] has found that certain phases of carbohydrate metabolism are speeded up in the cold. Furthermore, Hannon[3] has shown an increase in transaminase and glucose 6-phosphatase activity. Both of these enzymes help mobilize the critical metabolites, the transaminase also aiding in allowing amino acids to be used more readily as an energy source. Some of these effects are summarized in Fig. 11-1.

Behavioral effects

The behavioral patterns of cells can also be affected by imposing abnormal cold or heat on them. The motility of cells, particularly evidenced in flagellates and ciliates, is affected in such a way as would be predicted an a Q_{10} scale for biological reactions.

Division cycles are also modified in a manner paralleling the effects on enzymes. However, one unexpected effect is synchronization of certain organisms when shocked with cold or when a regimen of cold and warm is imposed on them. The mechanisms have not been elucidated, but experimenters enjoy the results of this—the synchronized division.

Heat death and thermophily

Considering the fact that most enzymes undergo reversible heat denaturation at temperatures slightly above optimum and irreversible denaturation at higher temperatures, one would have to postulate that the major cause of heat death would be enzyme inactivation. Although coagulation of cell protein can be observed on application of heat, this extreme denaturation is not necessary to bring about cell death. If a rate-limiting enzyme, or an enzyme having a critical role in metabolism, is the protein most easily affected, a mild increase in tem-

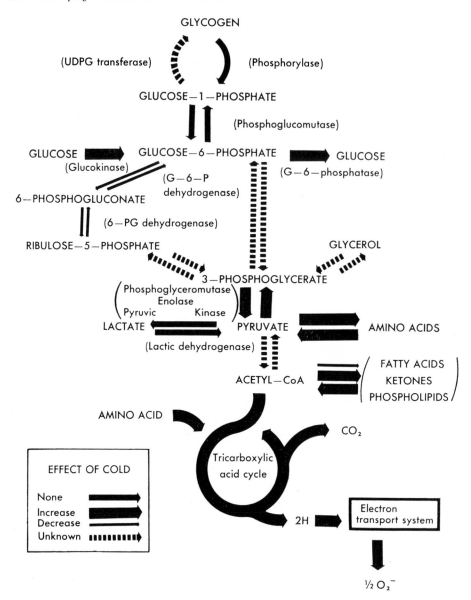

Fig. 11-1. Schematic summary of major alterations in intermediary carbohydrate metabolism induced by cold acclimatization. (From Hannon, John P. 1963. Current status of carbohydrate metabolism in the cold acclimatized mammal. Fed. Proc. 22:859.)

perature may bring about death even if the denaturation is still in the reversible phase. In fact, most heat-killing curves for simple one-celled organisms seem to imply that a single operational step brings about death. As the complexity of the organism increases, however, this singular event is lost and the curve shows a more complex picture. This does not preclude the possibility, though, that these more complex cells have a set of critical enzymes which are more susceptible to this increase of thermal energy.

Another factor which must not be overlooked is membrane integrity. Since a functional membrane is necessary for regulation of metabolite levels, any factor which would affect this could hasten, or cause, cell death. Each membrane has its own peculiar lipoid components, some of which may be melted at lower temperatures than others. Any disruption of the lipid would result in a malfunctioning membrane, again contributing to cell death.

Long exposure to a higher temperature may simply cause the cell to burn out by accelerating most of the reactions of the cell. If any metabolic pathways are affected in a different manner from others, the effect might not show up immediately. However, long exposure could lead to toxicity or other aberrancy of metabolism.

Finally, there is the possibility of activation of a coagulating enzyme as a factor in heat death. This may be caused by a divalent ion (probably Ca^{++}) being released from a bound state in conjunction with membrane lipid.

The physiology of thermophily has not been completely worked out. Certainly, some modifications must occur in the enzyme systems to prevent easy denaturation or to overcome the effects of this inactivation, and apparently there are two distinct methods of controlling this thermal effect. On the one hand, some organisms have a particular set of enzymes which are simply more resistant to high temperatures. This most probably infers stronger hydrogen bonding to lend greater thermal stability to the proteins. On the other hand, some organisms compensate for the normal denaturation of enzymes by heat by synthesizing the proteins at higher rates than at lower temperatures.

There are other factors which seem to be involved in thermophily. Those cells which are facultative thermophiles change their nutritional requirements at the higher temperatures. Thus the medium in which they are growing must have adequate supplies of the necessary metabolites at the various temperatures. Furthermore, both the presence of divalent ions and the smaller size of the cell seem to be characteristics of thermophilic organisms.

Cold death and cryophily

Cold death can be divided into two subcategories—that occurring above freezing and that occurring at freezing or below.

The possible reasons for the effects of cold above the freezing point parallel those given for heat death in many respects. If a rate-limiting enzyme, or an enzyme having a critical role, is depressed enough, death may occur. One would expect those reactions having a high Q_{10} to be particularly susceptible to the rate-lowering effect of cold. An altered electrolyte balance due to membrane impairment would also contribute to the physiological damage.

The cold death that occurs below freezing is not difficult to envision. The formation of ice crystals within the cell causes several major effects. First, the physical damage of ice crystals to the protein enzymes and the lipoprotein membranes could cause irreversible damage. Second, the removal of the active water by freezing causes concentration of the electrolytes and metabolites far above the normal physiological range.

Cryophily, in contrast to thermophily, is not easy to explain. It seems apparent:

1. That enzyme structure is protected from the damage of ice crystals
2. That there must be a higher tolerance to any electrolyte or metabolite concentration

These psychrophilic cells seem to have a lower water concentration than mesophilic cells; also the proportion of water in the bound state may be more. The lower amounts of water would tend to reduce the damage of crystallization.

In addition to the lower free water content, metabolic compensation and a thickened outer wall may also help to explain cryophily. As was indicated earlier, certain biochemical reactions are increased upon exposure to cold. This may postpone the effects of the lower temperatures. The heavy outer coating of cells that produce spores or cysts prevents much water exchange from occurring. If the inside contents are already low in water, neither cold nor heat will have as great an effect as on those cells which are relatively permeable to water.

SUMMARY

Cells function best at a temperature which is optimum for each particular cell. Although most survive and thrive in temperatures between 10° to 45° C., there are those which are acclimated to life outside this range.

Regardless of the thermal interval in which a cell exists, the reactions within the cell are affected by change in temperature. For the most part, reactions occur faster at the higher temperatures, provided that the temperatures compared are in the normal range for that cell. The Q_{10} and critical thermal increment are quantitative approximations of the effect of temperature on these reactions.

Not all cells, nor even all the reactions within one cell, are equally susceptible to thermal changes. Many factors are involved in this variation.

The specific effects of high and low temperatures on the physiology of the cell include the assortment of enzymes which are affected, heat death, and cold death. The concepts embodied in thermophily and cryophily help to explain some of the resistance of certain cells to these effects.

Literature cited

1. Tanford, C. 1963. The structure of water and of aqueous solutions, vol. 3, p. 123. In Herzfeld, C. M. (editor-in-chief), and J. D. Hardy (editor); Temperature: Its measurement and control in science and industry. Reinhold Publishing Corp., New York.
2. Stoner, H. B. 1963. Carbohydrate metabolism in some pathological conditions and in the cold. Fed. Proc. 22:851.
3. Hannon, J. P. 1963. Current status of carbohydrate metabolism in the cold-acclimatized mammal. Fed. Proc. 22:856.

General references

Allen, M. B. 1960. Utilization of thermal energy by living organisms, vol. 1, p. 487. In Florkin, M., and H. S. Mason (editors): Comparative biochemistry. Academic Press, Inc., New York.

Bayliss, L. E. 1960. Principles of general physiology, vol 2. 5th ed. John Wiley & Sons, Inc., New York.

Bruce, Victor G. 1957. Synchronization of cell division by changes in temperature. In Johnson, F. H. (editor): Influence of temperature on biological systems. American Physiological Society, Washington, D. C.

Casey, E. J. 1962. Biophysics: Concepts and mechanisms. Reinhold Publishing Corp., New York.

Davson, H. 1959. A textbook of general physiology. 2nd ed. Little, Brown & Company, Boston.

Herzfeld, C. M. (editor in chief). 1962. Temperature, vol. 3. Reinhold Publishing Corp., New York.

Smith, A. U. 1958. The resistance of animals to cooling and freezing. Biol. Rev. 33:197.

12

Radiation and its biological effects

T INTRODUCTION

The existence of life is ultimately dependent upon the natural radiations which exist in the environment. In our sphere of life, the primary producers, the photosynthetic organisms, depend on energy which their cells can glean from light. The whole story of photosynthesis, which will be developed in Chapter 23, is only one of the effects that radiation has on living material. The influences which this force has run the gamut from overt behavioral responses to subtle enzyme changes. As in all the other ecological factors affecting the cell, radiation is a constant and prevailing element of the environment.

CLASSIFICATION OF RADIATION

There is no classification system of radiation which does not overlap either within itself or with other systems. At the risk of confusion, several different nomenclatures will be illustrated and used.

Operational separation of radiation into natural, ionizing, ultraviolet, and laser does permit us to delineate the artificially imposed radiation of the last three from that which occurs normally in the environment—in this case primarily light. However, it is obvious that natural radiation does include some ionizing and ultraviolet components, but, for the sake of discussion, they will be maintained somewhat separately.

More correctly, radiation could be divided into corpuscular emissions, such as beta particles, protons, deuterons, alpha particles, or neutrons, and the electromagnetic radiations which include a large number of categories (Table 12-1).

The corpuscular emissions are thrown out from the atomic nucleus under a variety of conditions. The fact that these particles have weight, and often charge, gives this type of emission its basic characteristics. The penetrating ability into the cell, for instance, is dependent upon the weight and charge as well as upon the velocity with which the particle is moving. The penetrating ability and the potential ionizing-inducing property are directly related to the biological effects.

Table 12-1. Radiations in the environment*

Radiation	Characteristics
	Electromagnetic
Cosmic	λ, variable
Gamma rays (γ)	$\lambda = 6 \times 10^{-11}$ to 2×10^{-8} cm
X rays	$\lambda = 3 \times 10^{-10}$ to 2×10^{-6} cm
Ultraviolet rays	$\lambda = 8 \times 10^{-7}$ to 4×10^{-5} cm
Visible rays	$\lambda = 3.5 \times 10^{-5}$ to 8×10^{-5} cm
Infrared rays	$\lambda = 8 \times 10^{-5}$ to 3×10^{-2} cm
Radio waves	$\lambda = 8 \times 10^{-2}$ to 5×10^{6} cm
Electric waves	$\lambda = 1 \times 10^{6}$ to 6×10^{12} cm
	Corpuscular
Alpha (α)	Heavy, positive particle; contains 2 neutrons and 2 protons
Beta (β^- or β^+)	Fundamental particle of either positive or negative charge
Deuteron (d)	Positive particle containing 1 neutron and 1 proton
Electron (e^-)	Very small mass; fundamental, negative particle
Positron (e^+)	Very small mass; fundamental, positive particle
Proton (p)	Atomic weight of $\sim$1; positive charge
Neutron (n)	Neutral particle of atomic weight $\sim$1

*Data from Spector, W. S. (editor). 1956. Handbook of biological data. W. B. Saunders Co., Philadelphia.

The precise nature of electromagnetic radiation is still cryptic, although certain properties of electromagnetic waves are known. The electromagnetic wave has two components that vibrate at 90° from each other. These two, the magnetic and the electric elements, vibrate in phase and oscillate about an average value—the oscillation frequency and wavelength determining the energy of the wave.

Like light, all electromagnetic waves show both wave and particle phenomena. As far as biological effects are concerned, they are quite important in that the radiation can be focused or deflected as waves and can also deliver energy in quanta to various parts of the cell. The energy, it should be noted, is inversely proportional to the wavelength. Casey[1] has divided electromagnetic radiations according to their biophysical importance. His classification of the warming region (infrared), visible region, photochemical region (ultraviolet), and ionizing region is very useful in describing general effects on the physiology of the cell.

MEASUREMENT OF RADIATION

There are basically five units of measurement of radiation: (1) the roentgen, (2) the rem, (3) the rad, (4) the linear energy transfer (LET), and (5) the median lethal dose (LD$_{50}$).

The roentgen, which was the earliest quantitative term for radiation, is defined as either that quantity of X or gamma irradiation which will produce one electrostatic unit (esu) of electricity in 1 cc of dry air at standard temperature and pressure or that quantity of irradiation which, when absorbed, increases the energy of dry air at STP by 83 ergs/gm.

The rem, or roentgen equivalent-man, is defined as the amount of damage to a cell or tissue caused by radiation of any type which will produce the same biological effect as 100 ergs of energy from incident X or gamma rays per gram of tissue.

The rad, or radiation absorbed dose, is a more operational term in that it is the amount of X or gamma radiation which, when absorbed, adds 100 ergs of energy per gram of tissue. One rem damage is caused by 1 rad of absorbed incident radiation.

These terms are fairly much restricted to electromagnetic radiation, but LET and LD_{50} can be applied to any type. The LET, or linear energy transfer, is a term which indicates the amount of energy transferred per centimeter of path traveled. Penetrance, charge, and energy are all factors in LET determination. The LD_{50}, which is the most flexible and least quantitative of all of the terms, is defined as the dose in rads which will kill (lethal dose) 50 percent of the cells or organisms irradiated. The time at which observations are to be made is arbitrary, but it must be stated for any valid comparisons to be made.

NATURAL RADIATION

Although natural radiation includes cosmic rays, certain ionizing radiations, and ultraviolet, infrared, and radio rays, the discussion here will primarily be concerned with those electromagnetic waves in the visible zone. The sun, which supplies a majority of all the natural radiation, is, of course, responsible for those emissions in the 3500 to 8000 Å which is called the visible spectrum.

Incident light on an organism or cell may be absorbed as quanta—a reaction both random and independent of temperature. This primary reaction of light energy is dependent to a large extent upon the absorptive ability of the material upon which the light is incident. That is, for specific absorption and channeling of the energy from light, the cell must be adapted to absorb. This adaptation is usually in the form of colored pigments, although any living material is capable to some extent of participating in this primary reaction. Any secondary reactions of light, such as fluorescence, resonance, and activation, are peculiar to each cell type and may be affected by temperature and other environmental conditions.

Photoreception

Most cells are capable of responding to visible light, although the threshold may spread over a large range. Many simple one-celled organisms are capable of exhibiting some phototropism, but only those with specialized organelles are adapted for photoreception. This special receptor, termed eyespot, stigma, or pigment spot, simply lowers the threshold for the light stimulus. There is no "vision" per se in any of these forms.

Some of the cells of multicellular forms also have localized pigmented areas which are sensitive to incident light. The only cells, however, which are particularly adapted for the function of photoreception are the cells in the eyes of some invertebrates and all vertebrates. These cells are adapted to receive light waves and transmit them as electrical impulses to other portions of the nervous system. The particular response to light, vision, has reached its apex in

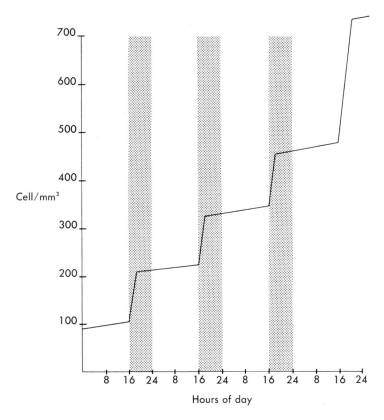

Fig. 12-1. The effect of an imposed light-dark regimen on the division of the alga *Brachiomonas submarina*. An eight-hour dark period in each twenty-four hour cycle was the regimen. The cells divided only during the dark period. Once synchronized, they continued to divide during the "dark" period, even when the cycle was changed to continuous light. (Data from R. H. Trumbore. Unpublished study.)

the higher vertebrate eye. We will not belabor the point here, as this discussion should be included in a vertebrate physiology or comparative physiology textbook.

Photoperiodism and diurnal rhythms

Photoperiodism is the regulation of certain physiological patterns by an imposed light-dark regimen. In plant cells, photosynthesis and subsequent respiration are, of course, affected by the exposure to light. Experimentally, flowering and growth hormones are released from plant cells under the stimulus of light. Various responses caused by absorption of light in the red range (6600 to 6800 Å) by the phytochrome pigment can be reversed by exposing the cells to a far red (7300 to 7500 Å) range.

An imposed light-dark regimen has been found to cause the alga *Brachiomonas submarina* to divide synchronously.[2] This synchronous division persists even after the organisms are returned to continuous light (Fig. 12-1). This sets up, then, a diurnal rhythm-mimicking response. Any photoperiodic response in animals at the cellular level has not been shown satisfactorily. The events which seem to be influenced by light-dark intervals are more behavioral than physio-logical. This does not preclude the possibility that physiological mechanisms at the cellular level do occur and will eventually be elucidated.

The role that light plays on diurnal rhythms has not been completely elaborated. These on-off endogenous patterns are known to be modified, delayed, and inhibited by light, but what part these electromagnetic radiations play in normal maintenance of the rhythms is uncertain. The intricacies of the biological clocks are such that experimenters are delighted to find mainsprings, let alone supporting cogs.

IONIZING RADIATION

The line between radiation which merely excites and that which brings about ionization is extremely thin in most cases. The mechanisms are at once quite similar. Moving particles are capable of exerting transient electrical force on the electron clouds of molecules which lie in the vicinity of their paths. This interaction will cause some quantum transitions, and as a result the target molecule may become excited or ionized, depending on the amount of energy transferred. By the same token, the particles, themselves, may lose energy and velocity.

In the case of electromagnetic radiation, the quantum energy of the particle phase of the electromagnetic wave (photon) is absorbed by the target molecule. The photon may then interact in several ways with a target:

1. By photoelectric absorption the photon will disappear and an electron will be ejected or agitated.
2. The initial incident energy may be divided into a photon of lower energy and an agitated or ejected electron.
3. The photon disappears, yielding a pair of energetic electrons—one a true negative electron and one a positive electron.

Regardless of the mechanisms, radiation of high enough energy can cause an ionizing effect on the biological material upon which it is incident. Absorption, scattering, energy loss, and energy transfer are dictated by principles of physics and will not be dealt with here. Suffice it to say, some radiations are capable of a range of ionizing effects, and this range leads to a variety of biological consequences.

Biological effects

It is impossible to enumerate all of the biological effects which have been found to be caused by ionizing radiation. For the most part, the damages incurred are proportional to the incident dose. Three major effects will be considered, with examples of each discussed briefly.

Biochemical effects

The cell contains anywhere from 75 to 90 percent water, on the average. As a result, on a purely random hit of a cell by ionizing radiation, the water

Table 12-2. Some radioactive isotopes used in biological work

Isotope*	Half-life
Carbon-14	5570 yr
Sodium-22	2.6 yr
Sodium-24	15 hr
Phosphorus-32	14.3 days
Sulfur-35	87.1 days
Chlorine-36	$\sim 3 \times 10^5$ yr
Potassium-42	12.5 hr
Calcium-45	164 days
Calcium-47	4.8 days
Iron-55	2.94 yr
Cobalt-60	5.38 yr
Copper-64	12.84 hr
Zinc-65	245 days
Bromine-82	35.9 hr
Strontium-90	28 yr
Iodine-131	8.05 days
Radium-226	1620 yr
Uranium-233	1.62×10^5 yr
Uranium-238	4.51×10^9 yr

*The element and the atomic weight to the nearest integer are given.

component should be affected proportionally more than the biological materials. There appears little doubt now that incident radiation can cause hydrolysis of water, with enough energy remaining to force the hydrogen and hydroxyl apart to allow them to react with other molecules. In addition, in the intermolecular reaction among water, H^+ and OH^- can yield the free radicals [OH] and [H]. These radicals, which are quite unstable because of the odd electron in the outer shell, are attracted to areas from which they can trap an electron or share it with another molecule. In other words, these free radicals combine quite readily with the organic constituents of the cell. The resultant oxidation by these radicals may cause much of the damage attributed to ionizing radiation. The decreased sensitivity to radiation in low oxygen tension seems to bear this out. Another consequence of the [H] and [OH] radicals is that, when they are in the presence of oxygen, peroxides form which are toxic, particularly in cells with low peroxidase or catalase levels.

The sulfhydryl-disulfide reactions in the cell are also susceptible to the presence of oxidative by-products. Inasmuch as the secondary structure of proteins is dependent to a large extent upon certain intact disulfide bridges, the destruction of these or the creation of new bridges could cause loss of biological activity. The presence of large amounts of free sulfhydryls in the cell may prevent disruption of the disulfide bridges.

Hydrogen bonding can also be disrupted by ionizing radiation. Again, the biological activity of a molecule may be lost, and in addition, those processes which depend on a certain hydrogen bonding or concentration may be altered.

The studies of ionizing radiation on subcellular particles are just becoming an important part of the literature. Here, the electron deficiency of the formed radicals may again be directly involved. In fact, Scaife[3] reports that ionizing radiation interferes with the electron transport mechanisms in thymus mitochondria because of these radicals.

Finally, many molecules may have their solubility affected by the radiation; that is, there is partial damage to the structure. Once the molecule goes into solution, however, it retains its normal activity.

These by no means are the sum total of the ionizing radiation effects on the biochemistry of the cell. The examples should serve, however, as indications of the general types of damage which can be imposed by this class of radiation.

Biophysical effects

The stability of many biological colloids depends on the adsorbed layer of solvent molecules (Chapter 9). Because irradiation can cause disturbance of this critical layer, the micelles can more easily clump or form abnormal cross-linkages among themselves. Breakdown of the colloidal structure of the cell can lead to further damage to, and impairment of, the normal physiological processes.

The transport mechanisms of the cell are contingent on a distinct structural framework of the membrane as well as upon a definite electrostatic configuration of the transported particle. Ionizing radiation, by effecting any of the results discussed in the previous section, could either accelerate or inhibit the normal movement of metabolites. At this point, other than some observations, there are no definitive works describing this effect in any detail.

Genetic effects

The effects of ionizing radiation on the nucleic acids are of such importance that they should be considered separately from the biochemical and biophysical effects just outlined, although the damages and alteration to the nucleic acids and chromosomes are obviously biochemical or biophysical in nature.

At the molecular level, the DNA is quite susceptible to radiation. In recalling the structure of this macromolecule (Chapter 7), it can be seen that the base pairs are held together by hydrogen bonds. The skeleton, on the other hand, depends on intact phosphate bridges. The hydrogen bond is an easy target of the ionizing effect, and X-ray exposure may split the phosphate bridge.[4] Other types of damage to the molecule may include loss of amine groups or active hydrogens, freeing of the purine or pyrimidine bases from the helix, and complete rupture of the nucleotide chains. At the cellular level, ionizing radiation has been shown to cause chromosomal breaks, the percentage of breaks being proportional to the applied radiation dose.

As will be seen later (Chapter 26), it only takes a subtle change in this genetic material to bring about a lasting effect. If critical coding areas are affected, the result may be an aberrant cell or a mutant. The genetic result of the damage is difficult to predict. With an overt change, such as a chromosome break, one could foresee some type of aberrancy. It is the small, seemingly insignificant changes which make ionizing radiation damage such a widespread phenomenon.

ULTRAVIOLET RADIATION

How fortunate it is that ultraviolet waves have a low penetrating ability. The effects of these electromagnetic waves are so specifically detrimental to biological material that if they had the ability to penetrate deeply damage from this radiation would be extreme. The major source of natural ultraviolet radiation is the sun, but because of an ozone layer surrounding the earth, a relatively small proportion reaches the surface.

The low penetration of these rays prevents much damage to the internal cells and organs of multicellular animals and plants. Epithelial cells do receive enough incident radiation to bring about some injury, including, at least experimentally, skin cancer.

Ultraviolet damage on unicellular forms, on the other hand, can be dramatic. Bacteria, protozoa, algae, and a variety of other cell types can be killed by exposure to ultraviolet irradiation. Cell death can be almost immediate, or as in many cases, the ultimate cause of death is the division block which results from the damage (Fig. 12-2). The fact that DNA and its components have maximum absorption near the wavelengths of ultraviolet suggests that this macromolecule may be involved.

Early experimentation with ultraviolet irradiation and its damage was fraught with frustration and nonrepeatable results. Finally, in 1949, it was shown that visible light, particularly at the blue end of the spectrum could bring about some reversal of the ultraviolet damage.

This reversal, termed *photoreactivation,* turned out to be both incomplete and not universal. When the process did occur, however, all phases, including mutations, could be partially reversed. Strangely, this phenomenon was found to occur only in the presence of cytoplasm. Individual nuclei exposed to ultraviolet showed no reversal when reexposed to visible light. This suggested that

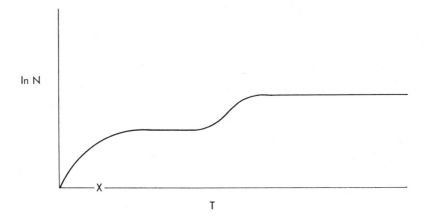

Fig. 12-2. Division block caused by exposure to ultraviolet radiation (*X*).

the reaction was mediated by a constitutive cytoplasmic enzyme. A possible scheme is offered below:

$$DNA + \lambda(UV) \longrightarrow DNA^*$$
$$DNA^* + En \longrightarrow DNA^* \cdot En$$
$$\overset{\text{Blue light}}{DNA^* \cdot En \longrightarrow DNA + En}$$

where DNA* is the affected DNA and En, the constitutive enzyme.

Beukers and Berends[5] in 1961 demonstrated that thymine forms a dimer on exposure to ultraviolet light and that this dimerization is the major source of damage by ultraviolet irradiation. This finding opened the door to a host of investigations on the effect of this radiation on the various purine and pyrimidine bases. Not only were specific reactions found to occur in bases other than thymine, but also a whole new field of radiosensitization was begun. The susceptibility to damage of cells grown in media containing certain halogenated purine and pyrimidine analogs gave a new tool for investigating ultraviolet effects on the cell, particularly at which stages in the life cycle it is most susceptible.

LASER BEAMS

The newest branch of radiation biology involves the study and use of laser beams. The first operating laser was not developed until 1960, but since then the fields of investigation have widened and grown rapidly.

The theory and physics of laser emission are beyond the scope of this book, but we might describe some of the unique properties of this nonionizing radiation. A laser is a monochromatic beam in wavelengths ranging from ultraviolet to infrared, with a majority in the visible range. The beam itself is collimated to the extent that the emitted rays are nearly parallel. A peculiar property of the laser beam, which for the most part complies with the laws of physics, is the coherence of the wave itself. A final property is that extremely high-energy fluxes can be produced.[6] It is this high energy, which can be focused as light waves, which causes the biological damage.

Because of the range of the electromagnetic spectrum which is involved, the biological effects of lasers on the higher organisms is primarily ophthomalogical and dermatological. The individual cells, however, can also be affected, and the effects on the cells depend on the presence of a suitable substance for absorbing the laser energy at any given wavelength.[7]

Specific cellular consequences of laser radiation are of varied nature. For instance, it has been reported that exposure of the NAD-linked lactic acid dehydrogenase system to laser emission results in a significant decrease in the ability of the enzyme to convert NADH·H[+] to NAD.[7] Further, it has been demonstrated that whole mitochondria can be selectively destroyed.[8]

It seems that laser radiation may hold a key to yielding methods whereby the internal machinery of the cell can be explored. Like ionizing and ultraviolet radiation, laser beams could be developed into a standard tool of cell physiologists.

SUMMARY

Incident radiation, whether it be natural, ionizing, ultraviolet, or laser, has profound effects on living material and is thus an important component in the ecological environment of the cell. Visible light of low energy can modify and initiate behavioral patterns and their allied physiological processes. Quantum transference of energy from ionizing radiation can alter protein configuration, change pH, clump colloids, and disrupt DNA molecules. On the other hand, ultraviolet irradiation has a more specific effect on the nucleic acids alone, although other sites may be affected under certain conditions. Different from ionizing radiation, much of the damage due to ultraviolet exposure can often be reversed by photoreactivation; that is, exposure to the blue end of visible light returns normal activity. Laser radiation, a newcomer to radiation biology, holds much promise as an exciting tool for delving into some of the intricacies of the cell.

Literature cited

1. Casey, E. J. 1962. Biophysics: Concepts and mechanisms. Reinhold Publishing Corp., New York. p. 82.
2. Ducoff, H. S., B. D. Butler, and E. J. Geffon. 1965. X-ray survival studies on the alga *Brachiomonas submarina* Bohlin, Radiation Res. 24:563.
3. Scaife, J. F. 1963. Effect of ionizing radiation on the oxidation of succinate by rat thymus mitochondria. Can. J. Biochem. & Physiol. 41:1486.
4. Wacker, A. 1963. Molecular mechanisms of radiation effects, vol. 1, p. 369. In Davidson, J. N., and W. E. Cohn (editors): Progress in nucleic acid research. Academic Press, Inc., New York.
5. Beukers, R., and W. Berends. 1961. The effects of UV-irradiation on nucleic acids and their components. Biochem. Biophys. Acta 49:181.
6. Daniels, R. G., and B. Goldstein. 1965. Lasers and masers—health hazards and their control. Fed. Proc. 24 (suppl. 14), p. S-27.
7. Rounds, D. E. 1965. Effects of laser radiation on cell cultures. Fed. Proc. 24 (suppl. 14), p. S-116.
8. Malt, R. A. 1965. Effects of laser radiation on subcellular components. Fed. Proc. 24 (suppl. 14), p. S-122.

General references

Augenstine, L. G. 1962. The effects of ionizing radiation on enzymes. Advances Enzymol. 24:359.
Casey, E. J. 1962. Biophysics: Concepts and mechanisms. Reinhold Publishing Corp., New York.
Epstein, H. T. 1963. Elementary biophysics. Addison-Wesley Publishing Co., Inc., Palo Alto, Calif.
Hollaender, A. (editor). 1956. Radiation biology. McGraw-Hill Book Co., New York. 3 vol.
Marmus, J., and L. Grossman. 1961. Ultraviolet light induced linking of deoxyribonucleic acid strands and its reversal by photoreactivating enzyme. Proc. Nat. Acad. Sc. 47:778.
McElroy, W. D., and B. Glass (editors). 1961. Light and life. Johns Hopkins University Press, Baltimore.
Patt, H. M. (editor). 1954. Basic mechanisms in radiobiology. Part III. Biochemical aspects. National Academy of Science, Washington, D. C.
Setlow, R. B., and E. C. Pollard. 1962. Molecular biophysics. Addison-Wesley Publishing Co., Inc., Reading, Mass.

Section IV

Bioenergetics

The functional cell is bound by many chemical parameters, but the open system of the biological world provides new meaning to these terms. The basic concepts of thermodynamics as developed for physical systems can be applied to the cell, with minor modifications. The problem of entropy level is handled by the cell by the constant influx of compounds with low entropy into the system. Their conversion allows the maintenance of the low entropy level, or high orderliness, required for a biological system. The concept of free energy— the energy available for use—is important to the energy problems of the cell. The fundamental thermodynamics are discussed in Chapter 13.

The enzymes (Chapter 14) are directly involved in flow of energy through the cell. By controlling the reactions of the cell through their catalytic properties and high specificity, the enzymes help regulate the energy gain and loss. Although the enzymes are only biological catalysts, they contribute more to the cell than their basic property suggests.

One means by which energy in the cell is kept from being dissipated is explained in the concept of the high-energy bond (Chapter 15). Trapping of energy into chemical bonds which can be used by the cell at a later time permits an exothermic reaction to drive an endothermic one by a coupled reaction, which prevents the entropy of the system from increasing.

The mechanisms by which high-energy bonds are produced are through the process of biological oxidation (Chapter 16). The removal of hydrogen and electrons from metabolites, defined as oxidation, occurs through regular pathways. In aerobic cells, the cytochrome system is the index of a respiring cell.

Bioenergetics, then, is a complex subject when applied to the living cell. The fundamental thermodynamics are modified for use by enzymes, high-energy bonds, and specific systems for biological oxidation.

13

Fundamental thermodynamics
in biological systems

T **INTRODUCTION**
The dynamic, living cell is constantly involved with energy fluxes among its various physiological processes. Rarely does one encounter a cellular phenomenon which does not either yield or require energy. Thus, some background should be provided in thermodynamics, both classical and as applied to biological systems, before an attempt to dissect the biochemical processes of the cell is made. However, according to Prigogine,[1] classical thermodynamics is a necessary and well-thought out sequence of knowledge, but it is only fragmentary when applied to biological systems. Nonetheless, the basic concepts of classical thermodynamics must be appreciated in order to expand these maxims to biological systems.

THERMODYNAMIC PARAMETERS

Any organic compound could be placed in a bomb calorimeter and reduced to its major elements. The heat generated during this process is dependent upon the structure and components of the original molecule. This heat, which is the energy content of the molecule, is also called the enthalpy. This term, designated H, is subject to change under a variety of conditions. The enthalpy or heat content (heat energy) is a base point from which the other thermodynamic terms are derived. To be absolutely correct, one must take into consideration that the basic elements to which the compound is degraded still have some residual energy residing in their structure. Thus, the heat content, or enthalpy, should be calculated from absolute zero ($0° K$).

Free energy is that portion of the enthalpy which is available for work. Since energy derived from biochemical or physiological processes comes primarily from chemical changes, the cell physiologist is particularly interested in free energy as an index of how utilizable the energy is to drive other reactions

125

or how it can be used to control physiological phenomena. The free energy level between two compounds also indicates whether energy must be put into a system or gleaned from it when going from $a_1 \rightarrow a_2$. The free energy concept is most important in predicting whether or not the reaction should go and to what degree. The dependence of reaction rates will be discussed in Chapter 15.

The third, and final, thermodynamic parameter, entropy, or ΔS, is the most difficult to understand. Perhaps the easiest definition is that entropy is an index of the disorder of the system. Any system, if left alone, will go toward a state of maximum entropy. Take glucose, for example, and degrade it to CO_2 and H_2O. Here, the orderliness of the sugar molecule is replaced by a more disordered situation. After all, now there are six CO_2 instead of the original single, more complex, glucose. Thus, in going from $C_6H_{12}O_6 \rightarrow 6CO_2$, there is an increase in entropy. In many cases, the conventions of thermodynamics as far as sign and direction seem somewhat unorthodox to a biologist's way of thinking. It must be kept in mind, however, that the higher the entropy component of a system, the lower is the degree of order; that is, the system is in a state of disorder.

Entropy is temperature-dependent, and when the changes in enthalpy, free energy, and entropy are related by formula, this becomes apparent.

$$\Delta F = \Delta H - T\Delta S$$

This relationship clearly shows that at a given temperature and a constant ΔH any increase in entropy will decrease the free energy which is available for work. This makes sense, really, when one considers there is much less to be gained energetically from six CO_2 than from one glucose molecule. As the temperature increases, the free energy decreases, if the ΔH is held constant. The thermal energy causes greater agitation of the molecules, leading to a more disordered state.

ENERGY FORMS

As in physical systems, biological systems show potential and kinetic energies. In addition, however, there are a number of special forms of energy which are particularly applicable to living systems.

Surface energy has already been mentioned as an important component of the total energy of a colloidal system. In the discussion in which this was described (Chapter 9), the two factors affecting surface energy were elucidated. These, the capacity factor and the intensity factor, also apply to the other forms of special energy (Table 13-1). The terms *extensive* and *intensive* are sometimes used as synonyms for capacity and intensity, respectively.

Electrical energy, or that force built up over a potential difference, is quite important to the cell. The nerve cell makes obvious use of this, but only on a greater scale than other cells. All cells can have a potential buildup across their membranes.

Radiant energy from the sun or artificial sources is used by autotrophic cells to produce metabolizable by-products. Employment of this energy necessitates

Table 13-1. Capacity and intensity factors of various forms of energy

Energy	Capacity	Intensity
Electric (joules)	Coulombs (amp-sec)	ΔE (volts)
Heat (calories)	Heat capacity (cal./deg)	ΔT (deg.)
Kinetic (ergs)	½ mass (g)	Vel^2 ($(cm/sec)^2$)
Mechanical (ergs)	Change in distance (cm)	Force (dynes)
Movement of charged particle (electron volts)	Charge	Volts
Potential (ergs)	Mass (g)	Height $\times$ acceleration ($(cm/sec)^2$)
Surface	Change in area (cm^2)	Surface tension (dynes/cm)
Volume expansion (ergs)	Change in volume (cm^3)	Pressure (dynes/cm^2)

specialized compounds to trap the energy as high-energy bonds (Chapters 12 and 23).

WORK IN BIOLOGICAL SYSTEMS

Available energy is of no use to the cell unless it can be channeled to do work. In biological systems, work has special qualities which may be somewhat different from the classical property.

Mechanical work, or force applied through distance, is applicable to living systems as well as to inanimate systems. Muscular movement and other forms of motion use this mechanical work. *Electrical work* can also be seen to operate in biological systems. Electron transport, or the movement of hydrogen across a potential difference, is one example.

Osmotic work, or the movement of material against a concentration gradient, is quite prevalent in the cell. Transport of many metabolites and ions across membranes involves this class of work. Directing of energy to this use is a major problem in active transport (Chapter 24).

Chemical work is the use of the free energy of a system to drive a chemical reaction against an energy gradient. In other words, synthesis of biological molecules by cells creates compounds with a higher energy level than the precursors from which they were formed. The cell is capable of doing this at isothermal conditions, a situation which does not readily occur in nonliving systems. Finally, a subcategory of this class is *photochemical work,* in which chemical work is directed toward production of radiant energy, such as in bioluminescence.

THE LAWS OF THERMODYNAMICS

The basic laws of classical thermodynamics should be reviewed here so that they can be placed in their correct context when applied to a biological system.

The first law of thermodynamics states simply that the sum total of all of the energies in an isolated system is constant. This implies that energy cannot be created or destroyed, but that it may be converted from one form to another. We have seen that if the enthalpy remains a constant the free energy and the entropy are dependent variables; that is, the change in one must be compensated for by a change in the other.

The second law of thermodynamics may be stated several ways:

1. In an isolated system, there is a tendency to reach an equilibrium.
2. The entropy of an isolated system tends to reach a maximum.
3. An isolated system approaches a condition of maximum probability.

These three statements all are variations of the definition of the second law, and although they appear distinct, almost contradictory, they, in fact, are saying the same thing.

According to the concepts embodied in this second law, a system, if left to itself—that is, without additional energy or temperature—will tend to approach the most disordered state since this state requires the least amount of energy to maintain. This approach, which will reach an equilibrium, results in the system's having a maximum entropy, the index of disorder. For any particular isolated system, the state of maximum entropy is also the state of maximum probability.

The third law of thermodynamics states that the entropy level of any crystalline system approaches zero as the temperature approaches absolute zero. In other words, the crystal has its most ordered structure at absolute temperature where bond vibration and intracrystalline forces are eliminated.

THE OPEN SYSTEM AND STEADY STATE

One often has to return to classical works to be brought up-to-date on a subject, and such is the case with the open system and steady state. von Bertalanffy pioneered the concept of the open system in the biological organism in 1932, but the idea was to some degree lost during World War II. Literature began appearing again in the late forties and finally, in 1950, von Bertalanffy published *The Theory of Open System in Physics and Biology*,[2] a paper which is a classic in its own right.

Open system defined

Prigogine[1] has very nicely delineated the three basic classes of thermodynamic systems.

1. There is the *isolated system*, in which there is no exchange of either energy or matter.
2. In the *closed system*, there may be exchange or interconversion of energy, but no matter is lost or gained.
3. In the *open system*, both energy and/or matter may be exchanged.

An open system thus implies constant influx and efflux of some component of the system such as energy or metabolites. In other words, an open system depends upon an import-export balance with the environment.

Several models have been proposed to show how this open system works. At the risk of insulting the intelligence of the student, a more simple model is proposed here which, I must admit, removes some of the mathematics (Fig. 13-1).

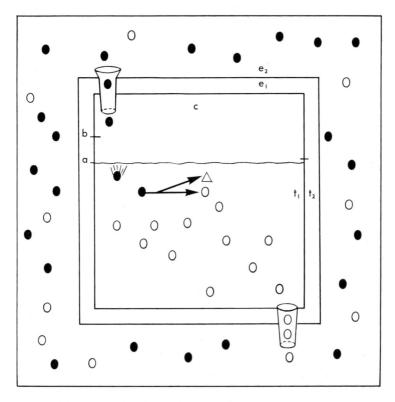

Fig. 13-1. Model of an open system. (See text.)

Assume that there is a biological system, *c*, enclosed in a limiting membrane in contact with two environmental conditions, e_1 and e_2. Let e_1 represent the potential energy drain to the enclosed system, *c*, represented here as two separate temperatures, t_1 and t_2. That is, there is a constant efflux of energy from system *c* to e_1. The other environmental component, e_2, supplies metabolites (solid circles) and accepts products (open circles). Because the phase, *c*, undergoes exchange with the environment, it is therefore classified as an open system. To extend on this, now assume that the rate of metabolites (closed circles) entering *c* equals the rate of products leaving *c*, and furthermore assume that the conversion of the metabolites to the products supplies enough energy, represented as $\triangle$, to maintain a constant t_1—that is, to balance the drain out to t_2. The condition here described is called a steady state. A steady state implies that the system as a whole maintains constant energy and matter levels. Note that this end result describes a closed system, the difference being the balanced influx and efflux of components.

To extend one more step, assume that the energy-matter level, *a*, of this system changes to a new level, *b*. To attain this, the system must temporarily lose its steady state by one of the following mechanisms:

1. Increasing the rate of metabolites entering
2. Decreasing the rate of products leaving

3. Changing the rate of conversion of the metabolites to products
4. Losing less energy in the t_1-to-t_2 efflux
5. Reversing this latter to get energy influx
6. Any combination of these

Regardless of the mechanism, once b is attained, a new steady state could be reached where the parameters are again balanced.

This abstract model does, hopefully, illustrate the conditions involved in both an open system and a steady state.

Biological versus inanimate systems

One of the general properties of a living system is the built-in self-regulatory mechanism. This can be seen in the model just described, where several of the rates of influx and efflux and conversion can be changed and still have mainte-nance of the steady state.

Feedback control in an open system may typically show an overshoot or oscillation around the new level of steady state; that is, the approach to a new steady state is not always asymptotic. This fluctuation around a new steady state level is one of the basic premises of error control and other feedback mechanisms found in nature (Chapters 30 and 31).

A distinct difference between biological and inanimate systems is expressed by the concept of equifinality.[2] In most physical systems, the initial conditions determine what final state will be attained, and any change in the initial conditions or the parameters in which they are operating will change the final state. In a behavior called *equifinal*, the final state of a biological phenomenon may be reached from different initial conditions and by various paths. The equifinality is sometimes predictable in that the system seems to approach a distinct final state, regardless of prevailing conditions.

The largest hurdle which the concept of the open system had to overcome was the apparent disregard for the second law of thermodynamics. While it is true that biological systems attempt to avoid the trap of attaining a high entropy level, this does not mean that the second law—a system must reach maximum entropy—is invalid. In the irreversible processes of a closed system, entropy must increase, but entropy is also produced in the living system. The influx of compounds high in negative entropy offsets this production.

Denbigh[3] has shown that entropy can increase in a biological system. He points out that in the conservation of energy principle the rate of increase of energy in a system equals the rate of passage of energy out of the system. However, the entropy can be produced in a living system, which requires that an additional term be incorporated in discussing interrelationships concerning energy:

(Rate of increase of the entropy of the system) +
(Rate of passage of entropy from the system) =
(Rate of production of entropy in the system)

The last term must be greater than, or equal to, zero, and if it is zero, the system described is a reversible reaction.

In growing or dividing cells, the entropy must decrease because of synthesis of the many ordered compounds necessary for these two processes.

In cells at rest, where the catabolic processes closely balance the anabolic ones (dynamic equilibrium), the other basic physiological processes of the cell are ramifications of the open system steady state. Metabolism, by its very nature of taking metabolites and converting them to energy or other biological compounds, is an integral must in steady state maintenance. Such phenomena as irritability, conductivity, and contractility are temporary situations imposed on the cell which may force it to attain some new steady state level. All of these processes are special cases of open systems.

APPLICATION OF THERMODYNAMIC TERMS OF BIOLOGY
$-\Delta F$ and $+\Delta F$

There are certain basic conventions associated with thermodynamic terminology with which one should become familiar before applying these expressions to more concrete phenomena.

The third law of thermodynamics states that the entropy of a system is zero at $0°$ K. This assumption allows calculation of entropy, then, at any other temperature. When the example given by Eyring and associates[4] is used, the reaction $A + B \leftrightarrows C + D$ could be taken to $0°$ K. At this point, ΔS, or entropy, is zero. Warming of the reactants to $T°$ K would allow calculation of the entropy at this temperature. Entropy is thus a positive term. If we go back to the equation

$$\Delta F = \Delta H - T\Delta S$$

and rearrange the terms, the following relationship is seen

$$\Delta S = \frac{\Delta H - \Delta F}{T}.$$

Since ΔS is always positive and ΔH is always constant at any one temperature, it can be seen that the ΔF value must become more negative if the entropy increases. In other words, in going from an ordered state to one of less order (increasing the entropy), the free energy would be more negative. Any reaction which is accompanied by a decrease in the free energy level is called exergonic, or exothermic. Conversely, any reaction with a positive ΔF is considered endergonic, or endothermic. The convention of indicating a reaction which will proceed "spontaneously" with a $-\Delta F$ has theoretical basis. Thus, use of $-\Delta F$ and $+\Delta F$ to indicate energy-yielding or energy-demanding reactions is widespread.

Energy barrier

If a reaction is to proceed in such a manner that the entropy increases, that is, the reaction has a $-\Delta F$, the system rarely attains this new level spontaneously. Assume a system as shown in Fig. 13-2. The compounds at ΔF_1 are considered to be in a state of metastability, a state in which a compound cannot release its energy or attain a new free energy state, although it is lower,

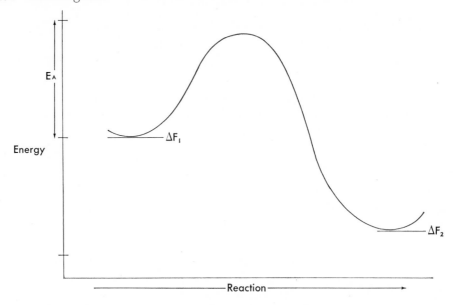

Fig. 13-2. Energy of activation, E_A, of a reaction going from one free energy level, ΔF_1, to a lower free energy level, ΔF_2.

without some outside force. This latter force must be supplied to overcome the energy barrier of the reaction; that is, a higher total ΔF value must be attained before the reaction will occur.

The difference between the initial free energy and the higher level which must be arrived at is called the activation energy. This may be designated by ΔH_a, E_a, $\Delta F^{\ddagger}$. In biological and nonbiological systems, this higher energy level is the result of some activated complex which can supply the energy required. Once this new level is reached, the reaction can glide downhill to the lower ΔF (higher entropy) level.

Many elementary texts very pictorially describe this process of raising the energy level in order to arrive at the lower level by use of the analogy of the stone at the top of the hill. The top of the hill (ΔF_1) has a rise in it near the edge which necessitates the stone's being pushed to the top of this rise ($\Delta F^{\ddagger}$) before the stone will roll to the bottom of the hill (ΔF_2). If an analogy teaches, it should be used, and thus it is included here.

Free energy in terms of other basic fundamentals

Free energy is so vitally important in biological systems that its application can be made to other basic biochemical phenomena. For example, it is extremely important, and convenient, that the free energy of a system can be related to the equilibrium constant, K, of a reaction:

$$\Delta F = -RT \ln K$$

or

$$= -2.303 \ RT \log K$$

Thus the free energy, which is difficult to measure, can be calculated if the reaction rate is known. This can only be accurately calculated, however, in an isolated reaction, but even in the open system with a flow of reactions a good approximation can be obtained.

In active transport mechanisms, osmotic work, and electrical wave propagation, the free energy of a system can be calculated from the formula

$$\Delta F = -nF\Delta E$$

where ΔE is the electropotential difference, n, the number of electrons, and F, the faraday. This calculation suffers from the same limitation as the previous one, but it is an extremely useful method of quantifying the free energy yield of such systems.

SUMMARY

The basic fundamentals of thermodynamics—enthalpy (ΔH), entropy (ΔS), and free energy (ΔF)—are interrelated in that in any given system any one value is dependent on the other two values. In order for a biological system to maintain itself, it must utilize various energy forms to perform the kinds of work necessary for the cell to survive.

The three laws of thermodynamics, although defined from the classical thermodynamics, are applicable to biological systems with some modifications. The system which is peculiar to a living complex is the open system pioneered by von Bertalanffy. This open system, which implies constant influx and efflux of energy and/or matter, often maintains a steady state condition in the cell. This steady state is described as that in which the energy and matter levels are maintained at a constant. This does not negate the open system; it merely signifies that the efflux and influx must be in balance.

The entropy of a living system is indicative of the physiological state of the cell. Increase in overall entropy infers degradation in the cell, possibly leading to death. A decrease in overall entropy indicates a large amount of synthesis, as might occur in growth or division.

For a reaction to go from a higher energy level (lower entropy) to one of lower energy (a higher entropy), it must overcome an energy barrier. This added energy level is brought about by formation of an activated complex. Exothermic, or exergonic, reactions are indicated by $-\Delta F$, whereas endergonic, or endothermic, reactions are shown by $+\Delta F$. The former are capable of giving up energy; the latter require energy.

Free energy can be related to both the equilibrium constant, K, of a reaction and the electropotential difference, ΔE. This allows calculation of free energy of most of the biological reactions of the cell.

Literature cited

1. Prigogine, I. 1961. Introduction to thermodynamics of irreversible processes. 2nd ed. Interscience Publishers, Inc., New York. p. 3.
2. von Bertalanffy, L. 1950. The theory of open systems in physics and biology. Science 111:23.

3. Denbigh, K. G. 1951. The thermodynamics of the steady state. Methuen & Co., Ltd., London. p. 39.
4. Eyring, H., R. P. Boyce, and J. D. Spikes. 1960. Thermodynamics of Living Systems, vol. 1, p. 15. In Florkin, M., and H. S. Mason (editors): Comparative biochemistry. Academic Press, Inc., New York.

General references

Baker, J. J. W., and G. E. Allen. 1965. Matter, energy, and life. Addison-Wesley Publishing Company, Inc., Palo Alto, Calif.

Bayliss, L. E. 1959. Principles of general physiology. 5th ed. John Wiley & Sons, Inc., New York.

Casey, E. J. 1962. Biophysics: Concepts and mechanisms. Reinhold Publishing Corp., New York.

Denbigh, K. G. 1951. The thermodynamics of the steady state. Methuen & Co., Ltd., London.

Edsall, J. T., and J. Wyman. 1958. Vol. 1. Biophysical chemistry. Academic Press, Inc., New York.

Fast, J. D. 1962. Entropy. McGraw-Hill Book Co., New York.

Karlson, P. 1963. Introduction to modern biochemistry. Academic Press, Inc., New York.

Kleiner, I. S., and J. M. Orten. 1962. Biochemistry. 6th ed. The C. V. Mosby Co., St. Louis.

Ling, G. N. 1962. A physical theory of the living state: The association-induction hypothesis. Blaisdell Publishing Co., New York.

Lumry, R. 1959. Some aspects of the thermodynamics and mechanism of enzymic catalysis, vol. 1, p. 157. In Boyer, P. D., H. Lardy, and K. Myrbäck (editors); The enzymes, Academic Press, Inc.

Prigogine, I. 1955. Introduction to thermodynamics of irreversible processes. Interscience Publishers, Inc., New York.

Setlow, R. B., and E. C. Pollard. 1962. Molecular biophysics. Addison-Wesley Publishing Co., Inc., Reading, Mass.

Tanford, C. 1961. Physical chemistry of macromolecules. John Wiley & Sons, Inc., New York.

West, E. S. 1963. Textbook of biophysical chemistry. 3rd ed. The Macmillan Co., New York.

White, A., P. Handler, and E. L. Smith. 1964. Principles of biochemistry. 3rd ed. McGraw-Hill Book Co., New York.

14

Enzymes, catalysis, and kinetics

E**INTRODUCTION**
nzymes are the proteins on whose surfaces are carried out the biochemical processes of the cell. They are biological catalysts which have their own peculiar ways of behaving in both their kinetics and their mechanisms of action.

The use of enzymes is an old art, with the fermentation processes in wine-making perhaps being the oldest historically. Many early studies of enzymes were for industrial purposes, but when Sumner, in 1926, isolated and crystallized urease, the door began to open to a more theoretical approach to the study of these catalysts.

There are three phases of enzymology which should be covered. First, there is a general consideration of the enzyme itself—its characteristics, classification, and working properties. Second, the topic of kinetics should be explored, developing the simple mass action equilibrium into a usable enzyme terminology. Implicit in a study of kinetics are those factors which either enhance or inhibit the normal rate of action of the enzymes. Finally, the mechanism of the action of enzymes must be discussed, for therein lies the overriding reason for enzyme studies—how do these proteins act to govern the rates of physiological processes of the cell.

DEFINITIONS AND TERMINOLOGY

Before the concept of catalysis is approached, perhaps it is better to pause and define some of the terminology which will be used in discussion.

A definition of an enzyme which is quite lucid is as follows: "*Enzymes* may be described as complex catalysts of biological origin which have a very high degree of specificity and a tremendous efficiency which allow in vivo reactions to occur very rapidly through well-defined pathways." This inclusive definition brings out the salient points concerning enzymes. The fact that they are bio-

135

logical catalysts has already been mentioned. The remainder of the definition, as just stated, elaborates their basic characteristics:

1. Specificity, which means that enzymes react only with certain substances
2. Efficiency, which is a prerequisite in a biological system where a large variety of molecules must operate in a small area
3. Reaction in vivo, which so often differs from in vitro reaction that extrapolation to in-the-cell conditions is often dangerous
4. Use of well-defined pathways, which indicates that enzymes catalyze reactions which occur in, or can lead to, basic metabolic patterns in the cell

Substrates, on the other hand, are those substances upon which the action(s) of the enzyme are directed. Not by definition, but by usage, the term *substrate* has come to mean those substances with which the enzymes *normally* react. Enzymes may combine or react with substances not normally found in the cell, but these substances are not referred to as true substrates.

Since enzymes are catalysts, their efficiency in this capacity can be compared. The *turnover number,* which is the number of moles of substrate acted upon per mole of enzyme per unit time, can be used for this comparison. This number is extremely high, ranging from 10,000 up to possibly 1 million. That is, one mole of enzyme is capable of converting up to 1 million moles of substrate per minute. This is a fantastic number, but the catalyst is present in such small amounts that it must react quickly in order for it to be reused again.

The activity of an enzyme is best defined in terms of its *specific activity.* This is the measured quantitative change per standard unit. Several examples should elucidate this nebulous definition. Many enzyme activities can be determined spectrophotometrically, and often the specific activity is reported as Δ E/mg N; that is, the change in extinction (optical density) per milligram of protein nitrogen. (Nitrogen is frequently used as the index of protein in the reaction vessel.) The higher specific activity values indicate a purer concentration of the enzyme being tested. Other, less exacting specific activities may use dry weight of material as the criterion—for example, ml O_2 consumed/mg dry weight of tissue.

CLASSIFICATION OF ENZYMES

Schemes of nomenclature of enzymes are quite inadequate. While it is true that there are several basic patterns which parallel known chemical ones, there are so many specialized reactions that do not fit into general categories that complete itemizing of the kinds of enzymes would take several chapters. Even the standard rule that enzymes should have the suffix *–ase* is not inviolate (for example, pepsin and chymotrypsin). In general, though, enzymes may be classified in large taxa, based on the type of biochemical reaction which is catalyzed. These groups, along with several examples of each, will be outlined.

Hydrolytic enzymes are those which introduce or remove water from a specific area of the substrate(s), with the introduction of the water resulting in an alteration of the substrate. As in all reactions which are reversible, one has to name the enzyme according to either the forward or reverse reaction, but it should be remembered that the same enzyme usually catalyzes in both directions. In fact, there are some reactions in which the equilibrium favors one direction completely over the reverse, and yet the enzyme nomenclature is based on the reverse reaction. Common examples of hydrolytic enzymes include the following:

1. Phosphatases

$$\underset{\underset{\displaystyle OH}{|}}{\overset{\overset{\displaystyle O}{\parallel}}{RO\overset{}{P}OH}} + H_2O \xrightarrow{\ \ En\ \ } ROH + P_i$$

2. Glycosidases

$$Sugar—O—Sugar + H_2O \xrightarrow{\ \ En\ \ } 2\ Sugars$$

3. Lipases and esterases

$$RCOOR' + H_2O \xrightarrow{\ \ En\ \ } RCOOH + R'OH$$

4. Proteases

$$RCONHR' + H_2O \xrightarrow{\ \ En\ \ } RCOOH + R'NH_2$$

Transferase enzymes catalyze transfer of reactive groups from one compound to another. Two examples are the transaminases and transphosphorylases. Their mechanisms are complex and will be discussed in the section on metabolism.

Isomerase enzymes are those which catalyze intramolecular rearrangement of groups. Many examples are seen in the glycolytic cycle and the pentose shunt. *Carboxylation* and *decarboxylation* enzymes are involved in addition and removal of carbon dioxide from the molecule. There seems to be no single mechanism for this transfer, as a variety of means of attaining the result have been found. *Addition enzymes,* of which the hydrases are a specific example, catalyze the addition to or removal of a group from the substrate. In the case of fumarase or aconitase, which are specific hydrases, water is added or subtracted. The *oxidation-reduction* enzymes have a full chapter devoted to them (Chapter 16).

COENZYMES AND COFACTORS

Very often enzymes do not work alone in performing their function. Early workers in the field found that if they attempted to purify enzyme extracts by dialysis (selective permeability where large molecules, but not small ones, are restrained from passing through an artificial membrane) the extract lost its activity. From this, and other more sophisticated evidence, several kinds of compounds were found to be essential for enzyme activity.

Terminology of the assorted groups of compounds is not stable. A consensus defines *coenzymes* as nonprotein organic substances necessary for activity of the *apoenzyme* (protein portion), but which are not permanently bound to the protein. A coenzyme may therefore participate in reactions with several or many apoenzymes. *Prosthetic groups* are nonprotein moieties bound tightly to the protein portion and are specific for that enzyme. *Cofactors* may be both organic or ionic. The organic cofactors are those compounds which seem to participate as coenzymes in enzymic reactions, but which have not been promoted to full status.[1] Ionic cofactors, or activators, on the other hand, are those ions which are apparently necessary to provide proper electrostatic configuration to allow the enzyme and substrate to combine and interact.

Coenzymes can be classified by their hydrogen-carrying ability or their capacity to transfer various groups (Table 14-1). Common hydrogen-carrying coenzymes are the pyridine nucleotides (nicotinamide adenine dinucleotide or NAD and nicotinamide adenine dinucleotide phosphate or NADP), the flavin nucleotides (flavin adenine dinucleotide or FAD and flavin mononucleotide or FMN), and lipoic acid.

NAD and NADP, also still reported in the literature as DPN and TPN, have a niacin base. Their hydrogen-carrying ability is characterized by the fact that only one hydrogen is carried per molecule, a deviation from the two hydrogens or electrons transported by other carriers.

FAD and FMN have the vitamin riboflavin as their base. They apparently transfer two hydrogens on each molecule of coenzyme, as does lipoic acid, a fatty acid with two sulfhydryl groups for hydrogen transfer.

The group-carrying coenzymes are those which are capable of transferring a particular group from one compound to another. The purine and pyrimidine phosphates, such as ATP, as well as the sugar phosphates, are involved in transfer of the phosphate group. Coenzyme A is an acetylating agent in its form as acetyl-coenzyme A.

3′-phosphoadenosine diphosphate   Pantothenic acid   β-mercapto-ethanolamine   Acetyl

Acetyl-CoA

Thiamine pyrophosphate, pyridoxal phosphate, and folic acid and its derivatives have more specific functions, which will be uncovered in the section on metabolism.

The organic cofactors include many vitamins or vitamin-like substances which

Table 14-1. Various coenzymes and organic cofactors

Hydrogen carriers	Group carriers	Cofactors
Flavin adenine dinucleotide (FAD)	Adenosine monophosphate (AMP)	Ascorbic acid
Flavin mononucleotide (FMN)	Coenzyme A (CoA)	Biotin
Lipoic acid	Cytodine monophosphate (CMP)	Choline
Nicotinamide adenine dinucleotide	Folic acid family	Glutathione
(NAD)	Guanosine monophosphate (GMP)	Inositol
Nicotinamide adenine dinucleotide	Pyridoxal phosphate	Vitamin B_{12}
phosphate (NADP)	Sugar phosphates	Vitamin K
	Thiamine pyrophosphate	
	Uridine monophosphate (UMP)	

participate in various ways to enhance enzyme activity. Some of these are biotin, vitamin K, choline, and ascorbic acid.

Ions and their effects on enzyme activity were previously outlined in Chapter 10. Recall that many enzymes have special ion requirements before activity is accomplished. Kinase (phosphate transfer) enzymes, for example, seem to require Mg^{++} or Mn^{++}, and Zn^{++} is necessary for peptidase activity.

CATALYSIS

In 1903, Henri[2] unequivocally stated that enzymes were true catalysts, and all work since then has verified this fact. Thus, in order to get at the mechanism of action of enzymes, one must be versed in catalysis and the major ramifications of this concept.

Simply, catalysts are those substances which can accelerate chemical reactions although they themselves are not usually changed. Furthermore, they tend to be specific and are effective in small amounts; this effect is not on equilibrium per se, but on the rate at which equilibrium is attained.

Formally, catalysts reduce the free energy of activation of the reaction catalyzed. This is quite evident in the example of hydrogen peroxide. Under noncatalyzing conditions, the energy of activation for decomposition is approximately 18,000 calories per mole. Catalytic iron and platinum reduce this figure to about 13,000 and 12,000 calories per mole, respectively. However, catalase, the cellular enzyme which is specific for this action, lowers the activation energy to a minimal 5000 calories/mole.

It has been previously stated that the energy barrier of a reaction must be overcome by forming an activated complex which provides the extra energy level needed to initiate the reaction. In a reversible reaction, this activated complex, and thus the energy level, must be overcome in both forward and reverse directions. Under noncatalyzed conditions this activated complex occurs randomly by collision among the various molecules. Arrhenius' theory that various molecules have different energy levels and that only a few attain levels high enough to be reactive applies here.

An inorganic catalyst, then, must increase the number of effective collisions, since there is no evidence that the collision rate is increased; it must bring about this increase by lowering the energy needed for this effective collision. Lumry[3] has stated that the prime function of catalysts is to weaken the strong bonds in reactants or to stabilize the fractional bonds formed in the activated complexes. He further elaborates on the modes by which these could occur:

1. By electrostatic interaction
2. By covalent interaction with unpaired electrons
3. By geometrical bond distortion
4. By enhancing any internal induction or resonance effects

Attention must then be focused on two questions:

1. To what degree do proteins mimic the action of inorganic catalysts (that is, increase the effective collisions)?
2. Which, if any, of these methods of lowering the activation energy are used by enzymes in performing their catalytic functions?

Proteins as catalytic agents

Solid crystalline catalysts can often supply sites which will donate or accept electrons, and in this sense proteins bear a strong resemblance to them.

Some other characteristics which both crystalline catalysts and proteins share are the following:

1. They both have large surfaces with some form of phase interface where the reaction occurs.
2. Both have active sites or areas.
3. Both can react with the substrate by forming multiple bonds to increase specificity.
4. Both are rigid or are capable of a certain amount of rigidity.

It is at these points where the similarities stop and differences begin to show. There is good evidence[4] that the protein molecule utilizes its flexible nature to better enhance the catalysis. It is also possible that the enzyme does not passively offer a surface on which substrates position themselves for action, but rather the enzyme actively participates in bringing substrates together.

Proteins also exhibit some ideal characteristics which allow dynamic involvement of their structure in the catalytic reaction. These traits, which will be utilized in the discussion of mechanisms, are the following:

1. The ability of the enzyme to enforce a certain orientation of functional groups through its secondary and tertiary structure
2. Those special electrostatic properties (derived from these structural conformations) caused by the interaction of ionized groups among themselves and with the substrates

Any further extension of discussion on proteins as catalysts would encroach upon the material in the section on enzyme mechanisms, and before we consider this latter subject, more background information is needed.

KINETICS

Law of mass action

One question which was posed concerning enzyme action was whether or not the equilibrium for the catalyzed reaction was such that it essentially follows that of the law of mass action or that of the law of chemical equilibrium. In order to develop some basic kinetic traits of enzyme action, one first should review these laws and their application to reaction orders.

The law of mass action states that the rate of any reaction is considered to be proportional to the concentration of the reactants. In the reversible reaction

$$A + B \underset{k_2}{\overset{k_1}{\rightleftharpoons}} C + D,$$

for example, the reaction rate forward, $R_f = k_1 [A] [B]$; the reaction rate in reverse, $R_b = k_2 [C] [D]$.

Thus, since $R_f = R_b$ at equilibrium

$$k_1 [A] [B] = k_2 [C] [D]$$

and

$$\frac{k_1}{k_2} = \frac{[C] [D]}{[A] [B]}$$

Since k_1 and k_2 are both constants, K can substitute for the ratio $\frac{k_1}{k_2}$. The term K is called the equilibrium constant and is an indication to what extent the reaction favors the right or left. A large value for K signifies that C and D are present in much larger concentration than A and B; thus, the reaction favors the forward direction.

The primary premise of enzymatic reactions is that the enzyme and substrate combine to give an enzyme-substrate complex.

$$E + S \underset{k_2}{\overset{k_1}{\rightleftharpoons}} ES$$

The question is immediately raised as to whether this reaction is normal, as described above, or is it, instead, an anomalous reaction peculiar to biological systems. Before attempting to resolve this, let us digress to briefly discuss reaction orders.

Reaction orders

Zero-order reactions are those reactions in which the rate is a constant and is thus unaffected by the concentration of the reactants. In other words, the change in the products per unit time is constant.

The simplest case of where concentration affects the rate of a reaction is in the *first-order reaction*. Here, the rate is proportional to the concentration of one of the reactants (or the reactant if the reaction is of the type $AB \rightarrow A + B$). Progressively, the second- and third-order reactions are dependent on the concentration of two or three of the reactants.

As far as enzymatic reactions are concerned, the reaction rate follows a zero-order course if the substrate level is high. If this level falls, either as the substrate is used up or is inadequately replaced, the rate more closely approximates a first-order reaction. It is therefore difficult to classify the overall enzyme reaction as to any rate order. It should be apparent, however, that the rate is always determined by the concentration of the enzyme, which is really the catalyst and not a reactant.

The Michaelis-Menten hypothesis and the resultant equation

Perhaps the Michaelis-Menten equation is overused and overrated, but the concepts behind its derivation are of such basic nature that they alone warrant its presentation.

In the hypothesis originally put forth by Michaelis and Menten in 1913, they proposed that the enzyme and substrate form a complex (ES) in enzyme-catalyzed reactions. Further, they assumed that the rate of conversion of the substrate to the products is determined by the rate of formation of the (ES) complex, and thus the step from (ES) to the products can be ignored.

$$E + S \underset{k_2}{\overset{k_1}{\rightleftharpoons}} (ES) \xrightarrow{k_3} P + E \tag{1}$$

In other words, k_3 is entirely dependent on the rate of reaction determined by k_1 and k_2. For simplicity's sake, therefore, one overall reaction constant, K_m, was assumed, which combines k_1 and k_2 and essentially ignores k_3 at this point.

$$E + S \overset{K_m}{\rightleftharpoons} (ES) \tag{2}$$

As in all equilibrium reactions, corrections have to be made for any reactants which appear in the product. However, in this instance, no correction is made for the substrate since it is present in such large quantities in comparison to the enzyme. Thus

$$(E - ES) + S \overset{K_m}{\rightleftharpoons} (ES) \tag{3}$$

applying the law of chemical equilibrium

$$K_m = \frac{[E - ES][S]}{[ES]} \tag{4}$$

which, by rearrangement, gives

$$[ES] = \frac{[E][S]}{K_m + S} \tag{5}$$

Equation (5) is unsatisfactory since it is extremely difficult (impossible!) to accurately measure the (ES) complex, and K is not known at this point.

From previous statements, it can be assumed that the velocity of the overall reaction is proportional to the formation (and breakdown) of the enzyme substrate complex:

$$v = k (ES) \tag{6}$$

Thus k must certainly be equal to the k_3 of equation (1). Thus

$$v = k_3 (ES) \tag{7}$$

substituting into equation (5)

$$v = \frac{k_3 [E] [S]}{K_m + [S]} \tag{8}$$

Furthermore, it has been stated that regardless of the reaction order the rate is dependent upon the enzyme concentration. Since maximum velocity occurs when all the enzyme is bound as (ES) to the substrate,

$$V_{max} = k (E) \tag{9}$$

Again, k_3 can be substituted for k

$$V_{max} = k_3 (E) \tag{10}$$

Substitute back into equation (8)

$$v = \frac{V_{max} [S]}{K_m + [S]} \tag{11}$$

Equation (11) is known as the Michaelis-Menten equation, and it does permit calculation of K_m inasmuch as the velocities of reaction and the substrate concentration can be determined. Notice that when the velocity is equal to one-half of the maximum velocity K_m equals the substrate concentration at that point. The K_m is more easily determined, then, when the reaction is allowed to occur at half of the maximum velocity.

The important assumptions which must be made to give any validity to the equation are as follows:

1. All enzyme reactions do, in fact, go through an (ES) complex.
2. The rate of conversion of the (ES) complex to the products is dependent upon the rate the (ES) complex is formed.
3. The substrate concentration is so much greater than that of the enzyme that no correction has to be made for the substrate appearing in (ES).
4. The velocity of an enzyme catalyzed reaction is proportional to the (ES) complex.
5. The maximum velocity is proportional to the amount of enzyme participating in the reaction.

These five assumptions are important corollaries to enzyme studies and catalysis in proposing a workable enzyme mechanism.

Lineweaver-Burke modification

Although the Michaelis-Menten equation in its original form can be used to calculate the K_m, determination is quite tedious and necessitates some approximations in that the curve of substrate versus velocity is asymptotic, with the V_{max} approached at infinite substrate concentration (Fig. 14-1).

One alternate form of this equation is the Lineweaver-Burke modification. Since a reciprocal plot often results in a linear relationship, the Lineweaver-Burke modification is the reciprocal of equation (11).

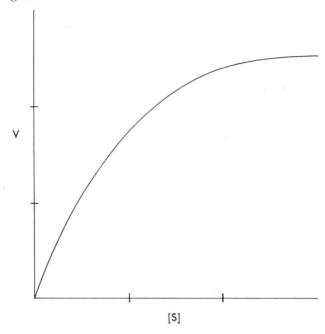

Fig. 14-1. Plot of Michaelis-Menten equation. To plot the curve accurately requires many determinations of *V* versus [*S*].

$$\frac{1}{V} = \frac{K_m}{V_{\text{max}}} \frac{1}{[S]} + \frac{1}{V_{\text{max}}} \tag{12}$$

or

$$\frac{[S]}{V} = \frac{K_m}{V_{\text{max}}} + \frac{[S]}{V_{\text{max}}} \tag{13}$$

For equation (12), a plot of $\frac{1}{V}$ versus $\frac{1}{[S]}$ gives a linear relationship where the y intercept is $\frac{1}{V_{\text{max}}}$, the x intercept $-\frac{1}{K_m}$, and the slope $\frac{K_m}{V_{\text{max}}}$ (Fig. 14-2). The significance of this linear plot is that the maximum velocity is at a finite point and can easily be determined by extrapolation from data of lesser velocities.

K_m

The Michaelis constant, K_m, is a complex constant which in reality is a close approximation of $\frac{k_2 + k_3}{k_1}$ (see equation (1)). It is therefore neither the dissociation nor the formation constant of (ES). Although there are approximations in its derivations and limitations to its use, it is still one of the fundamental constants in enzyme chemistry. Applications of it to enzyme studies include estimation of substrate concentration necessary for maximum velocity and determination of the (velocity)/(maximum velocity) ratio at any given substrate concentration.

The K_m, although constant only under rigorously specified conditions, does indicate that the formation of the (ES) complex follows predictable behavior based on the law of mass action. Finally, the K_m is an invaluable tool for studying enzyme kinetics.

Inhibition

A logical follow-up discussion to the Michaelis-Menten law is the subject of inhibitors, since they affect the kinetics of the reactions. Those agents which have been shown to be deadly to cell processes are, in fact, various kinds of inhibitors, and these substances exert their action in a variety of ways. Three areas of studies of inhibitors are as follows:

1. Their effect on the kinetics of the reaction
2. The mode by which they operate
3. Their use in the study of enzymes

Basically, there are two types of inhibition—competitive and noncompetitive—and they differ in both their kinetic effects and their modes of action.

Competitive inhibition

In competitive inhibition, the substrate and the inhibitor apparently vie for the same active site on the enzyme. A good inhibitor has a greater affinity for this site than does the natural substance. Usually, but not always, the inhibitor is unchanged by its attachment to the enzyme. The substance acting as a competitive inhibitor is structurally quite similar to the substrate. A now classical example of competitive inhibition demonstrates these properties quite well.

The enzyme succinic dehydrogenase removes two hydrogens from succinic acid, yielding fumaric acid as a product:

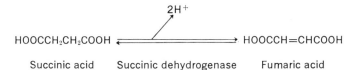

2H$^+$

HOOCCH$_2$CH$_2$COOH $\rightleftharpoons$ HOOCCH=CHCOOH

Succinic acid   Succinic dehydrogenase   Fumaric acid

This reaction is specifically affected in the presence of malonic acid, HOOCCH$_2$COOH. This acid, whose similarity to succinic acid can be seen, combines with the enzyme at the same site where the succinic acid attaches. In addition, no dehydrogenation of malonic occurs.

The effect of this attachment by the inhibitor in the kinetics of the reaction is quite severe. In addition to the normal (ES) formation

$$E + S \rightleftharpoons (ES)$$

there is also the formation of an enzyme-inhibitor complex

$$E + I \rightleftharpoons (EI)$$

However, since all of these are present at once, there are additional interactions.[5]

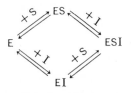

This complexes the kinetic picture. In deriving the Michaelis-Menten equation, one now has to take into account this new (EI) term. To avoid the tedium of going through the derivation, suffice it to say that the values of the slope and the x intercept are changed (Fig. 14-2). In true competitive inhibition, the maximum velocity remains the same; that is, the y intercept of a Lineweaver-Burke plot is unchanged. This occurs because as the natural substrate concentration increases the chances of it attaching at the active site are greater. At very large [S], the effect of the competitive inhibitor is negligible. The inhibition, then, is in effect reversible.

Noncompetitive inhibition

Noncompetitive inhibition may involve a compound combining with either the enzyme or the enzyme-substrate complex to form the inactive (EI) and

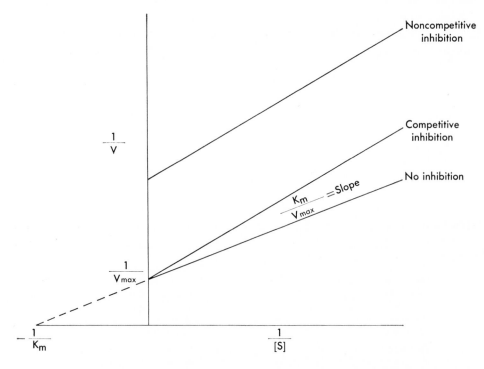

Fig. 14-2. Lineweaver-Burke plot and the effect of inhibitors. Reciprocal plots of $\frac{1}{V}$ versus $\frac{1}{[S]}$ result in a straight line. Competitive inhibition shifts the slope, but not the maximum velocity. In noncompetitive inhibition, both the slope and maximum velocity are altered. In all cases, the maximum velocity $\left(as \dfrac{1}{V_{max}}\right)$ is at the y intercept.

(ESI) (p. 146). Different from competitive inhibition, these inactive forms are generally not reversed by the presence of larger amounts of substrate. The inhibitor effectively ties up the enzyme or the (ES) complex, preventing both the enzyme from attaching to the substrate (EI) and the enzyme-substrate complex from separating into the product and the free enzyme. Since this consequently removes active enzyme from the system, the maximum velocity is depressed. In fact, several parameters of the kinetic formula are altered (Fig. 14-2). Noncompetitive inhibitors are often the heavy metals such as mercury, lead, and silver, although organic compounds can also inhibit in this manner.

Antimetabolites and metabolic analogs

The fact that an enzyme may be inhibited by compounds which are structurally similar to the natural substrates has opened wide areas of investigation. These compounds, the antimetabolites or metabolic analogs, are being used as drugs, in research on enzyme kinetics, and in studies on enzyme mechanisms, to name a few of the areas of application.

Several examples of metabolic analogs have already appeared in this text. Elaidic acid, an analog of oleic acid, is used to study lipid turnover in vivo. The halogenated purines and pyrimidines increase radiosensitivity of the cell or organism; their role in studying DNA and RNA synthesis is no less important.

Which compounds will actually act as antimetabolites is not always predictable, but those which do act in this capacity share common electrostatic configuration (Table 14-2).

p-Aminobenzoic acid   Sulfanilamide

Table 14-2. Some common metabolic analogs or antimetabolites

Metabolite	Analog
Acetic acid	Fluoroacetic acid
Adenine	Diaminopurine
β-Alanine	Propionic acid
p-Aminobenzoic acid	Sulfanilamide
Cytidine	Adenosine; fluorocytidine
Guanine	Azaguanine
Methionine	Ethionine
Phenylalanine	Fluorophenylalanine
Pteroylglutamic acid	Xanthopterin
Succinic acid	Malonic acid
Testosterone	Estradiol
Tyrosine	Fluorotyrosine
Uracil	Fluorouracil; bromouracil
Vitamin K	Dicumarol

$$\overset{\text{H}}{\underset{\text{H}}{\overset{|}{\underset{|}{\text{H}_2\text{NC}}}}}\text{—CH}_2\text{—COOH}$$

β-Alanine

$$\overset{\text{H}}{\underset{\text{H}}{\overset{|}{\underset{|}{\text{HC}}}}}\text{—CH}_2\text{—COOH}$$

Propionic acid

One would expect this, really, in light of the specificity of enzyme action and the attachment of the substrate to the protein.

Physiochemical factors that affect activity

All of the phenomena discussed in Section III are applicable to enzyme activity. In order to exert maximum catalysis, an enzyme has optimal requirements as far as pH, temperature, and ion environment are concerned. Even ionizing radiation has been reported to affect the activity of some enzymes.[6]

MECHANISMS OF ENZYME ACTION

The development of a universal model to describe the mechanism of enzyme action is impossible because of the many variations in the proteins, substrates, coenzymes, and actions involved. A good body of data is accumulating, however, which is beginning to show some basic trends and unifications. Uncovering of enzyme mechanisms is at the synthesis stage where areas of information from various sources are compared, and an attempt is made to apply these data to other situations. Still and all, as was indicated, enough material is available to more concretely present some ideas on enzyme mechanism.

Protein denaturation

The fact that enzyme reactions are dependent on a specific set of physiochemical conditions is well accepted. At the physiological limits of temperature and pH, the protein may become denatured, and if controlled correctly, this denaturation is reversible.

$$En \underset{\longleftarrow}{\overset{\longrightarrow}{}} En_{dn}$$

The enzyme when in the denatured state often loses its catalytic ability, and yet it regains its reactivity when conditions are altered and it returns to the normal state. This certainly infers that the tertiary structure of the protein is necessary for activity, and even minor alterations in this three-dimensional framework may render the protein inactive.

(ES)

The proof of the formation of the enzyme-substrate complex is beyond refute. Chance[7] clearly showed the presence of the elusive (ES) by means of mass spectrograph analysis. His data indicate a distinctly different absorption peak for the enzyme alone and the substrate alone and a separate short-lived peak which must be the enzyme-substrate complex. This biophysical evidence supports the chemical kinetic evidence previously discussed.

The implications of the formation of an enzyme-substrate complex are several. First, one must consider the fact that this complex is fairly labile and yet rigid and long-lasting enough to allow some modification of the substrate. What the nature of this attachment is remains unresolved, although some ideas are presented later. There is some excellent evidence that in at least some enzymes (aconitase, for example) this attachment is mediated through three distinct points of contact between the enzyme and the substrate.

Second, the question must be posed as to whether the physical attachment of the substrate to the enzyme is the force which increases the enthalpy, that is, effectively lowers the activation energy, or whether the enzyme merely mediates and provides an area for contact of molecules to enhance the effective collisions. Competitive inhibition studies indicate that the natural substrate may not attach to the enzyme as easily as does the inhibitor. The electrostatic configuration of the enzyme and substrate must closely match, but there is the possibility that the fit is not perfect. This would mean that in order to form the (ES) the natural substrate would have to have some small force, in the form of bending the bonds, applied to it. With a possible three-point attachment and the fact that covalent enzyme-substrate intermediates are formed,[8] the required force could be derived to increase the enthalpy of the molecule.

Active site—specificity of enzyme attachment

At or near the point of attachment of the substrate to the enzyme is an area designated the *active site*. This locus is that portion of the protein molecule which expresses the biological activity of the enzyme.

The fact that enzymes are quite specific suggests that this site demonstrates a high degree of specificity. This specificity is first spatial. That is, the substrate compound must have the correct configuration for attachment. Second, the locus shows an absolute specificity which is dependent on the action to be performed. This absolute specificity implies that only one substrate is acted upon by the enzyme, or that one specific group of the substrate is attacked.

Relative specificity also has a dual meaning. It may be defined in terms of the relative degree of activity on the members of the group of compounds it normally attacks. For example, a deaminase may be designated as having absolute specificity since an α-amino group must be present for activity. The degree of activity on the substrate, however, may be determined by the molecule having the α-amino group. This relative specificity is dependent on the ease of action, or attachment, on the substrate. On the other hand, the term *relative specificity* is also used to indicate those cases where an enzyme may alter substrates outside its normal sphere of activity.

Finally, as might well be expected, enzymes show optical specificity. The fact that organisms preferentially metabolize only certain optical isomers infers *a priori* that their cells must contain enzymes which show this optical specificity which can also be subdivided into absolute and relative.

This active site, with its specificities for attachment, comprises only a small portion of the enzyme molecule. The size of the active site may vary, depending on the type of substrates acted upon, but there is some indication that enzymes of diverse action may have the same sequence of amino acids at the active site. Often serine is involved as one of the acids in those sites which have been studied, and apparently the reactive groups of the amino acids are fully exploited in this locus where the (ES) complex occurs. The sulfhydryl group, which has an affinity for forming covalent bonds due to its ease of giving up electrons or hydrogens, as well as its participation in hydrogen bonding, is ideally suited for the active site. The list of enzymes whose activities are inhibited by sulfhydryl poisons is impressive. This inhibition is confirming evidence of the importance of this group. Fraenkel-Conrat[9] has listed the other reactive groups in enzymes which may operate in the active site. His list includes the various acids which can contribute to ionic attraction, form hydrogen bonds, create van der Waals forces, or form a link directly with the substrate. These reactive groups are listed in Table 6-1 (Chapter 6).

The active site on the enzyme may not, in fact, be the locus of activity of the enzyme. The contact amino acid sequence of the place of attachment of the substrate may work with auxiliary amino acids in other parts of the protein chain to bring about the required reaction.

Thus, the active site seems to carry out two functions. First, it provides a specific area where the substrate can attach, and, second, the appropriate changes on the substrate are made while the substrate is attached to the locus, although other areas of the protein may be active in the reaction to be carried out. An enzyme may have more than one active site, each active site carrying out a different, but related, function. A whole sequence of events may be mediated by one enzyme with several active sites.

Enzyme mechanisms

The discovery of an active site on the enzyme molecule made it tempting to propose a *template mechanism* for the enzymatic action. The active site could then be considered to be a three-dimensional depression where the substrate could enter, attach, and have the alteration occur, with cell components of the system located stereospecifically in adjacent areas so that the reaction could proceed. This theory may very well be correct for many enzyme-substrate interactions, but it does not explain all of the data and phenomena which have been observed. Koshland[4,8] proposes an alternate theory which, although only a modification of the template hypothesis, provides some new concepts for enzyme mechanism. The postulates of his theory, termed the *induced-fit theory* are as follows:

1. The attachment of the substrate to the enzyme at the active site causes a change in the geometry of the enzyme.
2. The change occurs in order to correctly orient the catalytic groups.
3. The substrate "induces" this alteration of geometry; other substances and inhibitors do not (Fig. 14-3).

This proposal, which is based on the fact that the protein molecule is flexible enough to go through these required conformation changes, is quite

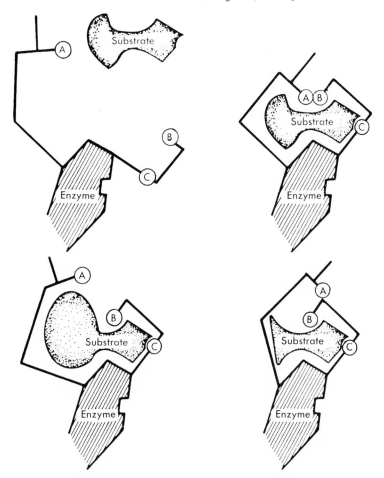

Fig. 14-3. Schematic model of flexible active site mechanism. Black lines indicate protein chains containing catalytic groups *A* and *B* and binding group *C*. *Upper left:* Substrate and enzyme dissociated. *Upper right:* Substrate with induced change of protein chains to bring *A* and *B* into proper alignment for reaction. *Lower left:* Bulky group added to substrate prevents proper alignment of *A* and *B*. *Lower right:* Deleted group eliminates buttressing action on chain containing *A*, so that thermodynamically stable complex has incorrect alignment of *A* and *B*. (From Koshland, D. E., Jr. 1964. Conformation changes at the active site during enzyme action. Fed. Proc. 23:724.)

attractive in that it can be used to explain the action of inhibitors and hormones on the activity of the enzyme (Figs. 14-4 and 14-5).

Many models of specific enzyme systems have been proposed (Fig. 14-6), with the most work having been done on transfer enzymes and chymotrypsin. Some evidence now points to the fact that most cleavage mechanisms require the presence of a nucleophilic area (an electron donor) in the active site or in the auxiliary areas. Serine seems to participate as an active group by temporarily capturing and thus stabilizing intermediate products in both hydrolysis and group transfer reactions. Pooling of these data, and others, may eventually lead to some concrete mechanisms of action.

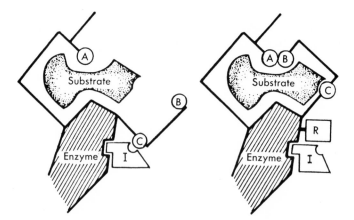

Fig. 14-4. Effect of inhibitors and reagents on flexible active site enzyme. *Left:* Inhibitor attracts group *C* and prevents proper alignment of catalytic group *B*. If net affinity of substrate is unchanged, noncompetitive inhibition would be observed. If *B* chain is involved in binding, competitive inhibition is observed. *Right:* Reagent *R* prevents juxtaposition of group *C* with inhibitor *I*, and effect of *I* is nullified without changing binding affinity of *I*. (From Koshland, D. E., Jr. 1964. Conformation changes at the active site during enzyme action. Fed. Proc. 23:725.)

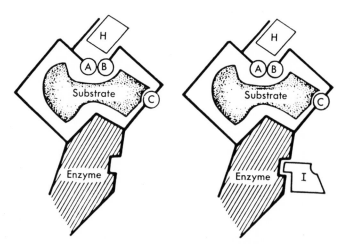

Fig. 14-5. Effect of hormone or activator on flexible site enzyme. *Left:* Hormone stabilizes active conformation by attracting chains containing *A* and *B*. *Right:* Hormone overcomes effect of inhibitor *I* by attracting chains containing *A* and *B*. (From Koshland, D. E., Jr. 1964. Conformation changes at the active site during enzyme action. Fed. Proc. 23:725.)

ENZYME ACTIVITY OF THE CELL

Study of the enzyme activity of the cell is often hampered by difficulty in distinguishing between *endogenous* and *exogenous* activity. Endogenous enzyme activity is that degree of reaction which occurs in the cell with the presence of those substrates, activators, coenzymes, and enzymes which are located there at that particular time. Exogenous activity is the degree of reaction which occurs

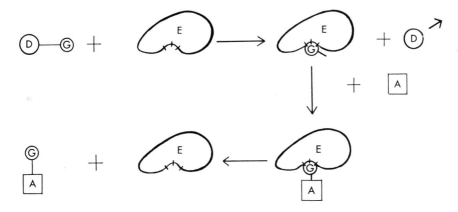

Fig. 14-6. Model of group-transfer enzyme. Enzyme, *E,* picks up group, *G,* from donor, *D,* and transfers it to acceptor, *A.*

when additional amounts of any of the above are introduced into the medium of the cell or into the cell itself. Total enzyme activity as experimentally determined is a sum of the endogenous and exogenous components.

The enzymes which are in the cell at any one point in physiological time are of two types. The *constitutive enzymes* are those which are always present in the cell, the fluctuation in level being the only variable. *Induced enzymes,* however, are those which are formed only when the substrate is present. Enzyme induction involves a change within individual cells and not a change in the makeup of the population. The process involves synthesis of an enzyme rather than subtle activation, but the exact biochemical role of the inducer has not been elucidated. This control mechanism for enzyme levels is considered in more detail in Chapter 31.

SUMMARY

The subject of enzymes warrants some detailed study because they, the biological catalysts of the cell, are the mediators of the physiological phenomena of the cell. The proteins, either working alone or in conjunction with coenzymes, prosthetic groups, or activators, are generally classified according to the types of reactions in which they participate. An attempt is made to make the nomenclature as consistent as possible by use of the suffix *-ase.*

The fact that enzymes chemically act as catalysts infers that the kinetics of their action should follow a somewhat predictable course, particularly since the enzyme combines with the substrate to yield an enzyme-substrate complex (ES). Since catalysis involves reduction of free energy of activation, formation of this (ES) complex should provide that extra energy. The structure of the protein, with its large surface area, flexible nature, three-dimensional configuration, and potential for forming uniting bonds, seems ideal for biological catalysis.

The kinetics of enzyme reactions follow those imposed by the law of mass action, which states that the equilibrium constant is proportional to the concentrations (activities) of the reactants and products involved in the action. With several assumptions based on experimental evidence, K_m, the Michaelis constant, is described as a fundamental constant in enzyme chemistry. Through the Michaelis-Menten equation, or modifications such as the Lineweaver-Burke, the kinetics of an enzyme reaction can be characterized as far as (1) maximum velocity which can be attained, (2) substrate concentration necessary to reach this maximum, (3) K_m, and (4) velocity at any substrate concentration.

Linear plotting of kinetic data allows the detection of the two basic types of inhibition—competitive and noncompetitive—since the linear plots shift, depending on the kind of inhibition imposed. In competitive inhibition, a compound competes for the same attachment site as the normal substrate. This type is usually reversible at high substrate concentration. Noncompetitive inhibitors bind the enzyme or the (ES) complex so that activity cannot occur and usually causes irreversible damage.

The outcrop of inhibitor studies is in the area of antimetabolites and metabolic analogs. These agents are used as tools for the study of enzymes and as instruments to control diseases.

The mechanisms involved in enzyme reactions have not been elucidated fully for any group of these proteins. There are, however, accumulated data which have been gleaned from various sources.

1. The enzyme and substrate must come into physical contact by a surface phenomenon. This contact may be mediated by activator ions.
2. The resultant contact, the (ES), may also have a coenzyme present, forming a ternary complex.
3. The protein portion of the enzyme is substrate-specific; the coenzyme may be reaction-specific.
4. By virtue of the formation of the complex, there is lowering of the energy barrier, or energy of activation.
5. The attachment is at an active site on the protein. These active sites, which have the same or similar amino acid sequences for many enzymes, are quite specific for substrate attachment. This specificity resides in the three-dimensional structure and the kinds of reactive groups present.
6. The action of the enzyme may not occur at the active site, but at auxiliary points on the protein.
7. The template hypothesis does not seem to fit all of the data; an alternate, the induced-fit theory, proposes a geometric change in the enzyme on exposure to the substrate—the change orienting the catalytic groups.

Most enzymes in the cell are constitutive and are thus present at all times. There are some, however, which are produced only when the substrate is present. This condition is called induced-enzyme formation.

The story of enzymes is incomplete, but great strides have been taken in the past ten years. The next decade should see exciting developments in those areas in which the seed has just begun to sprout.

Literature cited

1. Neilands, J. B., and P. K. Stumpf. 1959. Outlines of enzyme chemistry. 2nd ed. John Wiley & Sons, Inc., New York, p. 204.
2. Henri V., 1903. Lois générales de l'action des diastases. Hermann, Paris.
3. Lumry, Rufus. 1959. Some aspects of the thermodynamics and mechanism of enzymic catalysis, vol. 1, p. 157. In Boyer, P. D., H. Lardy, and K. Myrbäck (editors): The enzymes. Academic Press, Inc., New York.
4. Koshland, D. E., Jr. 1964. Conformation changes at the active site during enzyme action. Fed. Proc. 23:719.
5. Hearon, J. Z., S. A. Bernhard, S. L. Fuess. D. J. Botts, and M. F. Morales, 1959. Enzyme kinetics, vol. 1, p. 49. In Boyer, P. D., H. Lardy, and K. Myrbäck (editors): The enzymes. Academic Press, Inc., New York.
6. Augenstine, L. G. 1962. The effects of ionizing radiation on enzymes. Advances Enzymol. 24:359.
7. Chance, B. 1951. Enzyme-substrate compounds, Advances Enzymol. 12:153.
8. Koshland, D. E., Jr. 1959. Mechanisms of transfer enzymes, vol. 1, p. 305. In Boyer, P. D., H. Lardy, and K. Myrbäck (editors): The enzymes. Academic Press, Inc., New York.
9. Fraenkel-Conrat, H. 1959. Other reactive groups of enzymes, vol. 1, p. 589. In Boyer, P. D., H. Lardy, and K. Myrbäck (editors): The enzymes. Academic Press, Inc., New York.

General references

Alberty, R. A. 1956. Enzyme kinetics. Advances Enzymol. 17.1.

Bayliss, L. E. 1959. Principles of general physiology. 5th ed. John Wiley & Sons, Inc., New York.

Boyer, P. D., H. Lardy, and K. Myrbäck (editors): 1959-1963. The enzymes. Academic Press, Inc., New York. 8 vol.

Brookhaven Symposia in Biology. 1962. Enzyme models and enzyme structure. Brookhaven National Laboratory, Upton, N. Y.

Epstein, H. T. 1963. Elementary biophysics. Addison-Wesley Publishing Co., Inc., Palo Alto, Calif.

Karlson, P. 1963. Introduction to modern biochemistry. Academic Press, Inc., New York.

Kleiner, I. S., and J. M. Orten. 1962. Biochemistry. 6th ed. The C. V. Mosby Co., St. Louis.

Kosower, E. M. 1962. Molecular biochemistry. McGraw-Hill Book Co., New York.

Ling, G. N. 1962. A physical theory of the living state: The association-induction hypothesis. Blaisdell Publishing Co., New York.

Neilands, J. B., and P. K. Stumpf. 1958. Outlines of enzyme chemistry. 2nd ed. John Wiley & Sons, Inc., New York.

Neurath, H. 1964. Mechanism of zymogen activation. Fed. Proc. 23:1.

Niemann, Carl. 1964. Alpha-chymotrypsin and the nature of enzyme catalysis. Science 143:1287.

Setlow, R. B., and E. C. Pollard. 1962. Molecular biophysics. Addison-Wesley Publishing Company, Inc., Reading, Mass.

Synthesis and structure of macromolecules. 1963. Cold Spring Harbor Symposia on Quantitative Biology. Vol. 28.

Tanford, C. 1961. Physical chemistry of macromolecules. John Wiley & Sons, Inc., New York.

West, E. S. 1963. Textbook of biophysical chemistry. 3rd ed. The Macmillan Co., New York.

White, A., P. Handler, and E. L. Smith. 1964. Principles of biochemistry. 3rd ed. McGraw-Hill Book Co., New York.

Woolley, D. W. 1952. A study of antimetabolites. John Wiley & Sons, Inc., New York.

15

High-energy bonds and
coupled reactions

T INTRODUCTION

The laws of thermodynamics preclude the use of heat as an energy source under isothermal conditions, and thus the problem of a utilizable form of energy is imposed upon biological systems. The free energy of a compound can be changed to a lower level with the resultant increase in entrophy and the release of energy (recall $\Delta F = \Delta H - T\Delta S$). If this occurs by hydrolysis or by a similar degradation process, however, it is again thermodynamically not feasible to utilize this energy. The cell must have a mechanism of trapping this chemical energy in some sort of high-energy bond whose energy source can be tapped when the physiological demands are placed on it. The many phenomena and processes of a dynamic cell have energy-requiring reactions and would thus depend upon some energy-yielding compound as a driving force; that is, there must be catabolic processes which will couple with anabolic ones to give this energy (Fig. 15-1).

THE CONCEPT OF THE HIGH-ENERGY BOND

The free energy ($\Delta F°$) of hydrolysis

Lipmann[1] and Kalckar,[2] working independently, realized that various chemical bonds had different energy levels and thus proposed classifying compounds into energy-rich or energy-poor categories. They suggested that the energy level of a compound arbitrarily be assigned a value as if the compound underwent hydrolytic cleavage. For example, hydrolysis of a simple phosphate ester to an alcohol and inorganic phosphate, $ROPO_3H_2 + H_2O \rightarrow ROH + P_i$, has a free energy difference of -2000 to -3000 calories. This exergonic hydrolytic value, termed the $\Delta F°$ (free energy) of hydrolysis, is the energy level assigned to that ester.

This revolutionary concept of bond energy as proposed by Lipmann and

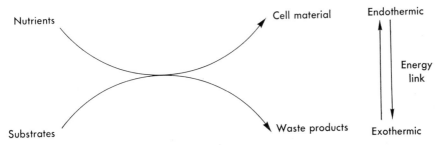

Fig. 15-1. Basic energy coupling in the cell. Nutrients are converted to cell material at the expense of the substrate as it is converted to waste products and energy. The energy from this exothermic reaction is what drives the endothermic synthesis.

Kalckar received much criticism from physical chemists as well as from biologists. Their basis for argument against this arbitrary assignment of energy was that the total energy of a compound cannot be determined by hydrolysis but must be calculated from the products of the reactions and the resonance of the bonds in the structure. Furthermore, they stated that the energy is not just in certain bonds, but instead is distributed throughout the molecule.

Counterarguments arose which insisted that this bond energy concept was quite useful in biochemical processes. Admittedly, assignment of the energy to that derived from hydrolysis is arbitrary, but no more so than assigning of oxidation-reduction values in the electromotive series. In an aqueous medium, the bonds most often involved in reactions are those which can be hydrolyzed or hydrated.

The concept has persisted and is one of the fundamental principles in characterizing biological reactions. The free energy of hydrolysis, which is always negative for hydrolytic reactions because of the increase in entropy, can be used to predict not only whether a reaction will occur, but also to what degree it goes. Examples will be given later. A list, albeit incomplete, of the free energy of hydrolysis of many compounds is given in Table 15-1.

The high-energy bond

The question of what makes certain molecules have more energy in their bonds than others was, in part, answered by Kalckar.[3] Working with phosphate compounds, he proposed that the higher energy level of some structures is due to an "opposing resonance" phenomenon. The inherent resonance of the phosphate group at times opposes the natural resonance or inflexibility of the organic moiety. This sets up stress on the bond, yielding a higher enthalpy and, in this case, a higher free energy. Those phosphate bonds which have this high energy are designated by $\sim$P.

Consider the structural characteristics of the compounds which have a high energy bond, and if the discussion is restricted to only the phosphate bonds, the following observations can be made:

1. The phosphate group has a high degree of internal resonance due to the

Table 15-1. Approximate $\Delta F°$ of hydrolysis values of some classes of compounds (STP)

Class of compound and example	Structure	$\Delta F°$ value (cal.)
Amides (peptide)	RCONHR	$>-3000*$
Carboxylic (simple fat ester)	RCOOR	-2000 to -3000
Simple phosphate (glucose-6-PO₄)	$ROPO_3H_2$	-2000 to -3000
Glycosides (maltose)	ROR	<-3000
Pyrophosphate	$HOPO_2HOPO_3H_2$	-6000
Phosphoric anhydrides (ATP)	$ROPO_2HOPO_3H_2$	$-8000†$
Thiol esters (acetyl-CoA)	RCOSR	-8000
Amino phosphate (creatine phosphate)	$RNH_2{}^+PO_3H_2$	-8000 to $-11,000$
Thiol phosphate (S-phosphoryl-CoA)	RSP	-9000
Carbamyl phosphate	$NH_2COOPO_3H_2$	-9000
Acyl phosphate (glyceryl phosphate)	$RCOOPO_3H_2$	$-11,000$
Enol phosphate (phosphoenol pyruvic)	RC=C—R $\quad\quad\vert$ $\quad OPO_3H_2$	$-11,000$ to $-12,000$
Acyl imidazole (acetyl imidazole)	$\quad\quad\quad$ H$\quad$H $\quad\quad\quad$/C=C RCON<$\quad\quad\vert$ $\quad\quad\quad$\C=N $\quad\quad\quad\quad$H	$-13,000$
Substituted acyl phosphate	$RCOOPO_3HR$	$-17,000$
Phosphosulfates (adenosine phosphosulfate)	$\quad$O$\quad$O $\quad$||$\quad$|| RP—S—OH $\quad$|$\quad$|| $\quad$O$\quad$O	$-18,000$

*Greater than (>) denotes a more positive number.
†Reported values vary in that there is a different value for ATP, depending on whether the hydrolysis is to AMP or ADP.

double bond to one oxygen and the dissociable hydrogen on at least one of the other oxygens.

$$
\begin{array}{c}
O \\
\| \\
-O-P-OH \\
\vert \\
O^-
\end{array}
$$

2. When the phosphate is attached to an organic moiety which has inflexibility in its structure due to a double bond, the phosphate group cannot exert its inherent rotation and thus causes a stress to be set up in the bond. Examples are phosphoenol pyruvic, acetyl phosphate, and carbamyl phosphate.

3. A portion of the moiety may have an internal rotation of its own which is not in harmony with the phosphate group. This also can put a stress on the bond. Examples are the phosphoric anhydride compounds.

The stress on the bond increases the enthalpy of the molecule. An analogy would be the building of a molecule using colored balls, sticks, and springs. If two atoms (colored balls) were attached by a spring, and the first of the balls were twisted, the second would respond with little stretch occurring in the spring. Little energy is lost or gained. If the second ball were now attached by a rigid stick to another "atom" and the first ball were turned, the spring would be twisted because of the inflexibility imposed by the stick. This increases the enthalpy of the system because when the first ball is released the twisted spring unwinds, yielding energy. Similarly, if two balls are attached by a spring and twisted in opposite directions, the energy is again increased in the "bond." The "twisting of the spring" in natural molecules is due to opposing resonance which is set up by the internal patterns of electron spin.

The phosphate pool

The importance of the phosphate esters as high-energy compounds has been recognized for many years. Phosphocreatine was known to be necessary for muscle contraction as early as 1927, and in 1931 ATP was shown to be a major high-energy component of the cell. More and more phosphate compounds were found to be energy rich. The combined thermodynamic lability with physiological stability made the phosphate group perfectly suited for its role. As can be seen in Table 15-1, other groups can participate as energy-donors in addition to the phosphates.

All of the known phosphate compounds which are classified high energy are either acid anhydrides, enol esters, or phosphamic acid derivatives.

According to Huennekens and Whitley,[4] the universal distribution of energy-rich compounds in microbial, animal, and plant cells suggests that the presence of these compounds should be considered a basic attribute of life. The system which is most universal is the adenylic acid system.

This group contains adenosine triphosphate (ATP), adenosine diphosphate (ADP), and adenosine monophosphate (AMP). The exchange of phosphate and energy among these compounds is of great importance to the cell—so important that the *raison d'être* of most metabolic pathways is the production of the ATP. The adenosine triphosphate can undergo two basic reactions which can yield energy.

$$\text{ATP} \xrightleftharpoons{\hspace{2cm}} \text{ADP} + \text{P}_i \tag{1}$$

$$\text{ATP} \xrightleftharpoons{\hspace{2cm}} \text{AMP} + \text{PP}_i \tag{2}$$

Reaction (1), the reversible breakdown to adenosine diphosphate and the inorganic phosphate, is the more common method of deriving energy from ATP. The free energy change is approximately $-$ 8000 calories, the value varying somewhat in the literature.

Reaction (2) is used by the cell quite often when group transfer requires a high energy source. The AMP usually complexes with the group to be transferred:

$$\text{ATP} + \text{XOH} \xrightleftharpoons{\hspace{2cm}} \text{AMP} \cdot \text{X} + \text{PP}_i$$

Many cells, as well as cell organelles, have an ATPase enzyme system. This enzyme, or set of enzymes, controls the release and storage of energy from the ATP. In other words, the ATPase system catalyzes the reversible hydrolysis of ATP to ADP or AMP, as shown in the previous equations.

Since most all of the physiological processes involve changes in energy, it is not too surprising that cells should contain compounds which can act both as a reservoir for the energy and as a means for channeling this energy into those processes which require it. In addition to the adenylic acid system, most cells also store energy in the inosine and guanosine phosphates and creatine phosphates. The entire complex of phosphate compounds which can store and release energy is called the *phosphate pool.*

The phosphate group does not have a monopoly on the high-energy systems in the cell. Many other compounds can exhibit this property, the most important being the ubiquitous coenzyme A, with its sulfhydryl end potentially forming the esters (RCOSR) which have a $\Delta F°$ of hydrolysis of -8000 calories.

COUPLED REACTIONS

Thermodynamically, it has been shown that the breakdown of ATP into ADP or AMP yields a free energy change of about -8000 calories; that is, ATP hydrolysis is an exergonic reaction. How and why the energy is necessarily channeled to drive endergonic reactions is embodied in the concept of coupled reactions.

The concept

Consider the reaction for the formulation of an ester:

$$R'COOH + ROH \rightleftarrows R'COOR + H_2O \qquad \Delta F = 3000 \qquad (1)$$

This is an endergonic reaction and thus requires energy to drive it to the right. Assume this energy comes from the hydrolysis of a glycoside

$$GOR^2 + H_2O \rightleftarrows GOH + R^2OH \qquad \Delta F = -3000 \qquad (2)$$

By adding these two equations, the sum total would be

$$GOR^2 + R'COOH + ROH \rightleftarrows R'COOR + GOH + R^2OH \qquad \Delta F = 0 \qquad (3)$$

This seems thermodynamically feasible because the free energy change of the exergonic reaction balances that of the endergonic. However, this coupled reaction will not go because the energy gained by the breakdown of the glycoside by hydrolysis is lost as heat with no available mechanisms for trapping the energy.

There must be some way in which the energy that is present can be channeled to get the required end products.

Assume

$$GOR^2 + ROH \rightleftarrows GOR + R^2OH \qquad \Delta F = 0 \qquad (4)$$

$$GOR + R'COOH \rightleftarrows GOH + R'COOR \qquad \Delta F = 0 \qquad (5)$$

the sum total is

$$GOR^2 + R'COOH + ROH \rightleftarrows GOH + R'COOR + R^2OH \qquad \Delta F = 0 \qquad (6)$$

Equations (3) and (6) are identical, but the mechanisms involved are different. In equations (4) and (5) water is not used and the energy which would have been lost by hydrolysis of GOR^2 is retained by formation of the ester linkage. Thus, it is biochemically possible to couple reactions (4) and (5) to arrive at the overall equation (6) which is both thermodynamically feasible and biochemically functional since no energy is lost. The reaction can only occur if the two component reactions are coupled by way of a common intermediate. In this case GOR is this intermediate.

The previous example was with energy-poor compounds, but the same principle holds true for substances with high-energy bonds as well.

Consider the following coupled reaction:

	RCOOH + R'SH	$\rightleftarrows$ RCOSR' + H_2O	$\Delta F = +8000$	(7)
	ATP + H_2O	$\rightleftarrows$ ADP + P_i	$\Delta F = -8000$	(8)
overall	ATP + RCOOH + R'SH $\rightleftarrows$ RCOSR' + ADP + P_i		$\Delta F = 0$	(9)

Again, as before, this reaction will not proceed. The energy lost in the hydrolysis of the ATP is irretrievable to the system. The reaction can be made to go by the following mechanism where the reaction is coupled through a common intermediate:

	ATP + RCOOH	$\rightleftarrows$ $RCOOPO_3H_2$ + ADP	$\Delta F = +3000$	(10)
	$RCOOPO_3H_2$ + R'SH	$\rightleftarrows$ RCOSR + P_i	$\Delta F = -3000$	(11)
overall	ATP + RCOOH + R'SH $\rightleftarrows$ RCOSR' + ADP + P_i		$\Delta F = 0$	(12)

Here is a case of one high-energy compound, ATP, being used to generate another energy-rich molecule, RCOSR'. In spite of the fact that the energy level of these compounds is high, the energy still must be channeled through coupled reactions if it is to be utilizable.

The concepts of coupled reactions and energy of hydrolysis can also be used to predict whether or not a reaction will go. In addition, if the reaction does proceed, the overall free energy change can be calculated.

Consider the reaction

$$RCOOPO_3H_2 + ROH \rightleftarrows ROPO_3H_2 + RCOOH \qquad (13)$$

The energy of hydrolysis can be used to determine whether this reaction will proceed. Taking the compounds on both sides which can be hydrolyzed

	$RCOOPO_3H_2$ + H_2O $\rightarrow$ RCOOH + P_i		$\Delta F = -11{,}000$	(14)
	ROH + P_i $\leftarrow$ $ROPO_3H_2$ + H_2O		$\Delta F = +3000$	(15)
overall	$RCOOPO_3H_2$ + ROH $\rightleftarrows$ $ROPO_3H_2$ + RCOOH		$\Delta F = -8000$	(16)

From this the following can be noted:

1. The reaction (13) will proceed because the overall free energy change is
   — 8000, a strongly exergonic reaction.

2. The overall energy change is the difference of the free energy of hydrolysis of compounds involved.

3. The sum reaction of the hydrolysis to the right of the phosphate compounds on the left of the overall reaction and the hydrolysis to the left of the phosphate compounds on the right yields the same overall reaction, (16), as the original, (13).

4. The preceding is *not* the mechanism of the reaction; it is the hydrolysis energies which are being determined.

The apparent inefficiency of reaction (13) is a necessary part of at least the homeothermic cells. The 8000 calories lost in this reaction are given off as heat, and this output of thermal energy is a necessary by-product of metabolism.

Thermodynamic applications

A reaction with a $+ \Delta F$ can occur in a biological system even without a coupled mechanism, but only under certain conditions. This possibility is a reflection of the relationship between ΔF and the equilibrium constant:

$$\Delta F = -2.303 \ RT \log K$$

For simplicity, assume a reaction to be occurring at $25°$ C., where

$$\Delta F = -1370 \log K$$

Further, assume a reaction

$$A + B \rightleftarrows C + D$$

where the ΔF is $+1370$. Thus

$$1370 = -1370 \log K$$

for that reaction. Solving for K

$$-1 = \log K$$
$$0.1 = K$$

When this value is applied to the equilibrium equation, it means that if the concentration of A and B initially were 0.01M, at equilibrium the following relationship must hold if $K = 0.1$.

$$0.1 = \frac{[C] \ [D]}{[A] \ [B]}$$

$$= \frac{[X]^2}{[0.01 - X]^2}$$

$$= \frac{[2.4 \times 10^{-3}]^2}{[7.6 \times 10^{-3}]^2}$$

or

$$= \frac{[0.0024] \ [0.0024]}{[0.0076] \ [0.0076]}$$

Thus, about one fourth of the reactants, A and B, are converted to C and D, even though the ΔF of the reaction is positive.

On the other hand, assume an hydrolysis reaction

$$A + B \rightarrow C + H_2O$$

with the same conditions of $K = 0.1$. Since free water in a biological system is 55M, the H_2O generated in this reaction is insignificant in comparison to that which is already present. The activity value of water is assigned as 1.

Thus

$$0.1 = \frac{[C][H_2O]}{[A][B]}$$

$$= \frac{[0.00001][1]}{[0.0099][0.0099]}$$

These calculations show that only 0.1% of the reactants will go to the product, C, when H_2O is the other product. Reactions producing water in the aqueous biological medium would not proceed at a fast enough rate to be useful. The question is then raised, can these reactions with a high $+ \Delta F$ be useful in the cell if the equilibrium is so far to the left. The concept of the coupled reactions shown previously explains how these $+ \Delta F$ reactions can be driven. One must keep in mind that we are dealing with an open system and not just isolated reactions. In the following scheme, an open system is shown.

Precursors

$\uparrow\downarrow$

$A + B \rightleftarrows C + D$

$\uparrow\downarrow$

Products

If the isolated reaction $A + B \rightleftarrows C + D$ is endergonic and proceeds extremely slowly, the overall reaction rate from precursor to products can still be rapid because of coupling of the steps. For the one reaction,

$$\Delta F = -RT \ln \frac{(C)^c (D)^d}{(A)^a (B)^b},$$

it can be seen that if any condition removes C or D as fast as it forms, making the ratio of concentration smaller, the ΔF value will be lowered. The reaction will then be forced to the right, effectively overcoming the high free energy barrier. Herein lies the value of coupled reactions.

SUMMARY

In a biological system where energy is at a premium, particularly if entropy is to be kept at a minimum, high-energy bonds are used to trap and store chemical energy. These high-energy compounds, mostly found in the phosphate pool, can yield their energy for both synthetic processes and to drive physiological phenomena which require energy.

The exergonic reaction where there is a release of energy by the breakdown of high-energy compounds such as ATP can be coupled to a reaction which is endergonic. If these reactions are coupled in such a way as to share a common intermediate, the exergonic reaction can drive the endergonic one.

Reactions with a small $+ \Delta F$ can proceed far enough to be useful to a biological system even if not coupled, provided that water is not one of the products.

The open system flow of reaction utilizes the coupled reaction concept to keep metabolites moving through the metabolic pathways.

Literature cited

1. Lipmann, F. 1941. Metabolic generation and utilization of phosphate bond energy. Advances Enzymol. 1:99.
2. Kalckar, H. 1941. The nature of energetic coupling in biological synthesis. Chem. Rev. 28:71.
3. Kalckar, H. 1947. Aspects of the biological function of phosphate in enzymatic synthesis. Nature 160:143.
4. Huennekens, F. M., and H. R. Whitely, 1960. Phosphoric acid anhydrides and other energy-rich compounds, vol. 1. p. 107. In Florkin, M., and H. S. Mason (editors): Comparative biochemistry. Academic Press, Inc., New York.

General references

Karlson, P. 1963. Introduction to modern biochemistry. Academic Press, Inc., New York.

Kleiner, I. S., and J. M. Orten. 1962. Biochemistry. 6th ed. The C. V. Mosby Co., St. Louis.

Kosower, E. M. 1962. Molecular biochemistry. McGraw-Hill Book Co., New York.

Neilands, J. B., and P. K. Stumpf. 1958. Outlines of enzyme chemistry. 2nd ed. John Wiley & Sons, Inc., New York.

White, A., P. Handler, and E. L. Smith. 1964. Principles of biochemistry. 3rd ed. McGraw-Hill Book Co., New York.

16

Biological oxidation

INTRODUCTION

The physiological processes of the cell and oxidation-reduction systems are so closely intertwined that the cell is almost a continuous oxidation-reduction reaction. In order to understand and use the terminology of redox reactions, it is necessary to discuss some of the concepts and quantitative terms which are applicable to biological oxidation.

All of the vital processes of the cell require energy, and the major means by which the high-energy bonds are produced to provide this energy is through the pathways involved in biological oxidation. Recall that the free energy which can be gained from a system is proportional to the difference in potential between components of the system.

$$\Delta F = -nF\Delta E \tag{1}$$

The fact that biological oxidation is the means toward an end adds more incentive for a detailed study of the mechanisms involved in these oxidation-reduction reactions.

OXIDATION-REDUCTION CONCEPTS

The older concept of oxidation as an addition of oxygen or a removal of hydrogen is no longer accepted as complete. The more general definition of oxidation, the loss of electrons, is a better way to describe an oxidative process. The redox potential, then, is a measure of the tendency for a substance to yield or to trap electrons. Equally, this potential is a means of calculating the free energy of a reaction in which there is an electron transfer, as shown in equation (1).

Recalling the configuration of the atom with its nucleus and electron rings, it should be remembered that chemical reactions involve interchanges and rearrangements of the electrons of the interacting atoms or molecules. Since nature seeks the lowest energy levels, or highest entropy, the electrons tend to either group in stable arrangements of pairs or octets or to be shared by two atoms.

In aqueous solution, however, the atoms or molecules very often lose their more stable configuration and take the structure of a free radical with unpaired electrons in the rings. The unpaired electron, bearing the negative charge, sets up a magnetic field as it rotates in its orbit; this condition is called paramagnetic. It is in this unpaired electron state that atoms and molecules more easily tend to give up or receive electrons and thus bring about oxidation or reduction. The unpaired state, though, is not always necessary to set up a redox reaction.

Consider the reaction:

$$Ag \longrightarrow Ag^+ + e$$

This is oxidation of the free silver to give the silver ion and the electron. Any atom or molecule which can produce an electron in a similar manner can be considered to be oxidizable. This freed electron cannot exist as such and thus must be trapped by some other atom or molecule which is deficient in electrons. Oxidation cannot, therefore, proceed unless there is a corresponding reductant to accept the freed electron. This is the reason that one refers to an "oxidation-reduction system." There must be two pairs of oxidation-reduction compounds. As one member of one pair is oxidized from its reduced form, the other pair must undergo conversion from the oxidized form to the reduced form. A system is thus set up in which there is coupled oxidation-reduction intermolecular conversion.

THE OXIDATION-REDUCTION POTENTIAL

By definition, oxidizing agents are substances accepting electrons, and reducing agents are those which give up electrons. The tendency to give up or attract electrons varies with the substance and forms a basis of comparison of the relative oxidizing and reducing capacity of any compound. The quantitative term for the comparison is the *electrode potential* or *oxidation-reduction potential*.

In theory, if any system is assigned an arbitrary oxidation-reduction value, then any other system can be compared to this arbitrary value. In practice, this essentially is what is done. Since it is impossible to measure the potential of a solution by a single electrode, a standard electrode is chosen as a standard of reference. Normally, the standard electrode against which all other electrodes are compared is the hydrogen electrode, which is arbitrarily assigned the value of 0.0. The actual measurement of the oxidation-reduction potential is performed against some secondary standard, as the hydrogen-electrode system is impractical to use in most circumstances.

The oxidation-reduction equation

The proof of the equation which relates the ratio of the oxidant and reductant to the measured potential is based on the fact that any oxidation or reduction can be treated as a reversible reaction which obeys the laws of mass action.

Consider the system

$$Fe^{++} \rightleftarrows Fe^{+++} + e$$

where the ferrous ion is reversibly oxidized to the ferric ion. Employing the mass action equilibrium formulation

$$k = \frac{[Fe^{+++}]\,[e]}{[Fe^{++}]} \tag{2}$$

The term $[e]$ can be seen to represent the concentration of free electrons. This term has been called the fugacity. Thus, the higher the fugacity, the more the system will give up electrons, and since the state of oxidation or reduction depends upon the movement of electrons, fugacity is an index of the oxidation-reduction potential. If electrons move into the system, the equation shifts to the left, forming more of the ferrous form; the system becomes more reduced. On the other hand, if there is a movement of electrons out from the system, the effect is an oxidation since more of the ferric form would be present.

Two salient points should be realized from the preceding discussion. First, a system may act as either an oxidant or reductant. Determination of which occurs depends upon whether the system on which it is acting is a stronger electron donor or electron receiver. Second, for a system to work at all, it must be coupled with some other system.

The movement of an electron against a gradient is osmotic work which can be formulated as $RT \int_{e_1}^{e_2} d[e]$ which balances the electrical work of the movement of the electron in the first place (EF). Setting these two equal and integrating between the two limits of electron concentration, the equation

$$EF = RT \ln [e_2] + RT \ln \frac{1}{[e_1]} \tag{3}$$

is derived.

If e_1 is the electron concentration of the system being measured against the standard (e_2), and if this latter concentration is a constant (k_1), then, substituting

$$E = k_1 + \frac{RT}{F} \ln \frac{1}{[e_1]} \tag{4}$$

Since

$$k = \frac{[Fe^{+++}]\,[e]}{[Fe^{++}]} \tag{2}$$

then

$$[e] = k \frac{[Fe^{++}]}{[Fe^{+++}]} \tag{5}$$

Substituting equation (5) into equation (4)

$$E = k_2 + \frac{RT}{F} \ln \frac{[Fe^{+++}]}{[Fe^{++}]} \tag{6}$$

Let $E_h = E - k_3$, where k_3 is the potential of the normal hydrogen electrode. Further, let $k_2 - k_3 = E'_0$, the constant for the system at a given pH. Finally,

$$E_h = E'_0 + \frac{RT}{F} \ln \frac{[Fe^{+++}]}{[Fe^{++}]} \tag{7}$$

and generalizing for any number of electrons moved,

$$E_h = E'_0 + \frac{RT}{nF} \ln \frac{[ox]}{[red]} \tag{8}$$

It can be seen that if E_h is the potential of the system at any one point and E'_0 is the potential under standard conditions which incorporates the constants when referred to the hydrogen electrode, the change in the actual potential is determined only by the ratio of the oxidant to the reductant. The gas constant, R, and F, the faraday, remain unchanged, whereas n, the number of electrons, and T, the absolute temperature, are variables which are known at the time of the determination.

The measured potential, E_h, equals E'_0, the standard potential, when the ratio of the oxidant to the reductant is 1:1; that is, E'_0 is the potential of a 50% oxidized system. The E'_0 is thus a measure of the intensity level of the system and enables the various redox systems to be graded. Although there is some confusion in terminology, consensus has it that the more positive the value of E'_0, the more the system will act as an oxidizing agent. Conversely, the more negative the value, the more easily the system will be oxidized; that is, it is

Table 16-1. Oxidation-reduction potentials of some biological systems

System (red/ox)	E'_0
$H_2O/\frac{1}{2} O_2$	+0.82
$H_2O_2/\frac{1}{2} O_2 + H_2O$	+0.30
Cytochrome a Fe^{++}/cytochrome a Fe^{+++}	+0.29
Cytochrome c Fe^{++}/cytochrome c Fe^{+++}	+0.26
Butyryl-CoA/crotonyl-CoA	+0.19
Ubiquinone red/ubiquinone ox	+0.10
Ascorbic acid/dehydroascorbic acid	+0.08
Cytochrome b Fe^{++}/cytochrome b Fe^{+++}	+0.04
Succinic acid/fumaric acid	+0.03
Leucomethylene blue/methylene blue	+0.01
Vitamin K	−0.06
Malic acid/oxalacetic acid	−0.10
$FMNH_2$/FMN	−0.12
Glutamic acid/α-ketoglutaric acid	−0.15
Lactic acid/pyruvic acid	−0.19
β-Hydroxybutyryl-CoA/acetoacetyl-CoA	−0.27
Lipoic acid —SH/lipoic acid S-S	−0.29
NADPH·H^+/NADP	−0.32
NADH·H^+/NAD	−0.32
Malic acid/pyruvic acid + CO_2	−0.33
$\frac{1}{2} H_2/H^+$	−0.42
α-Ketoglutaric acid/succinic acid + CO_2	−0.67
Pyruvic acid/acetic acid + CO_2	−0.70

acting as a reducing agent. The normal oxidation-reduction potentials of some biologically important systems are seen in Table 16-1.

The oxidation-reduction potential is always referred to the normal hydrogen electrode, which is arbitrarily assumed to be at zero. In practice, however, it is more convenient to use a calomel half-cell which is itself set in reference to the standard hydrogen electrode.

The effect of pH

Biological oxidation often involves movement of hydrogen as well as of an electron. As a result, the pH has a definite effect on the determination of the potential. The E'_0 values are generally recorded at pH 7, even though the pH of the hydrogen electrode is much lower. A correction can be made for the potential if it is desired to know it at some pH other than literature values. The correction term depends on the number of hydrogen that would be exchanged and the equivalents of substance oxidized or reduced by this change. However, for most biological material, the $\frac{dE'_o}{dpH}$ is 0.09 per unit of pH.

In summary, the oxidation-reduction potential depends on three conditions:
1. Tendency for a system to take up or give off electrons (fugacity)
2. Ratio of the oxidant to the reductant at the time of the determination of the potential
3. Hydrogen ion concentration

REDOX REACTIONS IN BIOLOGICAL SYSTEMS

In order to accomplish oxidation in a biological system, two prerequisites must be met. First, there must be a series of biological compounds which have as their primary function the accepting of hydrogens and electrons as the metabolites are oxidized. Second, in order to help maintain the low entropy level, the movement of electrons and hydrogen to oxygen in aerobic systems must yield energy. The first criterion will be dealt with here; the second will be handled in Chapter 21 under the topic of oxidative phosphorylation.

Oxidation and reduction in biological systems often occur in a stepwise fashion; that is, of a pair of electrons or hydrogen, only one will be transported at a time. This can lead to the temporary formation of free radicals, forming a structure similar to the semiquinone step in the conversion of hydroquinone to quinone.

Hydroquinone   Semiquinone   Quinone

The spin of the unpaired electron of the semiquinone produces a para-magnetic state. This single electron trap will be seen in some of the biological hydrogen acceptors and electron carriers.

Oxygen is the final acceptor of hydrogen in cellular respiration, and yet few substances known to be oxidized within the cell are spontaneously oxidized in the presence of oxygen. These reactions may be thermodynamically possible because all naturally occurring metabolites have redox potentials lower than oxygen. The difference in potential, however, is an intensity factor indicating the tendency for oxidation or reduction; this potential does not indicate the rate of the reaction. Thus, as in all other reactions, a specific set of enzymes is necessary to lower the activation energy the required amount necessary to allow the reaction to proceed.

The redox enzymes

Two basic classes of enzymes are involved in oxidation-reduction reactions in the cell. The oxidases are those enzymes which can transfer hydrogen from a metabolite directly to oxygen, and oxygen only.

$$MH_2 + \tfrac{1}{2} O_2 \xrightarrow{\text{Oxidase}} M + H_2O$$

The dehydrogenases, on the other hand, do not react in this manner. The aerobic dehydrogenases, although also capable of transferring hydrogen directly to oxygen, can transfer hydrogen to other compounds as well. These may be either artificial or naturally occurring substances. Methylene blue, for example, is often used as an artificial hydrogen acceptor. Equations involving aerobic dehydrogenases show two forms, as shown in examples (1) and (2).

$$MH_2 + \tfrac{1}{2} O_2 \xrightarrow[\text{dehydrogenase}]{\text{Aerobic}} M + H_2O \qquad (1)$$

$$MH_2 + MB \xrightarrow[\text{dehydrogenase}]{\text{Aerobic}} M + MBH_2 \qquad (2)$$

In example (2) the conversion from methylene blue (MB) to the colorless reduced methylene blue, or leucomethylene blue (MBH$_2$), is a good laboratory test for the presence of aerobic dehydrogenases. The test will only work if carried out under anaerobic conditions since oxygen will preferentially accept the hydrogen over the methylene blue.

The transfer of hydrogen to oxygen by oxidases or aerobic dehydrogenase pathways could result in the formation of hydrogen peroxide, H_2O_2. This compound is quite toxic to the cell, and the production of the peroxide cannot exceed the ability of the cell to decompose it. The breakdown of the H_2O_2 is catalyzed by two separate enzymes, catalase and peroxidase.

$$H_2O_2 \xrightarrow[\text{Peroxidase}]{\text{Catalase or}} H_2O + \tfrac{1}{2} O_2$$

The anaerobic dehydrogenases cannot catalyze the transfer of hydrogen from a metabolite directly to oxygen. As a result, the pathways involved with these enzymes must include other hydrogen or electron carriers which will transport them to oxygen to form water. These hydrogen acceptors and electron carriers are critical to the dynamics of the cell and are called the respiratory chain.

The redox coenzymes

The respiratory chain is composed of a series of special coenzymes which have as their primary function the passing of hydrogen or electrons in response to a difference in oxidation-reduction potential to the final acceptor, oxygen.

Pyridine nucleotides

This group of compounds, really two in number, is in the midst of a nomenclature clash. Since their structure was described some thirty years ago, diphosphopyridine nucleotide (DPN) and triphosphopyridine nucleotide (TPN) were known to be hydrogen acceptors. However, the Enzyme Commission of the International Union of Biochemistry recommended that the names be changed to nicotinamide adenine dinucleotide (NAD) and nicotinamide adenine dinucleotide monophosphate (NADP), respectively, and these are the names which are now appearing in the literature.

These coenzymes have as their most important single property the ability to undergo reversible oxidation-reduction, and under the influence of appropriate enzymes they can thus act as hydrogen carriers between substrates. Although there are many exceptions, NAD is mostly involved in those catabolic processes which yield energy. NADP is also used in some catabolic processes, but it is primarily involved in reductive biosynthesis operations.

The actual acceptance and transference of hydrogen by NAD and NADP is a two-electron transfer where the coenzymes pick up the equivalent of a hydride ion and liberate a proton into the medium. This "liberated" proton does not move out of the sphere of activity of the coenzyme unless the entire coenzyme is again oxidized. The attachment of the hydride is apparently stereospecific for the *para* position, that is, the position opposite from the attachment of the nucleotides to the pyridine ring.

As was pointed out previously, these coenzymes move freely in the metabolic pathways and can participate in a number of reactions. In the Embden-Meyerhof pathway, NAD apparently shuttles back and forth among the various enzymes. This hydrogen-shuttle role of NAD seems quite common and is very important in transporting hydrogen from one oxidation system to another. There are a number of dehydrogenases which can use either NAD or NADP, but the majority have a specificity for one or the other.

Flavoproteins

The riboflavin derivatives, flavin mononucleotide (FMN) and flavin adenine dinucleotide (FAD), participate in hydrogen and electron transfer also. These compounds are tightly bound to the protein moiety, forming flavoproteins which are the dehydrogenase enzymes. Some of these enzymes bind only one molecule of the flavin moiety, but many dehydrogenases have two FAD (or FMN) per molecule of apoenzyme.

The hydrogen transfer is not the same as it is in the NAD and NADP. Here, in FAD, for example, there is complete acceptance of the two hydrogens, forming FADH$_2$ or the equivalent. When two moles of FAD are present in the same enzyme, they may each accept one hydrogen, forming a double semiquinone.

$$\text{Enz} \Big\langle \begin{array}{l} \text{---FADH} \cdot \\ \text{---FADH} \cdot \end{array}$$

There are three roles which these flavoproteins serve in the cell:
1. Some are capable of transferring the hydrogen directly to oxygen.
2. Others can transfer the electrons and free protons to the cytochromes.
3. Some may funnel hydrogen from metabolic oxidation into other electron and hydrogen acceptors such as the quinones.

Cytochromes

In 1925 Keilin reported the presence of respiratory pigments which he named cytochromes, and thus the first members of the respiratory chain were discovered. These "cell pigments" are ubiquitously distributed in all cell types. All of the cytochromes are porphyrins, and as in the flavins, they may be bound tightly to the apoenzyme. Different from either of the previous groups, however, the cytochromes transport only electrons, releasing the free protons into the medium. The terminal member of the respiratory chain, that is, the enzyme which transfers the hydrogen and electrons to oxygen to form water, is cytochrome oxidase. This compound has been found to contain two distinct cytochromes, labeled a and a$_3$. In all, there are at least six separate cytochromes in mammals, but all six may not necessarily appear in one cell. Both the animal and plant kingdoms demonstrate a large variety of cytochromes, but in spite of this diversity, the pattern of electron transport does not fluctuate that much. The fact that the redox potentials of some of these are nearly identical implies that they may be able to substitute for each other in the respiratory chain.

A full discussion here of these very important compounds would be difficult without a feel for the strains that intermediary metabolism places on the hydrogen and electron carriers. The topic is discussed from this different approach in Section V.

Other hydrogen acceptors and electron carriers

Several other classes of compounds are believed to show the capacity for electron or hydrogen transport.

The quinones, of which ubiquinone, plastoquinone, and vitamin K are representatives, have been observed to act in this role. Coenzyme Q (ubiquinone) is believed by some investigators to be at a focal point in the respiratory chain. Plastoquinone is probably involved in the electron transport associated with photosynthesis, but the function of vitamin K is still uncertain.

Glutathione is representative of the compounds that can interchangeably form either sulfhydryl or disulfide bonds. This allows them to act as hydrogen carriers and also to prevent excessive oxidation.

$$NADH \cdot H^+ + GS—SG \rightleftarrows 2GSH + NAD$$

Ascorbic acid can be reversibly oxidized to dehydroascorbic acid. This transfer of hydrogen appears to be of some importance, particularly to plant cells, but the exact role is still uncertain.

Ascorbic acid   Dehydroascorbic acid

SUMMARY

Oxidation-reduction reactions are an important segment of all of the physiological processes of the cell. Not only does oxidation of metabolites yield by-products which are necessary for biosynthesis, but also the oxidative process itself can potentially yield the energy necessary for this synthesis and for the maintenance of cell dynamics.

The basic concepts of redox reactions as developed for inorganic systems apply to biological oxidation as well. The process of biological oxidation is carried out in a stepwise manner and is mediated by enzyme systems. These enzymes, the oxidases or dehydrogenases, specifically remove hydrogen from the substrate, bringing about oxidation, and transfer these activated hydrogen atoms to a hydrogen acceptor. These transferred hydrogens may then be transported further by specific hydrogen and electron carriers until they are finally combined

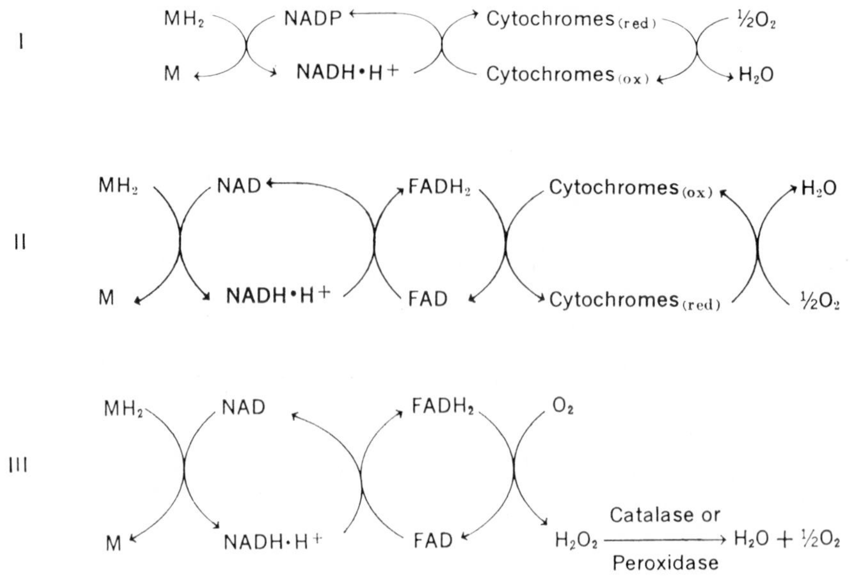

Fig. 16-1. Three different hypothetical respiratory chains, illustrating possible combinations of coenzymes in the chain. In III, the end product is hydrogen pero␣de and not water.

with oxygen to form water. The compounds which carry these hydrogens or electrons are generally assembled in a specific respiratory chain (Fig. 16-1).

The composition of respiratory chains may include NAD, NADP, assorted flavoproteins, various cytochromes, quinones, sulfhydryl compounds, and ascorbic acid. Neither the complete mechanism of the hydrogen or electron transport nor the role in the pathways has been worked out for all of these carriers.

General references

Boyer, P. D., H. Lardy, and K. Myrbäck (editors). 1963. The enzymes, vol. 7 and 8. Academic Press, Inc., New York.

Chance, B. (editor). 1963. Energy-linked functions of mitochondria. Academic Press, Inc., New York.

Conn, E. E. 1960. Comparative biochemistry of electron transport and oxidative phosphorylation, vol. 1, p. 441. In Florkin, M., and H. S. Mason (editors): Comparative biochemistry. Academic Press, Inc., New York.

Karlson, P. 1963. Introduction to modern biochemistry. Academic Press, Inc., New York.

Kleiner, I. S., and J. M. Orten. 1962. Biochemistry. 6th ed. The C. V. Mosby Co. St. Louis.

Kosower, E. M. 1962. Molecular biochemistry. McGraw-Hill Book Co., New York.

Lehninger, A. L. 1964. The mitochondrion. W. A. Benjamin, Inc., New York.

Lehninger, A. L. 1961. How cells transform energy. Sci. Am. (Sept.), p. 62.

Stewart, R. 1964. Oxidation mechanisms. W. A. Benjamin, Inc., New York.

West, E. S. 1963. Textbook of biophysical chemistry. 3rd ed. The Macmillan Co., New York.

White, A., P. Handler, and E. L. Smith. 1964. Principles of biochemistry. 3rd ed. McGraw-Hill Book Co., New York.

Wolstenholme, G. E. W., and C. M. O'Connor (editors). 1961. Quinones in electron transport. Little, Brown & Co., Boston.

Section V

Intermediary metabolism

Kluyver and van Niel proposed the unity of metabolism, or comparative biochemistry, theory which is a concept that suggests that there is a unified plan of life, and that the biochemistry of various organisms reflects this. Furthermore, it states that any complex biochemical process is a series of fundamental chemical reactions designed along basic pathways, and that the difference in metabolism of organisms is due to the degree of emphasis placed on these various pathways. Any one cell shares similar metabolic sequences and cycles with any other cell, regardless of the diversity in structure or function between them. The physiological differences mirror a difference in the use of these pathways. This does not preclude the possibility of specialized pathways being developed; however, even the specialized metabolic sequences take their root from more common paths.

The elucidation of the "wiring plan" of the metabolic cycles is made easier knowing that there is a thread of unity running throughout the living world. The establishing of a particular reaction in one cell may be applied to the understanding of the metabolism of another. Intermediary metabolism is the study and presentation of the interrelationships of the elaborate pathways through which metabolites course within and among the cells, a complex of interwoven threads which, on the surface, appears to be a true Penelope's web.

The discussion of the metabolic sequences is restricted to those which are pertinent to the cell. Multicellular forms often have their own interesting and important pathways, but they are not considered here. The section first develops the common pathways which are shared by virtually all cells (Chapter 17) and is followed by a look, in more depth, at the pathways of the carbohydrates, lipids, and amino acids (Chapters 18 to 20). The use of these paths for the production of high-energy bonds through the oxidative phosphorylation in the electron transport chain is discussed (Chapter 21). The interrelationship between structure and function is illustrated by this sequence which occurs in the mitochondrion.

Finally, some examples of specialized pathways are given in Chapters 22 and 23. Bioluminescence is an example of a fundamental process which does not have a unified mechanism. The importance of photosynthesis to the energy balance of the living world warrants some detailed discussion of this process.

17

Common pathways

INTRODUCTION

The problems in metabolism involve not only the theoretical postulation of certain pathways, but also the proof of the steps and the isolation of intermediates. Before one can conclude that any postulated compound is an actual intermediate in a biochemical process, three criteria must be satisfied:

1. It must be conclusively demonstrated that the compound in question will go to the products dictated by the overall pathway.
2. It must be demonstrated that the rate of conversion of the postulated compound is equal to or greater than the overall rate of reaction.
3. It, finally, must be shown that the postulated intermediates are produced by known precursors of the final end product and, furthermore, that these precursors go through these intermediates to arrive at the products.

Consider the stepwise reaction:

$$A \rightarrow (B) \rightarrow C \rightarrow D$$

If B is the intermediate in doubt, then, according to the preceding criteria, it must be shown

1. That B actually goes to C and D
2. That the rate of B to C is as great as or greater than that of A to D
3. That A goes to B and through B to get to D

The latter proof is necessary to eliminate the following possibility:

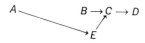

Metabolic pathways occur quite often in cycles, and if they are not in cycles, they present so many interrelationships among the pathways that there is always a feedback element. Because of these factors, any starting point in the study of intermediary metabolism is arbitrary, and any place from which a start is made is returned to in some form. Thus, it seems logical to start with a discussion of the common pathways which are shared by the catabolic and anabolic processes of carbohydrates, lipids, and proteins.

COENZYME A

One compound of great importance to the metabolic pathways is coenzyme A. This compound has not been discussed in any detail before, and therefore it seems appropriate to introduce some information about this ubiquitous molecule. As was previously mentioned, the active form of this coenzyme is acetyl coenzyme A, although several acyl coenzyme A forms also exist (for example, succinyl-CoA). The shorthand form CoASH or CoA is used for the unsubstituted compound and $CH_3COSCoA$ or acetyl-CoA for the acetylated derivative. The participation of this coenzyme, however, is not limited to acylation or acetylation reactions. The thiol ester form is a high-energy compound and, as such, can yield energy to drive various cellular reactions.

There are several mechanisms of synthesis of this compound.

1. *Acetokinase-transacetylase*—This mechanism involves ATP (as the energy source) which reacts with acetic acid to give acetyl phosphate which, as the common intermediate in a coupled reaction, transfers the acetyl group to CoASH.

$$CH_3COOH + ATP \underset{\longleftarrow}{\overset{\text{Acetokinase}}{\longrightarrow}} CH_3COOPO_3H_2 + ADP$$

$$CH_3COOPO_3H_2 + CoASH \underset{\longleftarrow}{\overset{\text{Transacetylase}}{\longrightarrow}} CH_3COSCoA + P_i$$

2. *NAD-linked alcohol and aldehyde dehydrogenation*—This mechanism involves two successive dehydrogenations mediated by two separate enzymes.

$$CH_3CH_2OH + NAD \underset{\longleftarrow}{\overset{\text{Alcohol dehydrogenase}}{\longrightarrow}} CH_3CHO + NADH \cdot H^+$$

$$CH_3CHO + CoASH + NAD \underset{\longleftarrow}{\overset{\text{Aldehyde dehydrogenase}}{\longrightarrow}} CH_3COSCoA + NADH \cdot H^+$$

3. *CoA transferase*—This mechanism, like the first, has ATP reacting with acetic acid, but the result in this case is the production of pyrophosphate and an AMP-acetyl complex; this latter is the intermediate in a coupled reaction combining with CoA to yield the acetyl-CoA. The reaction seems to be mediated by a single enzyme.

$$CH_3COOH + ATP \underset{\longleftarrow}{\overset{\text{CoA transferase}}{\longrightarrow}} AMP\overset{O}{\overset{\|}{C}}CH_3 + PP_i$$

$$AMP\overset{O}{\overset{\|}{C}}CH_3 + CoASH \underset{\longleftarrow}{\overset{\text{CoA transferase}}{\longrightarrow}} CH_3COSCoA + AMP$$

4. *Transesterase*—This mechanism occurs as a part of the pathway in converting pyruvic acid to a form which can enter the common metabolic cycles; in this case the form is acetyl-CoA. The conversion is so important that it will be considered separately in the discussion of the reaction that follows.

THE HUB REACTION

Biochemists for years called pyruvic acid the hub of both the catabolic and anabolic reactions involving carbohydrates, proteins, and fats. However, realization of the importance of acetyl-CoA forced modification of this designation of the hub to the reaction [pyruvic → acetyl-CoA], since together they share a central role in the metabolic picture.

The diagrammatic presentation (Fig. 17-1) of the confluence of pathways into the pyruvic → acetyl-CoA reaction demonstrates its importance. This reaction serves as the major link between the two most important common pathways, the Embden-Meyerhof and the Krebs, or tricarboxylic acid, cycles. In addition, the following are true:

1. Fat synthesis uses acetyl-CoA as the building block.
2. Amino acids approach the hub from various directions.
3. Carbohydrate metabolism often has pyruvic acid as its primary end product.
4. Innumerable synthetic processes derive their start from pyruvic acid or acetyl-CoA.

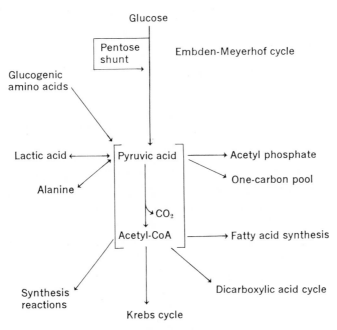

Fig. 17-1. Schematic diagram of the central position of the hub reaction in the metabolic pathways.

The development of the pathway from pyruvic acid to acetyl-CoA reflects the various stages of preciseness through which biochemistry has come over the past decades.

For many years, the reaction was considered to be a simple decarboxylation of the acid in the presence of CoASH.

$$CH_3COCOOH + CoASH \xrightarrow[\quad]{Enzyme \quad CO_2} CH_3COSCoA + H_2O$$

This was then sophisticated by the addition of a hydrogen acceptor. The enzyme was also given a name.

$$CH_3COCOOH + NAD + CoASH \xrightarrow{Cocarboxylase} CH_3COSCoA + CO_2 + NADH \cdot H^+$$

More and more research indicated that this "simple" decarboxylation involved more compounds than CoASH and NAD. Thiamine pyrophosphate (found to be synonymous with cocarboxylase), ATP, lipoic acid, FAD, and inorganic phosphate were also found to be necessary for decarboxylation and regeneration of the reactive forms of the various coenzymes and cofactors.

The initial step of the reaction is apparently the combining of a 2-carbon fragment of pyruvic acid with thiamine pyrophosphate to yield CO_2 and α-hydroxyethyl thiamine pyrophosphate, possibly going through an unstable α-lactyl-2-thiamine pyrophosphate intermediate.

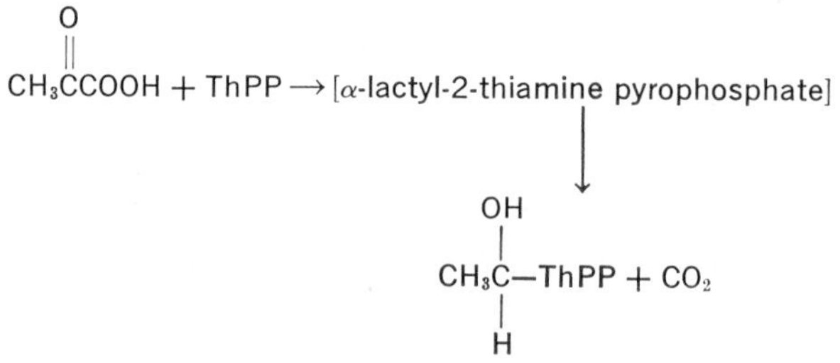

$$\overset{O}{\overset{\|}{CH_3CCOOH}} + ThPP \rightarrow [\alpha\text{-lactyl-2-thiamine pyrophosphate}]$$

$$\overset{OH}{\underset{H}{\overset{|}{CH_3C}}-ThPP} + CO_2$$

α-Hydroxyethyl thiamine
pyrophosphate

This thiamine pyrophosphate complex, the "active acetaldehyde," is on the surface of the enzyme, as is lipoic acid (6,8-dithiooctanoic). This lipoic acid, which may be linked to the ε-amino group of a lysine residue of the enzyme, is present as a disulfide compound.

In a two-step reaction, the acetaldehyde is oxidized to acetic acid, followed by the acetyl group being picked up by the lipoic acid.

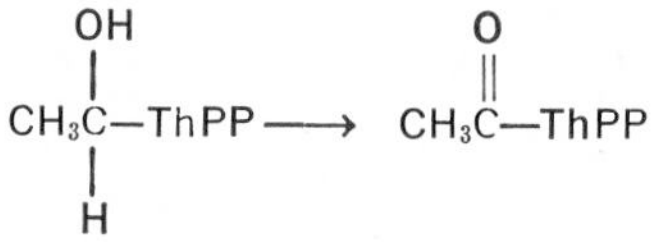

$$\overset{OH}{\underset{H}{\overset{|}{CH_3C}}-ThPP} \longrightarrow \overset{O}{\overset{\|}{CH_3C}}-ThPP$$

| α-Hydroxyethyl thiamine | Acetyl thiamine |
| pyrophosphate | pyrophosphate |

$$\text{CH}_3\overset{\overset{\text{O}}{\|}}{\text{C}}-\text{ThPP} + \underset{\text{S}}{\overset{\text{S}}{|}}\text{Lip} \longrightarrow \text{CH}_3\overset{\overset{\text{O}}{\|}}{\text{C}}-\underset{\text{HS}}{\overset{\text{S}}{\diagdown}}\text{Lip} + \text{ThPP}$$

Acetyl thiamine   Lipoic acid   Acetyl-lipoic
pyrophosphate   acid

Still attached to the same enzyme, the acetyl group is transferred to CoASH in the transesterase reaction previously referred to

$$\text{Lip}\underset{\text{SCOCH}_3}{\overset{\text{SH}}{<}} + \text{CoASH} \longrightarrow \text{Lip}\underset{\text{SH}}{\overset{\text{SH}}{<}} + \text{CH}_3\text{COSCoA}$$

The primary purpose of the pathway, production of acetyl-CoA from pyruvic acid, is now complete. However, for the lipoic acid to be recycled, it must give up its hydrogens to some form which can feed them to a respiratory chain.

The FAD coenzyme of lipoyl dehydrogenase removes the hydrogens from the reduced lipoic acid, transferring them to NAD from which they can then be fed into electron transport chains.

$$\text{En·FAD} + \text{Lip}\underset{\text{SH}}{\overset{\text{SH}}{<}} \rightleftharpoons \text{En·FADH}_2 + \text{Lip}\underset{\text{S}}{\overset{\text{S}}{<}}$$

$$\text{NAD} \longrightarrow \text{NADH·H}^+$$
$$\text{En·FAD}$$

The pathway is now complete, and there are certain features which should be noted. The lipoyl-enzyme complex is involved in four separate steps in the cycle. Reed[1] has called the type of participation of this complex the "swinging arm" mechanism. His designation of this term was based on the postulation that the lipoyl group "swings" from one active site of the enzyme to another, exchanging organic groups or hydrogen at each step. Second, NADH·H+ usually donates its hydrogen to a flavoprotein, the reverse of which is seen in the preceding pathways.

With this mechanism in operation, both pyruvic acid and acetyl-CoA can be utilized by other pathways. The Embden-Meyerhof cycle, which produces pyruvic acid, and the Krebs cycle, which has acetyl-CoA as its major input, will be considered next.

THE EMBDEN-MEYERHOF CYCLE

The Embden-Meyerhof, or glycolytic, cycle is probably the most universal of all of the pathways. In the anaerobes, it is the *only* major pathway and must thus serve as the prime energy source for other metabolism. In the aerobic cells, the Embden-Meyerhof cycle has much less of a role as a major source of ATP; the utilization of this glycolytic pathway is primarily a means of catabolic conversion of glucose and its isomers to pyruvic acid and on to acetyl-CoA. In addition, in photosynthetic cells, the components of the glycolytic cycle are the forms to which the by-products of this process eventually become channeled.

The pathway

There are several ways to approach the study of metabolic pathways. One aspect which will not be covered here is the historical development of the cycle. This is certainly an important phase of study; however, the events leading to

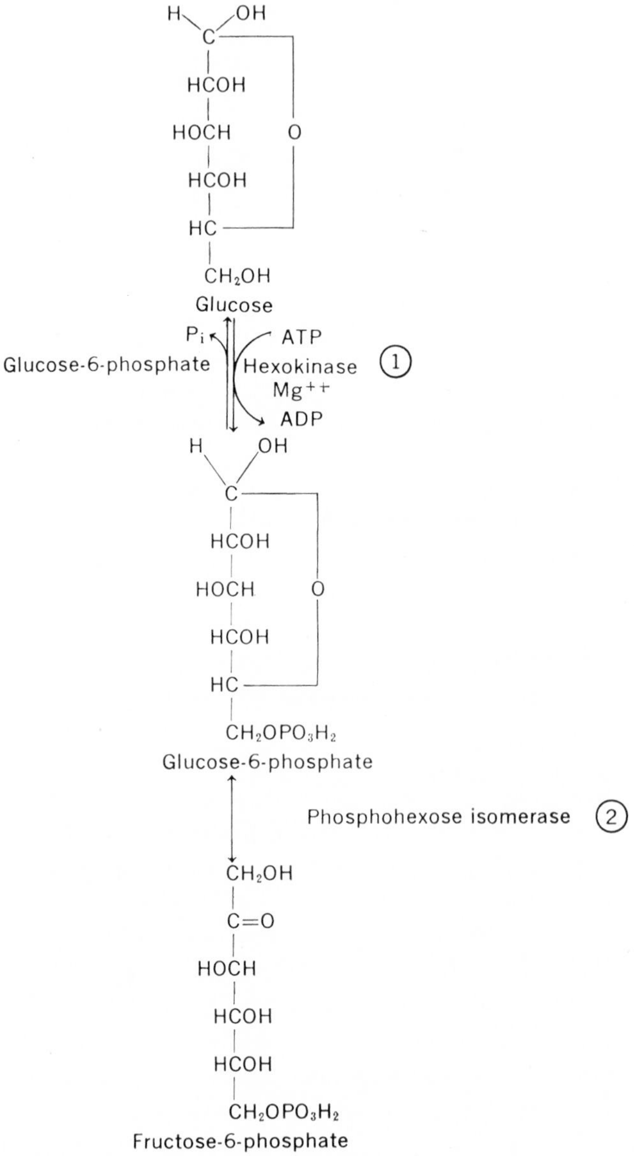

Fig. 17-2. The Embden-Meyerhof pathway.

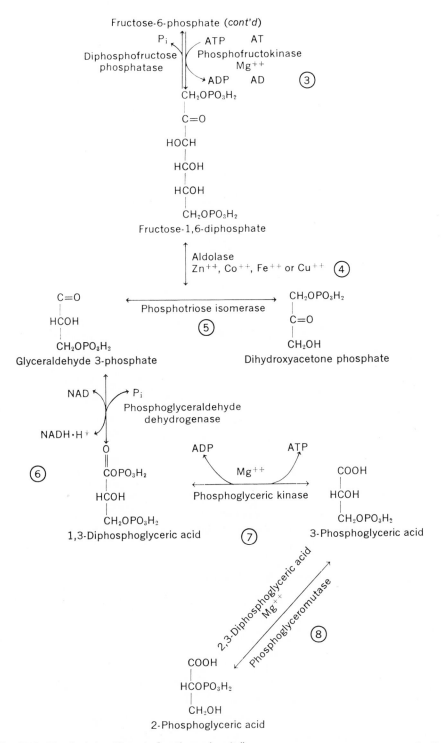

Fig. 17-2. The Embden-Meyerhof pathway (cont'd).   *Continued.*

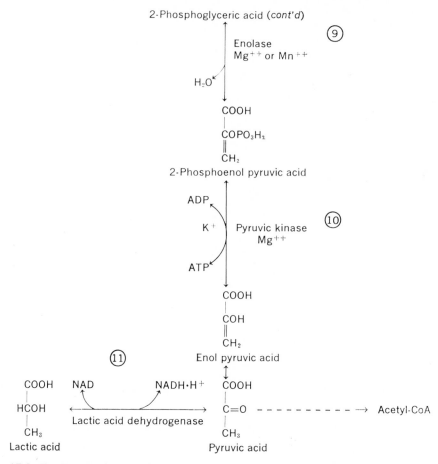

Fig. 17-2. The Embden-Meyerhof pathway (cont'd).

the final pathway can be developed better in a text restricted to biochemistry. The aspects which will be emphasized here are the following:

1. What the particular pathways contribute to the energy production or energy demand of the cell
2. The importance of the individual reactions
3. The place of the pathway in the overall scheme of the cell

The scheme for the Embden-Meyerhof cycle is seen in Fig. 17-2. To simplify the reading, word formulas are used in the text since the structural formulas are presented in the scheme.

Reaction 1. Rarely is free glucose found in the cell, and thus glucose-6-phosphate is the form to which conversion is directed. This conversion can be from glycogen or starch breakdown or from glucose in the outer medium being phosphorylated as it moves through the membrane. In order to form the glucose-6-phosphate, or Robison, ester, the energy of 1 mole of ATP has to be invested in the hexokinase reaction:

$$\text{ATP} + \text{Glucose} \xrightarrow[\text{Mg}^{++}]{\text{Hexokinase}} \text{Glucose-6-phosphate} + \text{ADP}$$

This reaction is essentially irreversible, the equilibrium being far to the right. This is not unexpected in that the $\Delta F°$ of hydrolysis of ATP is -8000 calories and that of the glucose-6-phosphate only -2500 calories. This large $\Delta F°$ difference makes reversibility thermodynamically improbable, particularly since the glucose is not removed from the medium to draw the reaction to the left. The conversion of glucose-6-phosphate to glucose is mediated by a separate enzyme, glucose-6-phosphatase, the reaction being the reverse of the kinase phosphorylation just mentioned.

The appearance of a kinase and a phosphatase at the same reaction is quite common. The large energy barrier created when ATP is used in phosphorylation necessitates the reverse reaction being under the influence of a separate enzyme. The kinase-phosphatase coupling appears in many ATPase systems.

Reaction 2. The intramolecular rearrangement in the shift of glucose-6-phosphate to fructose-6-phosphate is under the control of the enzyme phosphohexose isomerase. The fructose ester, named the Neuberg ester, has a slightly higher $\Delta F°$ than does glucose-6-phosphate. The equilibrium favors the formation of the glucose ester by about two to one.

$$\text{Glucose-6-phosphate} \underset{1\quad :\quad 2}{\overset{\text{Phosphohexose isomerase}}{\longrightarrow\!\!\!\longleftarrow}} \text{Fructose-6-phosphate}$$

Reaction 3. The fructose-6-phosphate is further phosphorylated to the diester, fructose-1,6-diphosphate (Hardin-Young ester), at the expense of another ATP. The reaction mimics the formation of glucose-6-phosphate from glucose in that there is one enzyme, phosphofructokinase, for the phosphorylating step and a separate enzyme, diphosphofructose phosphatase, for the reverse reaction.

$$\text{ATP} + \text{Fructose-6-phosphate} \underset{\substack{\text{Diphosphofructose}\\\text{phosphatase}}}{\overset{\substack{\text{Mg}^{++}\\\text{Phosphofructokinase}}}{\longrightarrow\!\!\!\longleftarrow}} \text{Fructose 1,6-diphosphate} + \text{ADP}$$

Reactions 4 and 5. The cleavage of the 6-carbon diphosphate ester of fructose produces two 3-carbon fragments, glyceraldehyde 3-phosphate and dihydroxyacetone phosphate. Zinc^{++}, Co^{++}, Fe^{++}, and Cu^{++} have been found to be the required activator ions in some cells.

$$\text{Fructose-1,6-diphosphate}$$
$$\updownarrow \quad \substack{\text{Aldolase}\\(\text{Zn}^{++}, \text{Co}^{++}, \text{Fe}^{++}, \text{or Cu}^{++})}$$
$$\text{Glyceraldehyde 3-phosphate} \underset{\text{Phosphotriose isomerase}}{\longrightarrow\!\!\!\longleftarrow} \text{Dihydroxyacetone phosphate}$$

Aldolase is the enzyme controlling the split of the 6-carbon fragment into the two trioses. These latter are in equilibrium with each other, a reaction catalyzed by phosphotriose isomerase. Two facts should be made explicit about this overall reaction. First, the equilibrium strongly favors the formation of the fructose ester by aldol condensation of the two 3-carbon fragments. The prime factor which pulls the reaction downward is the removal of the glyceraldehyde 3-phosphate. This 3-carbon phosphate ester is important in control mechanisms for this reason. Second, the dihydroxyacetone phosphate is essentially a blind alley, and if it were not for the equilibrium reaction with its triose mate, the potential energy of dihydroxyacetone phosphate would be lost to the cycle.

Reaction 6. The phosphorylation of glyceraldehyde 3-phosphate does not follow the same pattern as the previous phosphate additions:

Phosphoglyceraldehyde
dehydrogenase

$$\text{Glyceraldehyde 3-phosphate} + P_i + \text{NAD} \underset{\longleftarrow}{\xrightarrow{\hspace{2cm}}} \text{1,3-Diphosphoglyceric acid} + \text{NADH} \cdot H^+$$

This is an oxidative phosphorylation reaction where a 3-phosphoglyceryl-enzyme complex is formed, probably through a sulfhydryl group of the protein. Addition of the phosphate and stripping off of the hydrogen occur while the aldehyde is attached to the enzyme.

In an anaerobic system, this reaction is merely the addition of a phosphate group to the triose. In aerobic cells, however, the production of each mole of the reduced form of NADH·H$^+$ can potentially produce 3 moles of high energy phosphate if the reduced coenzyme is shunted to the electron transport system. This fact will have to be accepted at face value here until the proof is developed in Chapter 21.

A final point should be made concerning this and subsequent reactions. The compounds involved in these steps are trioses, and thus there are potentially two of each formed per molecule of glucose-6-phosphate with which the cycle started. This is a trivial point as far as the mechanism of the pathway is concerned; it is not trivial when the energetics are considered.

Reaction 7. The 1,3-diphosphoglyceric acid gives up one of its phosphate groups to the adenylic acid system, regenerating ATP in the process.

Phosphoglyceric kinase

$$\text{1,3-Diphosphoglyceric acid} + \text{ADP} \underset{\underset{Mg^{++}}{\longleftarrow}}{\xrightarrow{\hspace{2cm}}} \text{3-Phosphoglyceric acid} + \text{ATP}$$

The original two ATP molecules invested to start the cycle (reactions 1 and 3) are regained in this step. Per mole of 6-carbon fragment, reaction 7 yields 2 moles of ATP, replacing those lost in the previous phosphorylations.

Reaction 8. By an intermolecular phosphate transfer (see Chapter 18), 3-phosphoglyceric acid is converted into 2-phosphoglyceric acid, a reaction catalyzed by phosphoglyceromutase.

Phosphoglyceromutase

3-Phosphoglyceric acid $\xrightleftharpoons{\text{Mg}^{++}\ 2,3\text{-Diphosphoglyceric acid}}$ 2-Phosphoglyceric acid

Reaction 9. The phosphate group is transferred to the second carbon where a high-energy bond will appear. Water is stripped from the 2-phosphoglyceric acid, yielding an enol-phosphate. This is one of the basic high-energy forms of phosphates.

Enolase H_2O

2-Phosphoglyceric acid $\xrightleftharpoons{\text{Mg}^{++}\ \text{or}\ \text{Mn}^{++}}$ 2-Phosphoenol pyruvic acid

Reaction 10. The high-energy enol-phosphate is transferred to the adenylic acid system, ADP picking up the phosphate.

Pyruvic kinase

2-Phosphoenolpyruvic acid + ADP $\xrightleftharpoons{\text{Mg}^{++},\ \text{K}^+}$ Pyruvic acid + ATP

Again, per mole of 6-carbon fragment, 2 moles of ATP are formed. This gives a net gain of 2 ATP for this pathway under anaerobic conditions.

Reaction 11. Under aerobic conditions, the pyruvic acid just formed is further utilized as acetyl-CoA after undergoing the decarboxylation sequence previously described. Under anaerobic conditions, however, the pyruvic acid may take a series of pathways. The one which is quite common is the conversion of pyruvic to lactic acid.

Lactic acid dehydrogenase

Pyruvic acid + NADH·H$^+$ $\rightleftharpoons$ Lactic acid + NAD

The reduced NAD used in this conversion is that which is produced in reaction 6; that is, there is a coupled relationship between these two reactions. The value of this can be seen as a way of preventing the buildup of too much of either the reduced or oxidized coenzyme since, unlike aerobic cells, those functioning under anaerobiosis cannot shunt these reduced coenzymes to an electron chain.

Importance of the Embden-Meyerhof cycle

In addition to the fact that the Embden-Meyerhof cycle is the most ubiquitous of all of the metabolic pathways, the glycolytic cycle has some general considerations which should be made. The role of this cycle as a source of energy in the form of ATP should not be minimized. Although the percentage of contribution in aerobic cells is low, the energy production in anaerobic cells is primarily from the Embden-Meyerhof cycle. In anaerobic conditions, or in situations where pyruvic acid metabolism is impaired, the glycolytic cycle has a built-in shunt mechanism. The lactic acid–pyruvic acid reaction has an equilibrium ratio of 300,000:1. This means that if pyruvic acid is not pulled out of the system by some other pathway it will be converted to lactic acid. The pile up of lactic acid thus allows glycolysis to continue, which could not

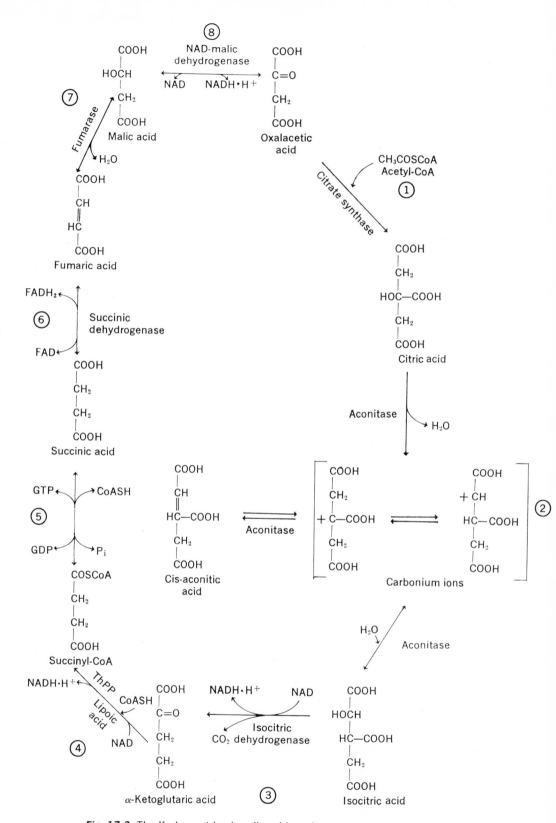

Fig. 17-3. The Krebs, or tricarboxylic acid, cycle.

occur if it were pyruvic which was being accumulated. Finally, in aerobic systems, the Embden-Meyerhof cycle supplies the hub with pyruvic acid which, in turn, feeds the other pathways of the cell.

The energy efficiency of the glycolytic cycle is very low. The standard free energy $\Delta F°$ of glucose is $-686,000$ calories per mole. In an anaerobic system, where 2 ATP is the net gain from the pathway, the efficiency of trapping usable energy is only about 2 to 3%. In aerobic cells, where 6 ATP can be produced from the 2 NADH·H$^+$ formed, the percent efficiency increases to approximately 10% (a total of 8 ATP formed).

THE KREBS CYCLE

The other common pathway to be dealt with is the Krebs cycle, also called the tricarboxylic acid cycle or citric acid cycle. These names are all synonyms and all are correct to use; consensus probably favors Krebs cycle, since it gives credit to Hans Krebs who did so much of the work in elucidating the pathway.

The pathway

The scheme and the structural formulas for this cycle are seen in Fig. 17-3. Again, word reactions will primarily be used in the text.

Reaction 1.   The first step in the Krebs cycle is perhaps the most important since it represents the major input of new material. In this reaction, acetyl-CoA combines with oxalacetic acid to yield citric acid.

$$\text{Acetyl-CoA} + \text{Oxalacetic acid} \underset{\longleftarrow}{\overset{\text{Citrate synthase}}{\longrightarrow}} \text{Citric acid} + \text{CoASH}$$

The enzyme citrate synthase has also been called the condensing enzyme and citrogenase in the literature. The reaction equilibrium is far to the right because the high-energy bond of acetyl-CoA is essentially lost, the $\Delta F°$ of the total reaction being about -8000 calories.

Reaction 2.   Aconitase catalyzes the reversible interconversion among the citric acid formed in reaction 1 and the *cis*-aconitic and isocitric acids. The reaction suggests a common intermediate, which may be carbonium ions which are in equilibrium.

$$
\begin{array}{c}
\text{Citric acid 90\%} \\
\Big\updownarrow \text{Aconitase} \\
\text{Cis-aconitic acid} \underset{}{\overset{\text{Aconitase}}{\rightleftharpoons}} \text{[Carbonium ions]} \\
3\% \\
\Big\updownarrow \text{Aconitase} \\
\text{Isocitric acid} \\
7\%
\end{array}
$$

The percent of each form at equilibrium is shown, but these may not represent true values in vivo.

In this conversion, the symmetrical citric acid is changed to the asymmetrical isocitric The citric acid, however, does not behave as a symmetrical molecule in that the hydroxyl group of isocitric is never on the carbons introduced from acetyl-CoA. The $-CH_2COOH$ group of the oxalacetic acid is apparently bound to the enzyme surface, and in citric acid this attachment, plus two others, causes the citric acid to act as an asymmetric molecule. This three-point attachment causes the two $-CH_2COOH$ groups not to be geometric equivalents. As a result, the isocitric hydroxyl is always on the α-carbon at the end remote from where the acetyl-CoA condensed.

For reasons which are not yet apparent, aconitase requires the presence of a sulfhydryl group, either as reduced glutathione or cysteine, and iron, Fe^{++}, to attain maximal activity.

Reaction 3. The oxidation of isocitric acid to α-ketoglutaric acid further demonstrates the asymmetry which must have been present in the citric acid. It was in the α-keto acid that asymmetric labeling showed up when an isotope-labeled acetate ($-CH_2C^{14}OOH$) was added to form citrate. In the reaction that follows, the label is shown in α-ketoglutaric.

$$\text{Isocitric acid} + \text{NADP} \underset{\substack{\text{Isocitric} \\ \text{dehydrogenase}}}{\overset{CO_2}{\rightleftharpoons}} \text{NADPH} \cdot H^+ + \underset{\substack{| \\ CH_2 \\ | \\ H_2C-C^{14}OOH}}{O=C-COOH}$$

There seems to be two distinct enzymes which can catalyze this oxidative decarboxylation, one specific for NAD and one for NADP. The NADP-isocitric dehydrogenase reaction is reversible and is the more common enzyme of the two. This enzyme is also capable of converting added oxalosuccinic acid to α-keto-glutaric acid. The oxalosuccinic acid was at one time considered to be an intermediate in the Krebs cycle. The NAD-isocitric dehydrogenase reaction does not seem to be reversible, and also it does not seem to have the ability of using oxalosuccinic as a substrate.

Reaction 4. The oxidation of α-ketoglutaric acid to succinyl-CoA parallels the pyruvic acid to acetyl-CoA sequence. As in this latter reaction, this oxidative step of the Krebs cycle requires thiamine pyrophosphate, lipoic acid, and NAD. The overall reaction is

$$\text{CoASH} + \alpha\text{-Ketoglutaric} \overset{CO_2}{\rightleftharpoons} \text{Succinyl-CoA}$$

Reaction 5. The succinyl-CoA formed by the previous set of reactions loses its high-energy thioester bond to form succinic acid. The energy from the bond is transferred to the phosphate pool, the conversion involving the guanine diphosphate to guanine triphosphate.

$$\text{Succinyl-CoA} + \text{GDP} + P_i \underset{\substack{\text{Succinyl-CoA} \\ \text{synthetase}}}{\rightleftharpoons} \text{Succinic acid} + \text{GTP}$$

The high-energy phosphate is probably fed into the adenylic acid system, with ADP picking it up.

$$ADP + GTP \rightleftarrows ATP + GDP$$

The succinic acid apparently behaves as a symmetrical molecule in that the labeling localized at one end of the previous acids now appears at either end of the succinic acid molecule.

Reaction 6. Succinic acid is oxidized to fumaric acid by the flavoprotein enzyme succinic dehydrogenase.

$$Succinic\ acid + En \cdot FAD \rightleftarrows Fumaric\ acid + En \cdot FADH_2$$

Because of special circumstances, this oxidative step only yields 2 ATP from the electron transport chain, even though 1 mole of a reduced coenzyme is formed.

The fumaric acid formed is the *trans*-isomer; the *cis*-isomer, maleic acid, is not formed from succinic acid by this enzyme.

Reaction 7. Fumaric acid undergoes hydration to form malic acid, with fumarase being the enzyme involved. This enzyme reverses the symmetry, converting the *trans*-fumaric acid to an L-fatty acid.

$$
\begin{array}{ccc}
\text{HC—COOH} & & \text{H}_2\text{C—COOH} \\
\| & \xrightarrow{\text{Fumarase}} & | \\
\text{HOOC CH} \quad +\text{H}_2\text{O} & \longleftarrow & \text{HOC—COOH} \\
\textit{Trans}\text{-fumaric acid} & & \text{L-malic acid}
\end{array}
$$

Reaction 8. The final step, regeneration of oxalacetic acid, involves the reduction of malic acid by NAD-linked malic dehydrogenase.

$$Malic\ acid + NAD \underset{\text{dehydrogenase}}{\overset{\text{NAD-malic}}{\rightleftarrows}} Oxalacetic\ acid + NADH \cdot H^+$$

This reaction returns the cycle back to the point where the 2-carbon fragment is added.

Importance of the Krebs cycle

The Krebs cycle is one of the most versatile metabolic pathways of the cell. It is, first, truly cyclic in that the final step returns the pathway back to its original starting point. Second, it receives input from several sources, not the least of which is acetyl-CoA. This "active" 2-carbon fragment is the end product of the Embden-Meyerhof pathway and fat metabolism. The fact that it can easily enter a cycle such as the Krebs cycle ensures maximum energy yield from the metabolite. Third, as producer of ATP, the Krebs cycle is almost unsurpassed. Calculating from the point of addition of the acetate, the energetics add up as follows:

Isocitric acid ⟶ α-Ketoglutaric acid		3 ATP
α-Ketoglutaric acid ⟶ Succinyl-CoA		3 ATP
Succinyl-CoA ⟶ Succinic acid	1 GTP ⟶	1 ATP
Succinic acid ⟶ Fumaric acid		2 ATP
Malic acid ⟶ Oxalacetic acid		3 ATP
One revolution of Krebs cycle		12 ATP

For each molecule of acetate entering the cycle, there are potentially 12 ATP produced since each reduced NADH·H⁺ formed can yield 3 ATP by shunting into the electron transport system. The exception is the flavoprotein succinic dehydrogenase, which can yield only 2 high-energy bonds.

Aerobic metabolism is much more efficient than anaerobic metabolism insofar as trapping the energy from glucose in a usable form. Totaling up the total gain of ATP we arrive at 38 as the possible number *formed per mole of glucose*:

Embden-Meyerhof cycle		8 ATP
Pyruvic acid to acetyl-CoA	3 (×2)	6 ATP
Krebs cycle	12 (×2)	24 ATP
		38 ATP

The figure 38 ATP represents an efficiency of 50% of the energy trapped from glucose as high-energy compounds. Although this sounds wasteful, the efficiency is much higher than that of mechanical machines.

INTERCYCLIC PATHWAYS

Acetyl-CoA is one of the most important inputs of the Krebs cycle, and this importance is even greater because the reaction links these two major cycles, Embden-Meyerhof and Krebs, together. With the central role which both of these pathways play in overall metabolism, it is not surprising to see alternate intercyclic reactions occur. One feature of many biochemical pathways is the presence of alternate routes for getting from one reactant to another.

There are four basic reactions which link the Embden-Meyerhof and Krebs cycles together. The conversions are from 3-carbon compounds of the glycolytic cycle to 4-carbon fatty acids intermediates of the Krebs cycle. This means that in going from the Embden-Meyerhof cycle to the Krebs cycle, carbon dioxide or a 1-carbon fragment must be added. This carbon dioxide fixation mechanism is fully exploited in some bacteria.

The first reaction is the decarboxylation of oxalacetic acid to give pyruvic acid and CO_2.

$$\text{Oxalacetic acid} \xrightarrow[\text{Mg}^{++}]{\text{Carboxylase}} \text{Pyruvic acid} + CO_2$$

This reaction is irreversible for all intents and purposes because of the energy barrier created between the oxalacetic acid and the pyruvic acid.

The second reaction, called the Wood-Werkman or Ochoa reaction, involves the conversion of malic acid and pyruvic acid. This reaction is reversible. The Wood-Werkman reaction is used quite often by bacteria for carbon dioxide fixation.

$$\text{Pyruvic acid} + CO_2 + \text{NADPH·H}^+ \underset{\longleftarrow}{\xrightarrow{\text{NADP-malic dehydrogenase}}} \text{Malic acid} + \text{NADP}$$

Notice that the enzyme is NADP-linked; the NAD-linked dehydrogenase converts the malic acid to oxalacetic acid.

The third reaction is also involved in carbon dioxide fixation. This is an energy-requiring mechanism in that a high-energy phosphate is used.

$$\text{Phosphoenol pyruvic acid} + CO_2 + \text{IDP (inosine diphosphate)} \underset{Mg^{++}}{\overset{\text{Phosphoenol pyruvic carboxylase}}{\rightleftharpoons}} \text{Oxalacetic acid} + \text{ITP}$$

The fourth intercyclic reaction uses ATP as the energy source for the conversion.

$$\text{Pyruvic acid} + CO_2 + \text{ATP} \underset{Mg^{++}}{\overset{\text{Pyruvic carboxylase}}{\longrightarrow}} \text{Oxalacetic acid} + \text{ADP} + \text{Pi}$$

These reactions afford better control of the Krebs cycle activity. Shunting out of the oxalacetic or malic acids effectively slows the cycle down. Conversely, active carbon dioxide fixation allows more rapid activity in the Krebs cycle.

SUMMARY

Metabolic pathways occur in a regular stepwise fashion, and often they occur as cyclic mechanisms. The various pathways of the cell are so interrelated and interdependent that any starting point is arbitrary. The Embden-Meyerhof and the Krebs cycles are considered because of the central position they assume in the overall wiring diagram of the metabolic pathways. Because of this central position, these two cycles are referred to as the common pathways.

Acetyl-CoA is an extremely important component of metabolism. This end product of carbohydrate and lipid metabolism can enter the Krebs cycle as the major input molecule. In addition to its potential energy yield function, this "active" acetate is used in biosynthesis as well. The mechanisms of production of acetyl-CoA may involve the investment of a high-energy compound since the thioester itself has a high-energy bond.

The pyruvic to acetyl-CoA sequence is termed the hub reaction because of the important role both of these compounds have.

The Embden-Meyerhof pathway degrades glucose-6-phosphate to pyruvic acid in a catabolic sequence. The cycle potentially produces a net gain of 2 ATP under anaerobic conditions and 8 ATP under aerobic ones. The pathway is reversible so that a 6-carbon fragment can be produced from 3-carbon fragments. This pathway is the most universal of all of the pathways.

The Krebs cycle is a true cyclic pathway which has as its prime function the production of high-energy compounds. For each mole of acetate as acetyl-CoA which is fed into the cycle there is a net gain of 12 ATP (24 per mole of glucose). This high efficiency is due to the fact that reduced coenzymes can be shunted to the electron transport system where the actual production of most of the high-energy bonds occurs.

It is important that these two major common pathways, the Krebs and the Embden-Meyerhof, have several intercyclic links for greater flexibility of function. The paths which have been demonstrated are between the 4-carbon oxalacetic or malic acids and the 3-carbon pyruvic or enolpyruvic acids.

Literature cited

1. Reed, L. J. 1960. Lipoic acid, vol. 13, p. 195. In Boyer, P. D., H. Lardy, and K. Myrbäck (editors): The enzymes. Academic Press, Inc., New York.
2. White, A., P. Handler, and E. L. Smith. 1964. Principles of biochemistry. 3rd edition. McGraw-Hill Book Co., New York, p. 369.

General references

Karlson, P. 1963. Introduction to modern biochemistry. Academic Press, Inc., New York.

Kleiner, I. S., and J. M. Orten. 1962. Biochemistry. 6th ed. The C. V. Mosby Co., St. Louis.

Kosower, E. M. 1962. Molecular biochemistry. McGraw-Hill Book Co., New York.

Krebs, H. A., and J. M. Lowenstein. 1960. The tricarboxylic acid cycle, vol. 1, p. 129. In D. M. Greenberg (editor): Metabolic pathways. Academic Press, Inc., New York.

Lehninger, A. L. 1964. The mitochondrion. W. A. Benjamin, Inc., New York.

Lehninger, A. L. 1961. How cells transform energy. Sci. Am. (Sept.), p. 62.

White, A., P. Handler, and E. L. Smith. 1964. Principles of biochemistry. 3rd ed. McGraw-Hill Book Co., New York.

18

Carbohydrate pathways

INTRODUCTION

No attempt will be made to cover all aspects of the metabolism of each of the major classes of compounds contributing to the metabolic pathways. Apart from the biochemical interest per se, the focus of these chapters will be on the various pathways as alternate or ancillary to the common pathways just discussed. The physiological importance to the cell will also be stressed.

HEXOSE INTERCONVERSIONS

In the discussion on monosaccharides, it was pointed out that the value of most hexose sugars was in their ready conversion to glucose or a glucose ester, and that the mechanism quite often used was interconversion through enolization. This process is catalyzed by a series of stereospecific isomerases, one of which is the phosphoglucose isomerase encountered in the Embden-Meyerhof pathway.

Another hexose conversion mechanism is that of the mutase, as is evidenced in the pathway from glucose-6-phosphate to starch or glycogen. Here, the glucose-6-phosphate is converted to glucose-1-phospate, the enzyme being phosphoglucomutase.

$$\text{Glucose-6-phosphate} \xrightleftharpoons[\quad\quad\quad\quad\quad\quad\quad\quad]{\text{Phosphoglucomutase}} \text{Glucose-1-phosphate}$$

Early investigations demonstrated that pure glucose-6-phosphate would not be converted readily to the 1-ester, but that impure glucose-6-phosphate would be catalyzed. This paradox was solved when it was discovered that glucose-1,6-diphosphate, a "contaminant," was necessary for the reaction to occur.

The mechanism for this conversion is shown in the following reactions in which a serine hydroxyl of the enzyme apparently acts as a phosphate carrier.

En—OH + Glucose-1, 6-diphosphate $\rightleftarrows$ EnOPO$_3$H$_2$ + Glucose-6-phosphate (or glucose-1-phosphate)

Either hexose ester can be formed in this manner. When the diphosphate ester gives up one of its phosphates to the enzyme, the glucose-6-phosphate or glucose-1-phosphate can be formed. The phosphorylated enzyme then reacts with either glucose-1-phosphate or glucose-6-phosphate to give the diester again.

Another way of showing this reaction is as follows:

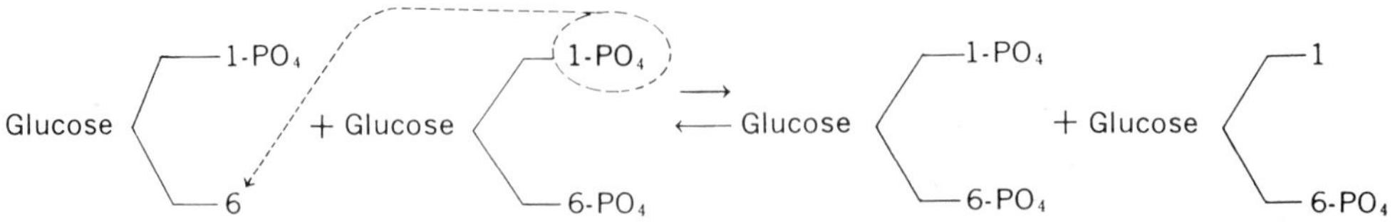

Glucose ⟨ 1-PO$_4$ / 6 ⟩ + Glucose ⟨ 1-PO$_4$ / 6-PO$_4$ ⟩ ⟶ ← Glucose ⟨ 1-PO$_4$ / 6-PO$_4$ ⟩ + Glucose ⟨ 1 / 6-PO$_4$ ⟩

The formation of the 6-phosphate is favored over the 1-phosphate because of an energy level difference between the two. The glucose-1,6-diphosphate is formed through a kinase reaction involving ATP.

$$\text{Glucose-1-phosphate} + \text{ATP} \longrightarrow \text{Glucose-1, 6-diphosphate} + \text{ADP}$$

NUCLEOSIDE DIPHOSPHATE ESTERS

Many of the carbohydrate pathways involve various nucleoside diphosphate esters as intermediates. Pyrophosphorylases are the group of enzymes catalyzing the formation of these esters. The general reaction is

$$\text{Sugar-phosphate} + \text{Nucleoside triphosphate} \rightleftharpoons \text{Nucleoside diphosphate-sugar} + PP_i$$

or, using glucose and uridine

Uridine-glucose
pyrophosphorylase
$$\text{Glucose-1-phosphate} + \text{Uridine triphosphate} \rightleftharpoons \text{Uridine diphosphate-glucose} + PP_i$$

This uridine diphosphate-glucose (UDP-G) is an important intermediate in starch and glycogen synthesis.

The number of nucleoside diphosphate esters is large and their composition is quite varied. Once considered an interesting, but unimportant, class of compounds, these sugar derivatives have demonstrated an important role in carbohydrate metabolism.

STARCH AND GLYCOGEN SYNTHESIS

The reaction in which uridine diphosphate glucose is involved, which is most important to the cell, is the synthesis of starch or glycogen as a reserve energy supply. The synthetic pathway is as follows:

Glycogen
synthetase
$$n\text{-Uridine diphosphate-glucose} \rightleftharpoons (\text{Glucose})_a + n\text{UDP} + n P_i$$

This is a polymerization reaction which forms the basic glycosidic 1-4 bond of the straight chain portion of starch and glycogen, the amylose. Since glycogen is a highly branched structure containing 1-6 linkages in addition to the 1-4 bonds, there is a separate reaction in which some of the straight chain amylose fragments are cleaved and transferred to other portions of the molecule in the 1-6 linkage.

$$\text{1-4 Polymer} \xrightleftharpoons{\text{Transglucosylase}} \text{1-4 Polymer} + \text{Fragments}$$
$$\Big\updownarrow \text{Transglucosylase}$$
$$\text{1-4 Polymer with 1-6 branches}$$

Equilibrium of the starch and glycogen synthesis favors the anabolic phase; thus, reserve glucose as glucose-1-phosphate is quickly incorporated into stored starch.

THE PENTOSE SHUNT

The Embden-Meyerhof pathway is one of two major pathways by which glucose can be metabolized. The second of these sequences is the pentose shunt, also called the hexose or sedoheptulose monophosphate shunt. This pathway is unique both in the compounds which are involved and in the fact that it is an aerobic mechanism. The latter implies that glucose metabolism can be carried out without the use of the anaerobic Embden-Meyerhof pathway, and, yet, the pentose shunt is very dependent on the glycolytic cycle for input and output purposes.

The shunt basically involves a series of intermolecular jugglings starting with the 6-carbon glucose-6-phosphate and going through a series of 5-, 7-, 4-, and 3-carbon intermediates. The scheme for this pathway is seen in Fig. 18-1. The format for discussing the pathway will continue as previously handled.

The pathway

Reaction 1. The first reaction is conversion of glucose-6-phosphate to 6-phosphogluconic acid, going through a lactone intermediate. Different from the Embden-Meyerhof pathway, the coenzyme involved here is NADP, not NAD.

$$\text{NADP} + \text{Glucose-6-phosphate} \xrightleftharpoons[]{\substack{\text{Glucose-6-phosphate} \\ \text{dehydrogenase}}} \text{6-Phosphoglucono-}\delta\text{-Lactone} + \text{NADPH·H}^+$$
$$\Big\updownarrow \substack{\text{Lactonase} \\ \text{Mg}^{++}}$$
$$\text{6-Phosphogluconic acid}$$

Reaction 2. In an oxidative decarboxylation, again involving NADP, the 6-phosphogluconic acid is converted to the 5-carbon sugar ester ribulose-5-phosphate.

$$\text{6-Phosphogluconic acid} + \text{NADP} \xrightleftharpoons[]{\substack{\text{6-Phosphogluconic} \quad CO_2 \\ \text{dehydrogenase}}} \text{Ribulose-5-phosphate} + \text{NADPH·H}^+$$

The ribulose-5-phosphate has a pivotal role in plant cells because of its conversion to an intermediate in the photosynthetic sequence, ribulose-1,5-diphosphate.

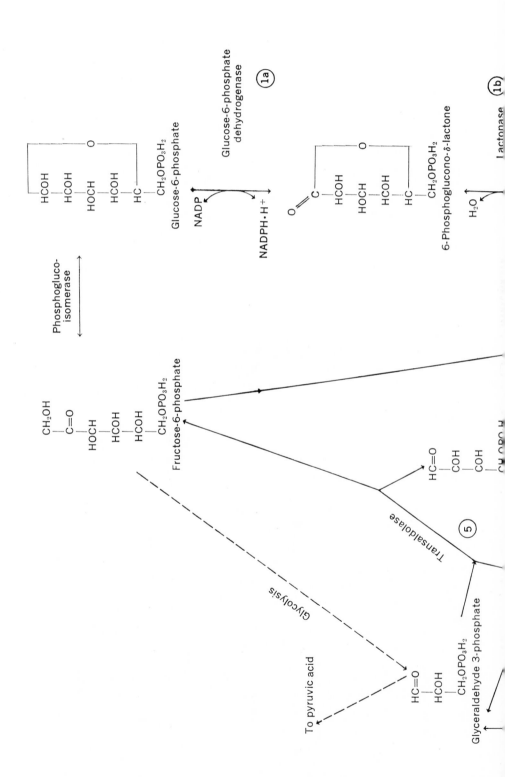

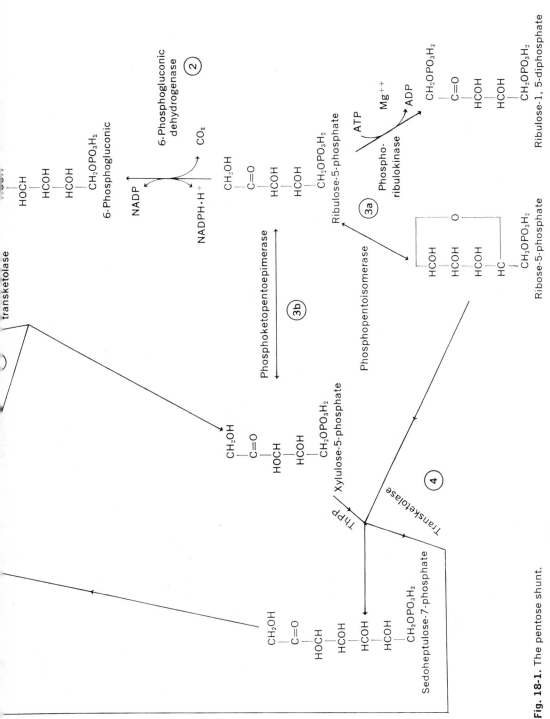

Fig. 18-1. The pentose shunt.

Phosphoribulokinase

Ribulose-5-phosphate + ATP $\xrightarrow{\hspace{3cm}}$ Ribulose-1,5-diphosphate + ADP

Reactions 3a and 3b.   Molecules of ribulose-5-phosphate undergo two pentose interconversions to give ribose-5-phosphate and xylulose-5-phosphate.

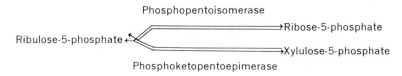

Phosphopentoisomerase

Ribulose-5-phosphate → Ribose-5-phosphate

→ Xylulose-5-phosphate

Phosphoketopentoepimerase

The ribose-5-phosphate can, of course, be shunted into nucleic acid synthesis by combining with purines and pyrimidines to form various ribose and deoxyribose nucleosides.

Reaction 4.   In a reaction which requires thiamine pyrophosphate, the two 5-carbon sugars from the previous reaction combine to give a 7-carbon and a 3-carbon product. This $5 + 5 = 7 + 3$ reaction yields sedoheptulose-7-phosphate and glyceraldehyde 3-phosphate.

Transketolase

Ribose-5-phosphate + Xylulose-5-phosphate $\overset{\longrightarrow}{\underset{\longleftarrow}{}}$

ThPP

Sedoheptulose-7-phosphate + Glyceraldehyde 3-phosphate

The importance of the reaction should be evident. The 3-carbon glyceraldehyde 3-phosphate is a definite link between the Embden-Meyerhof cycle, the Krebs cycle, and the pentose shunt. From glyceraldehyde, the Embden-Meyerhof cycle can reverse, leading to starch formation. This is an important factor in photosynthesis. The 3-carbon fragment can progress down the Embden-Meyerhof pathway to pyruvic acid and on to acetyl-CoA where it can enter the Krebs cycle for greater energy yield. Conversely, the reverse of the glycolytic pathway from pyruvic acid up to glyceraldehyde 3-phosphate can feed the pentose shunt.

Reaction 5.   The sedoheptulose-7-phosphate and the glyceraldehyde 3-phosphate formed in the previous reaction combine in a $7 + 3 = 6 + 4$ manner to yield fructose-6-phosphate and erythrose-4-phosphate.

Transaldolase

Sedoheptulose-7-phosphate + Glyceraldehyde 3-phosphate $\overset{\longrightarrow}{\underset{\longleftarrow}{}}$

Fructose-6-phosphate + Erythrose-4-phosphate

This reaction also feeds back into the Embden-Meyerhof pathway, again offering the possibility that the fructose-6-phosphate can take several paths of metabolism. The erythrose-4-phosphate formed is essentially a dead end and thus acts as a storage device for the sugar ester. This 4-carbon fragment can feed back into the glycolytic cycle by the last reaction in the sequence.

Reaction 6.   This is a $4 + 5 = 6 + 3$ reaction, as follows.

Transketolase

Erythrose-4-phosphate + Xylulose-5-phosphate $\overset{\longrightarrow}{\underset{\longleftarrow}{}}$

ThPP

Fructose-6-phosphate + Glyceraldehyde 3-phosphate

Importance of the pentose shunt

The oxidative metabolism of glucose by the pentose shunt affords the cell greater flexibility in its metabolic patterns. By the investment of only 1 ATP per mole of glucose, the pentose shunt allows glucose metabolism to reach pyruvic acid through the glyceraldehyde 3-phosphate. This 3-carbon fragment and fructose-6-phosphate are critical links between this shunt and the Embden-Meyerhof pathway.

The production of reduced $NADPH \cdot H^+$ is an important function of the shunt. Many reactions in the cell, particularly fatty acid synthesis, require $NADPH \cdot H^+$ rather than $NADH \cdot H^+$.

The intermediates of the shunt, specifically the pentose esters, are significant in their own right. Ribose-5-phosphate is necessary for nucleic acid synthesis, and ribulose-5-phosphate leads into the photosynthetic sequence.

Because of the combining and recombining reactions in the shunt, the energy gain is difficult to calculate. The true oxidative steps are reactions 1 and 2, where the specific dehydrogenases transfer 4 electrons and hydrogens per mole of glucose; that is, 2 $NADPH \cdot H^+$ are formed. By controlling the flow of the reactions, essentially all of the cycle can be funneled back to fructose-6-phosphate, and thus back to glucose-6-phosphate. The overall net reaction could then be represented as

$$6 \text{ Glucose-6-phosphate} + 12 \text{ NADP} \longrightarrow 5 \text{ Glucose-6-phosphate} + 6 \text{ CO}_2 + 12 \text{ NADPH} \cdot H^+ + P_i$$

This net reaction demonstrates two important aspects of the pentose shunt:
1. Glucose can be metabolized completely to CO_2 without going through the Krebs cycle.
2. The potential energy gain is probably 6 ATP per mole of glucose metabolized, but the value may vary because of all of the interactions.

Nevertheless, the pentose sequence does offer an important alternate pathway, and the shunt could be considered somewhat of a safety valve if malfunctions are occurring in the Embden-Meyerhof pathway.

GLYOXYLIC ACID PATHWAY

The final carbohydrate pathway to be considered is the glyoxylic acid pathway. This cycle seems to have as its prime function the conversion of fat into stored starch. The end product of fat degradation is acetyl-CoA. This, however, cannot be converted into pyruvic acid by reversal of the sequence of pyruvic acid to acetyl-CoA. By use of intermediaries of the Krebs cycle, however, acetyl-CoA molecules can be fed into the Embden-Meyerhof cycle for reversal up to starch. The scheme of this pathway is shown in Fig. 18-2.

The steps which are different from those already considered are given. First, there is splitting of isocitric acid into glyoxylic acid and succinic acid.

$$\text{Isocitric acid} \xrightarrow{\text{Isocitritase}} \text{Succinic acid} + \text{Glyoxylic acid}$$

One molecule of acetyl-CoA is combined with the glyoxylic acid formed to yield malic acid.

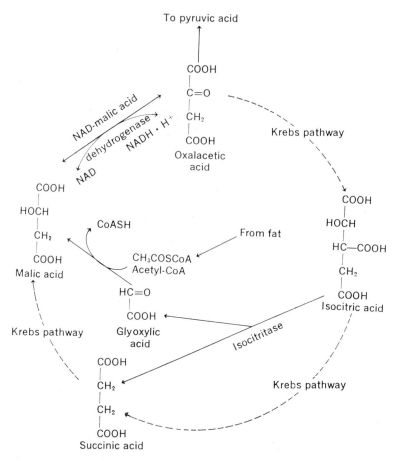

Fig. 18-2. The glyoxylic acid pathway.

$$\text{Acetyl-CoA} + \text{Glyoxylic acid} + H_2O \xrightarrow{\text{Malic synthetase}} \text{Malic acid} + \text{CoASH}$$

The malic acid, from both the malic synthetase condensation and that formed from succinic through fumaric acids, goes to oxalacetic acid in the Krebs cycle. At this point phosphorylation and decarboxylation occur, converting the oxalacetic acid to phosphoenol pyruvic acid.

$$\text{Oxalacetic acid} \overset{\text{Phosphoenolpyruvic}}{\underset{\text{carboxylase}}{\rightleftharpoons}} \overset{CO_2}{\longrightarrow} \text{Phosphoenolpyruvic acid}$$

This completes the glyoxylate pathway or shunt, demonstrating a means by which acetyl-CoA can feed back into the Embden-Meyerhof pathway. This pathway seems to be restricted to the plant kingdom.

SUMMARY

The efficiency of carbohydrate metabolism depends to some extent on the ability of various sugars, particularly hexoses, to undergo a series of interconversions. These molecular rearrangements allow the cell to produce the types of compounds most needed for the metabolic requirements.

One reaction to which all hexoses are directed is the formation of starch or glycogen. This process involves polymerization of uridine diphosphate glucose to the 1-4 straight chain starch, with the concomitant cleavage of some of this straight chain to also give the 1-6 linkage of the branched chain characteristic of glycogen.

The two carbohydrate pathways which are ancillary to the Embden-Meyerhof and Krebs pathways are the pentose shunt and the glyoxylate pathway.

The pentose shunt allows oxidative metabolism of glucose which does not involve the Krebs cycle. In a dynamic cell, the Embden-Meyerhof cycle and the pentose shunt are interdependent, both working on hexose esters to get an energy yield. The three main functions of the pentose cycle are to furnish intermediates for other cycles, reduced NADPH·H+ for fat synthesis, and energy in the form of ATP.

The glyoxylate shunt converts acetyl-CoA molecules into an Embden-Meyerhof intermediate. This process uses some of the same steps as the Krebs cycle.

The metabolism of carbohydrates, and glucose in particular, can take many forms. Microorganisms can convert glucose into a number of fermentation products including lactic acid, acetic acid, formic acid, propionic or butyric acids, ethyl or butyl alcohol, and acetone. Only the more common pathways, however, were considered here.

General references

Barker, H. A. 1956. Bacterial fermentations. John Wiley & Sons, Inc., New York.

Cabib, E. 1963. Carbohydrate metabolism. Ann. Rev. Biochem. 32:321.

Gale, E. F. 1959. Synthesis and organisation in the bacterial cell. John Wiley & Sons, Inc., New York.

Horecker, B. L. 1962. Pentose metabolism in bacteria. John Wiley & Sons, Inc., New York.

Karlson, P. 1963. Introduction to modern biochemistry. Academic Press, Inc., New York.

Kleiner, I. S., and J. M. Orten. 1962. Biochemistry. 6th ed. The C. V. Mosby Co., St. Louis.

Kosower, E. M. 1962. Molecular biochemistry. McGraw-Hill Book Co., New York.

Pon, N. G. 1964. Expressions of the pentose phosphate cycle, vol. 7, p. 2. In Florkin, M., and H. S. Mason (editors): Comparative biochemistry. Academic Press, Inc., New York.

Stetten, D., and M. R. Stetten. 1960. Glycogen metabolism. Physiol. Rev. 40:505.

White, A., P. Handler, and E. L. Smith. 1964. Principles of biochemistry. 3rd ed. McGraw-Hill Book Co., New York.

Wood, H. G. 1955. Significance of alternate pathways in the metabolism of glucose. Physiol. Rev. 35:841.

19

Lipid pathways

T **INTRODUCTION**
The lipids are an important structural unit in the cell, particularly in the membrane system. As a result, the maintenance of a steady dynamic turnover of these lipids is critical to the integrity of the membranes and the cell. The major pathways which will briefly be discussed in this chapter are the oxidation and synthesis of fatty acids (which may not share the same pathway), the synthesis of triglycerides and phospholipids, some special synthetic pathways, and metabolism of propionic acid as an example of the reactions of a fatty acid with an odd number of carbons. Again, no attempt will be made to cover all of the compounds and their metabolism; those just listed should serve, however, as representatives of the lipid pathways of the cell.

FATTY ACID OXIDATION

Back in 1904, Knoop proposed his β-oxidation theory to explain the oxidative degradation of fatty acids. He postulated that 2-carbon fragments were chopped off in sequence from the fatty acids, and although the theory was discarded off and on over the years, the sequence has become firmed as a basic lipid pathway.

The oxidation of the long-chained fatty acids occurs in a repetitive sequence of events, beginning with activation of the acid by coenzyme A, the reaction driven by hydrolysis of ATP.

$$RCH_2CH_2CH_2COOH + ATP + CoASH \rightleftarrows RCH_2CH_2CH_2COSCoA + AMP + PP_i$$

There are apparently three separate enzymes which catalyze this reaction, the criterion of which is involved being the length of the fatty acid chain. Hydrolysis of the pyrophosphate by an inorganic pyrophosphatase helps move this reaction to the right.

In some cells, formation of the acyl-CoA occurs by a thiophorase reaction where succinyl-CoA supplies the –CoA group.

$$RCH_2CH_2CH_2COOH + Succinyl\text{-}CoA \rightleftarrows RCH_2CH_2CH_2COSCoA + Succinic\ acid$$

In four successive steps after the acyl-CoA derivative is formed, the fatty acid is dehydrogenated, hydrated, dehydrogenated a second time, and then cleaved. These reactions occur between the α-carbons and β-carbons—thus the name β-oxidation.

Reaction 1. The activated fatty acid is dehydrogenated, with FAD acting as the hydrogen acceptor.

Acyl
dehydrogenase

$$RCH_2CH_2CH_2COSCoA + FAD \xrightleftharpoons{\hspace{2cm}} RCH_2CH=CHCOSCoA + FADH_2$$

There are three specific acyl dehydrogenase enzymes which catalyze this reaction. The length of the chain is again the determining factor as to which is used.

Reaction 2. The second step in the sequence is the addition of water across the double bond created by the dehydrogenation.

Enoyl hydrase

$$RCH_2CH=CHCOSCoA + H_2O \xrightleftharpoons{\hspace{2cm}} RCH_2CHOHCH_2COSCoA$$

The enoyl hydrase, also called crotonase, causes formation of the L-configuration of β-hydroxyacyl-CoA.

Reaction 3. There is a second dehydrogenation, with NAD serving as the hydrogen acceptor.

β-Hydroxyacyl

$$RCH_2CHOHCH_2COSCoA + NAD \xrightleftharpoons{\hspace{2cm}} RCH_2COCH_2COSCoA + NADH{\cdot}H^+$$

dehydrogenase

The enzyme β-hydroxyacyl dehydrogenase is specific for the L-isomer.

Reaction 4. Acetyl-CoA is split off from the end of the chain, with the concomitant formation of another acyl-CoA with two carbons less than the initial fatty acid.

Thiolase

$$RCH_2COCH_2COSCoA + CoASH \xrightleftharpoons{\hspace{2cm}} RCH_2COSCoA + CH_3COSCoA$$

Energetics and other considerations

The oxidation of fatty acids (Fig. 19-1) is a stepwise sequence which involves the investment of one coenzyme A molecule per 2-carbon fragment split off. The end product of this oxidation is acetyl-CoA which can enter the Krebs cycle for further breakdown and energy gain. The second source of energy in the form of high-energy compounds is the production of $FADH_2$ and $NADH{\cdot}H^+$ by the oxidative steps. The reduced coenzymes can transfer hydrogen and electrons to the electron transport chain where more ATP can be formed. Thus, per mole of fatty acid, the energy gain to the cell of its oxidation is very high, and therefore the lipids represent an excellent storage mechanism for energy.

An example of the high amount of energy stored in fats is shown by tallying

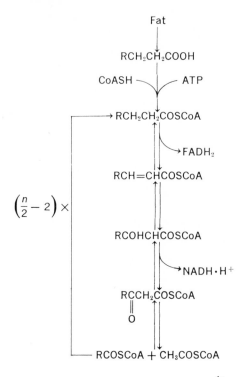

Fig. 19-1. The fatty acid oxidation sequence. The pathway is used $\left(\dfrac{n}{2}-1\right)$ times for each fatty acid. For example, an 18-carbon chain would go through the cycle eight times to yield the nine 2-carbon fragments as acetyl-CoA, that is, once through and seven repeats.

the number of ATP which can be gained from the oxidation of 1 mole of stearic acid. Starting with the 18-carbon stearyl-CoA, there will be 8 sets of β-oxidation sequences to yield 9 acetyl-CoA. In these reactions, 8 $FADH_2$ and 8 NADH·H⁺ will be formed. These two reduced coenzymes represent a total of 5 ATP formed through the electron transport chain for every mole of $FADH_2$ and NADH·H⁺ used (3 for NADH·H⁺ and 2 for $FADH_2$). The energy gain in the fatty acid oxidation to this point is 40 ATP. This amount is minor in comparison to the ATP which can be produced as the acetyl-CoA enter the Krebs cycle. Recall that for each turn of the citric acid cycle there is a yield of 12 ATP; thus, the 9 acetyl-CoA formed from the oxidation represent a potential of 108 ATP. The total ATP gain from the complete oxidation of the 18-carbon fatty acid is 148 ATP. The 148 ATP gain for the 18-carbon stearic acid oxidation (8.33 ATP per carbon) compares very favorably with the 38 ATP gain for glucose oxidation (6.33 ATP per carbon).

FATTY ACID SYNTHESIS

The cell has two separate pathways for producing fatty acids. One, which is essentially the reverse of the oxidative degradation, is localized in mitochondria. The second mechanism is not a reverse of the catabolic breakdown and is primarily extramitochondrial. This sequence is outlined on p. 207.

The basic building block for this pathway is malonyl-CoA. The 3-carbon malonyl ester can be formed by several separate mechanisms. One of the more common of these involves fixation of CO_2 by a biotin-enzyme complex. The CO_2, as the formate, HCO_3^-, combines with this vitamin-protein complex, the energy being donated by ATP.

$$HCO_3^- + ATP + \text{Biotin-En} \xrightarrow{Mn^{++}} CO_2\text{-biotin-En} + P_i + ADP$$

The "fixed" CO_2 is then transferred to acetyl-CoA to form malonyl-CoA.

$$CO_2\text{-Biotin-En} + \text{Acetyl-CoA} \rightleftarrows \text{Malonyl-CoA} + \text{Biotin-En}$$

Malonyl-CoA can also be formed by either of the following reactions:

$$\text{Malonic acid} + \text{CoASH} + ATP \rightleftarrows \text{Malonyl-CoA} + AMP + PP_i$$

This reaction parallels the activation of the long-chain acids, as seen in the preliminary step to the β-oxidation sequence.

$$\text{Succinyl-CoA (or acetoacetyl-CoA)} + \text{Malonic acid} \underset{\longleftarrow}{\overset{\text{CoA transferase}}{\longrightarrow}}$$

$$\text{Malonyl-CoA} + \text{Succinic (or acetoacetic) acid}$$

Conversion of malonyl-CoA to the higher chain fatty acids requires acetyl-CoA and NADPH·H⁺. The reaction demonstrating conversion to the higher acids is as follows:

$$\text{Acetyl-CoA} + \left(\frac{n}{2} - 1\right) \text{Malonyl-CoA} + 2\left(\frac{n}{2} - 1\right) \text{NADPH·H}^+ \longrightarrow$$

$$n\text{-Carbon fatty acid} + \left(\frac{n}{2} - 1\right) CO_2 + \frac{n}{2} \text{CoASH} + 2\left(\frac{n}{2} - 1\right) \text{NADP} + \left(\frac{n}{2} - 2\right) H_2O$$

All of the 1-carbon fragments which were fixed in the formation of malonyl-CoA are regenerated during the anabolic sequence. The malonyl-CoA is essentially behaving as a 2-carbon fragment.

The mitochondrial system, which is basically the reverse of the β-oxidation sequence, seems to incorporate steps 2, 3, and 4 given on p. 205, only in reverse. Step 1, however, in the oxidation sequence requires FAD and a specific dehydrogenase. The comparable step in the synthesis uses NADP and a reductase.

$$RCH_2CH{=}CHCOSCoA + NADPH·H^+ \underset{\longleftarrow}{\overset{\text{Reductase}}{\longrightarrow}} RCH_2CH_2COSCoA + NADP$$

The NADPH·H⁺ which participate in both of the preceding schemes often come from the pentose shunt.

Energetics and other considerations

Synthesis of fatty acids for the purposes of producing storage fat or for building and turnover of cell membranes is a process which drains large amounts of potential energy from the cell in two ways.

1. The reduced coenzymes which are oxidized in the process cannot enter

the electron transport chain for ATP production. That is, the $FADH_2$ and NADPH·H+ are oxidized in the biosynthetic sequence and are not available for participation in the events of the electron chain.

2. Many of the acetyl-CoA which are formed from carbohydrate and other pathways will not be shunted into the Krebs cycle if fatty acid synthesis is rapidly occurring.

It is implicit in metabolic pathways, though, that the anabolic energy drain can be regained on subsequent catabolic processes. Thus, in the steady state condition of the cell, the total energy picture should nearly balance.

The teleological reason for two separate pathways is not completely understood. It is probable that the mitochondrion and its pathway evolved at a later period than the pathway of fatty acid synthesis, and thus the nonmitochondrial portion of the cell accrued its own mechanism.

NEUTRAL TRIGLYCERIDES AND PHOSPHOLIPIDS

The fate of fatty acids is either to be incorporated into phospholipids or to be stored as neutral triglycerides. The pathway to both of these compounds is very similar, and for that reason they will be considered together.

At the end of fatty acid synthesis, the acids are found in the form of acyl-CoA. These coenzyme A derivatives of fatty acids combine with glycerophosphoric acid to yield phosphatidic acid.

$$\begin{array}{ccc} & CH_2OH & CH_2OOCR \\ & | & | \\ 2\ RCOSCoA + & HCOH & \rightleftarrows\ HCOOCR \quad + 2\ CoASH \\ & | & | \\ & CH_2OPO_3H_2 & CH_2OPO_3H_2 \end{array}$$

This phosphatidic acid then combines with choline, serine, or ethanolamine to give the lecithin and cephalins. The agent which seems to be involved in the transfer of these groups to the phosphatidic acid is cytidine diphosphate (CDP).

The neutral triglycerides can be formed from the phosphatidic acid by hydrolysis of the phosphate by a phosphatase.

$$\text{Phosphatic acid} + H_2O \underset{\longleftarrow}{\overset{\text{Phosphatase}}{\rightleftarrows}} \text{1,2-Diglyceride} + P_i$$

The diglyceride can then add a third fatty acid to form the neutral triglyceride.

$$\text{1,2-Diglyceride} + \text{Acyl-CoA} \rightleftarrows \text{Triglyceride} + \text{CoASH}$$

The interrelationship between these two pathways is striking, and from an efficiency standpoint, this is an excellent arrangement. The stored triglycerides can easily be converted to the phospholipids needed in membrane production without elaborate conversion or energy input.

KETONE BODIES

Ketone bodies are by-products of lipid or carbohydrate metabolism which may be toxic if present in large enough quantities. Heavy accumulation occurs

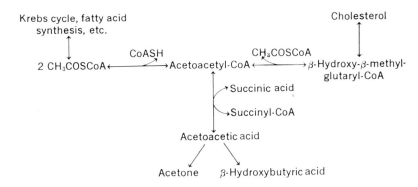

Fig. 19-2. Scheme showing possible fates of acetoacetyl-CoA.

only during aberrant metabolism, but the pathways are always functional in that they supply intermediates for synthesis of other compounds. All of these related pathways have as a starting point acetoacetyl-CoA, which is formed from two molecules of acetyl-CoA.

$$2 \text{ Acetyl-CoA} \rightleftharpoons \text{Acetoacetyl-CoA} + \text{CoASH}$$

A summary of the various fates of this 4-carbon acetoacetyl-CoA is seen in Fig. 19-2.

PROPIONIC ACID METABOLISM

Although most of the fatty acids which occur in nature have an even number of carbons, there are many cells which have the odd-numbered long-chain acids. Beta-oxidation of these acids occurs as it does in the even-carbon forms, but the final residue is a 3-carbon propionyl instead of the acetyl residue. This creates the need for propionic acid to have pathways which will convert it to forms which can be used by other cycles.

The basic pathway of propionic acid first involves its being activated with coenzyme A in the same CoA transfer mechanism as previously described. Then, a 1-carbon fragment is added via a biotin-enzyme complex to form methyl-malonyl-CoA(a). The latter is then converted to its isomer, methyl-malonyl-CoA (b). The final reaction, catalyzed by an enzyme having B_{12} as a coenzyme, shows the methyl-malonyl-CoA(b) converted to succinyl-CoA.[1] These reactions are seen in Fig. 19-3.

The succinyl-CoA thus formed can further react with another molecule of propionic acid to give propionyl-CoA and succinic acid, this latter acid entering directly into the Krebs cycle.

Propionic acid or propionyl-CoA can also be oxidized to a variety of end products in different cells. Pathways have been demonstrated leading to malonyl-CoA, acetyl-CoA, pyruvic acid, and alanine. Further, many amino acids are degraded to propionic acid, but the pathways are believed to be irreversible.

This 3-carbon fatty acid demonstrates well the interrelationships which exist in the metabolic pathways. Sequences have been shown where this lipid by-

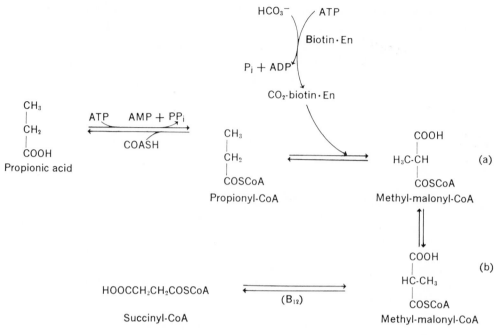

Fig. 19-3. One pathway of propionic acid metabolism, showing its conversion to succinyl-CoA which can feed into the common cycles.

product is converted to carbohydrates, amino acids, and intermediates of the common pathways.

SUMMARY

The cell uses lipids in a variety of ways—as an energy source, as a structural unit, and as intermediates in the synthesis of specialized compounds. These uses each require a separate pathway of metabolism. Some of these sequences are considered.

Oxidative degradation of fatty acids occurs in a sequence of 2-carbon fragments being cleaved from the acid (of n carbons) one at a time, with the final end products being $\frac{n}{2}$ moles of acetyl-CoA. The process is called β-oxidation.

Biosynthesis of these fatty acids can occur in two distinct sequences. One pathway is essentially the reverse of β-oxidation. The other differs in that the building block is the 3-carbon malonyl-CoA instead of the 2-carbon acetyl-CoA.

The biosynthesis of neutral triglycerides and phospholipids shares similar pathways. Both are derivatives of phosphatidic acid. Acetoacetyl-CoA, produced by condensation from 2 acetyl-CoA molecules, can follow several synthetic pathways leading to a variety of end products.

Propionic acid metabolism is considered in that it demonstrates the interrelationships among fatty acid metabolism and the pathways of carbohydrates and proteins. Propionic acid, the 3-carbon residue of β-oxidation of odd-numbered fatty acids, is metabolized to succinyl-CoA via a 1-carbon transfer mechanism. A number of other end products can also be derived from propionic acid.

It is becoming more evident with each class of compounds considered that the metabolic pathways cross and unite from their different starting points. Lipid pathways are an excellent example of some of these interrelationships.

Literature cited

1. Kaziro, Y., and S. Ochoa. 1964. The metabolism of propionic acid. Advances Enzymol. 26:283.

General references

Barker, H. A. 1956. Bacterial fermentations. John Wiley & Sons, Inc., New York.

Bloch, K. (editor). 1960 Lipide metabolism. John Wiley & Sons, Inc., New York.

Dawson, R. M. C. 1962. The metabolism of phospholipids, vol. 3A, pp. 265-285. In Florkin, M., and H. S. Mason (editors): Comparative biochemistry. Academic Press, Inc., New York.

Gale, E. F. 1959. Synthesis and organisation in the bacterial cell. John Wiley & Sons, Inc., New York.

Grant, J. K. 1962. Lipids: Steroid metabolism, vol. 3A, pp. 163-203. In Florkin, M., and H. S. Mason (editors): Comparative biochemistry. Academic Press, Inc., New York.

Green, D. E., and D. M. Gibson. 1960. Fatty acid oxidation and synthesis, vol. 1, pp. 301-340. In Greenberg, D. M. (editor). Metabolic pathways. Academic Press, Inc., New York.

Karlson, P. 1963. Introduction to modern biochemistry. Academic Press, Inc., New York.

Kennedy, E. P. 1957. Biosynthesis of phospholipides. Fed. Proc. 16:847.

Kleiner, I. S., and J. M. Orten. 1962. Biochemistry. 6th ed. The C. V. Mosby Co., St. Louis.

Kosower, E. M. 1962. Molecular biochemistry. McGraw-Hill Book Co., New York.

Popják, G., and E. Le Breton. 1956. Biochemical problems of lipids. Butterworth & Co. (Publishers), Ltd., London.

Stumpf, P. K., and G. A. Barber. 1960. Comparative mechanisms for fatty acid oxidation, vol. 1, pp.75-105. In Florkin, M., and H. S. Mason (editors): Comparative biochemistry. Academc Press, Inc., New York.

White, A., P. Handler, and E. L. Smith. 1964. Principles of biochemistry. 3rd ed. McGraw-Hill Book Co., New York.

20

Pathways of the nitrogen-containing compounds

I INTRODUCTION

In all of metabolism, the cell is faced with the task of maintaining physiologically determined levels of the metabolites necessary to carry out the various cell processes. This maintenance implies that there must be interconversions, syntheses, degradations, and adjustments of the cellular constituents to meet the needs which the cell dictates.

The nitrogen-containing compounds, in comparison to the carbohydrates and lipids, have problems which are more demanding on the cell. Enumerated, these are the following:

1. Availability of nitrogen or nitrogen-bearing metabolites.
2. Vast number of these compounds: for example, more than twenty common amino acids as compared to less than ten common monosaccharides.
3. The metabolic pathways of amino acids and other nitrogen compounds are not as directly involved with the common Krebs and Embden-Meyerhof cycles, and thus many have specialized pathways.
4. Both carbohydrates and lipids can be stored in a relatively inert form in the cell; the nitrogen-containing compounds are not stored as such.

The availability of nitrogen is a critical problem for many cells, particularly those which are free-living. The process of true nitrogen fixation is limited to only a few kinds of cells. Most cells thus depend on discarded, decayed, or digested organic material for the nitrogen source. The possibility of limited resources of nitrogen places a demand on the cell to be frugal with its nitrogenous materials.

The number of nitrogen-containing compounds which the cell uses or requires is extraordinary. In addition to the twenty or so amino acids found, plus the myriad of specific proteins, the cell contains many ring structures containing nitrogen. To just list all which are either end products of synthetic processes or intermediates in the pathways would take a good number of pages.

This large number of compounds with such a great variety of structures precludes using the more established pathways except as a starting point or as a locus for the feed in of end products. Thus, there are many individual sequences of biosynthesis and degradation which place an additional load on the enzyme system of the cell. Many of the individual pathways are so obscure that only a few intermediates have been isolated, or even postulated.

Finally, the dynamic turnover of the nitrogen compounds is very high. The lack of storage reserves such as starch and triglycerides necessitates maintenance of efficient, interrelated pathways among the different nitrogen compounds so that if one area needs to increase its synthetic activities, building blocks can be shunted from these other pathways.

As the metabolic picture of these nitrogen-containing compounds develops, it should become evident that greater precautions and many alternates are available for interrelationships and interconversion among the various members of the class. The story of protein synthesis will not be dealt with in this chapter because it is not only a biochemical phenomenon. This synthesis, as much as any process, meshes the functional cell with biochemical processes. A later chapter (Chapter 26) is devoted to this.

AMMONIA AND AMMONIA FIXATION

The level of nitrogen in the cell is critical to the synthetic activities which are going on. The primary source of this nitrogen for most cells is ammonia, with nitrate and nitrite also actively moved into the internal medium. Very few cells, however, can fix atmospheric nitrogen into a form which is metabolizable by the cell. Several genera of bacteria and a few isolated species of algae are capable of taking this atmospheric component and converting it to ammonia, nitrate, or nitrite. All other cells depend on the nitrogen fixed by these cells or the nitrogenous material which comes from organic breakdown of soluble minerals. The ammonia, then, which is a prevalent form of utilizable nitrogen, represents a major source of supply to the cell. Some of the processes producing it or utilizing it bear mentioning.

One of the degradative products of amino acid metabolism is ammonia. This group is split off from the α-carbon by a series of reactions which will be discussed later. Other nitrogen-containing compounds also yield NH_3 upon catabolic breakdown. In most microorganisms and plants, the nitrogen by-products of metabolism are reused for synthetic purposes because the external supply is relatively limited. Cells of higher animals exhibit a different situation in that they actively accumulate nitrogen metabolites, and often the supply is greater than the cell really requires. As a result, mechanisms for removal of excess nitrogen, usually in the form of NH_3, are present in these cells.

In microorganisms, plants, and lower animals, nitrogen is often presented to the cell in the form of dissolved N_2 or NO_3^-. Since most metabolic pathways utilize nitrogen as ammonia, the nitrogen gas and the nitrate have to be reduced to the NH_3 form. The mechanism for this reduction has not been fully elucidated, although there is some evidence that a specific hydrogenase functions in the fixation of nitrogen by reducing the nitrogen which has been chemiabsorbed to ions which are complexed with flavoproteins.

Ammonia utilization apparently occurs in all taxa in both the animal and plant kingdoms, and three major reactions dominate the means by which NH_3 can be incorporated into an organic molecule. These three, glutamic acid synthesis, glutamine synthesis, and carbamyl phosphate formation, occur in essentially all cells.

$$\text{(1)} \quad NADH \cdot H^+ + NH_4^+ + \alpha\text{-Ketoglutaric acid} \underset{Zn^{++}}{\overset{\text{Glutamic acid dehydrogenase}}{\rightleftharpoons}} NAD + \text{Glutamic acid}$$

This reaction may also use the reduced $NADPH \cdot H^+$. In either instance, the reaction is reversible. The fact that an intermediate of the Krebs cycle can be used to incorporate ammonia into an organic molecule is of great value to the cell. This link assures an aerobic, functional cell of a supply of nitrogen, provided, of course, that there is sufficient NH_3 in the external medium.

$$\text{(2)} \quad \text{Glutamic acid} + ATP \overset{\text{Glutamine synthetase}}{\rightleftharpoons} \text{``Activated'' glutamic acid} + ADP + P_i$$

$$\text{``Activated'' glutamic acid} + NH_4^+ \overset{\text{Glutamine synthetase}}{\longleftrightarrow} H_2NCOCH_2CH_2CHNH_2COOH$$
$$\text{Glutamine}$$

This is an extremely useful mechanism for adding additional nitrogen to the cell. Once glutamic acid is formed, the second amine group can be added and one, or both, can be transferred to other organic compounds. This diamino compound and asparagine, another amino acid with an additional $-NH_2$, may serve as a small storage device for nitrogen.

$$\text{(3a)} \quad CO_2 + NH_4^+ + H_2O + 2ATP \underset{\text{Acetyl glutamate}}{\overset{\text{Carbamyl phosphate synthetase}}{\longrightarrow}} \underset{\text{Carbamyl phosphate}}{H_2NCOOPO_3H_2} + 2ADP + P_i$$

The carbamyl phosphate is an important compound. It is the starting point for the urea cycle and is also an early intermediate in some synthetic pathways.

The reaction as written here is irreversible because of the large energy difference, with the 2 ATP being hydrolyzed. There is, however, a mechanism for forming carbamyl phosphate which is reversible. This reaction, found only in certain microorganisms, may actually be a means of producing ATP.

$$\text{(3b)} \quad ATP + CO_2 + NH_3 \underset{\text{synthetase}}{\overset{\text{Carbamyl phosphate}}{\rightleftharpoons}} \text{Carbamyl phosphate} + ADP$$

Since this enzyme requires only the presence of one ATP, the reaction is more easily reversed than (3a).

These are not all of the mechanisms by which nitrogen can get into the cell. In some organisms, for example, other amino acids may be formed instead of glutamic acid. In other organisms, preformed amino acids may be taken into the cell directly. The extent to which the cell depends on outside nitrogen sources determines the synthetic capacity which the cell must have. It is obvious that the cells which fix ammonia in only a minimal number of ways must manipulate the nitrogen much more once it is inside than those cells which transport many nitrogen-containing compounds and fix ammonia in a variety of mechanisms.

The role ammonia plays will become even more evident as the specific reactions, degradations, and syntheses of the nitrogen-containing compounds are considered.

AMINO ACIDS—BASIC REACTIONS

Very few substances can claim the diversity of use and biological properties of the amino acids. Their metabolic role as the precursors to the very enzymes which control their metabolism is of such prime importance that the cell has at its disposal many mechanisms for interconversion and modification of the structures.

The various levels of available amino acids compose what is termed the amino acid pool or, more generally, the nitrogen pool. The maintenance of this pool is dependent upon the functioning of the mechanisms which allow the amino acid interactions and reactions to occur.

The individual amino acids undergo so many different reactions, depending on the character of their structure, that they should not be included in this section under the guise of basic mechanisms. In fact, many are so specialized that their discussion should be restricted to the appropriate monographs.

There are, however, a series of reactions which are considered to be basic to amino acid metabolism in the cell. Some of these are primarily interconversion devices, whereas others are degradative in nature.

Transamination

One of the most important reactions which the amino acids can undergo so far as maintaining flexibility in the amino acid pool is transamination.

In a classical work published in 1937, Braunstein and Kritzmann reported a mechanism for the removal of the amine group from amino acids; the amine did not appear in the medium, but was apparently picked up by some keto-acid to form a new amino compound.

This reaction, termed *transamination,* was an intermolecular transfer of the amino group and could be summarized as follows:

$$RCHCOOH + R'CCOOH \rightleftarrows RCCOOH + R'CHCOOH$$
$$\overset{|}{NH_2} \qquad \overset{\|}{O} \qquad \overset{\|}{O} \qquad \overset{|}{NH_2}$$

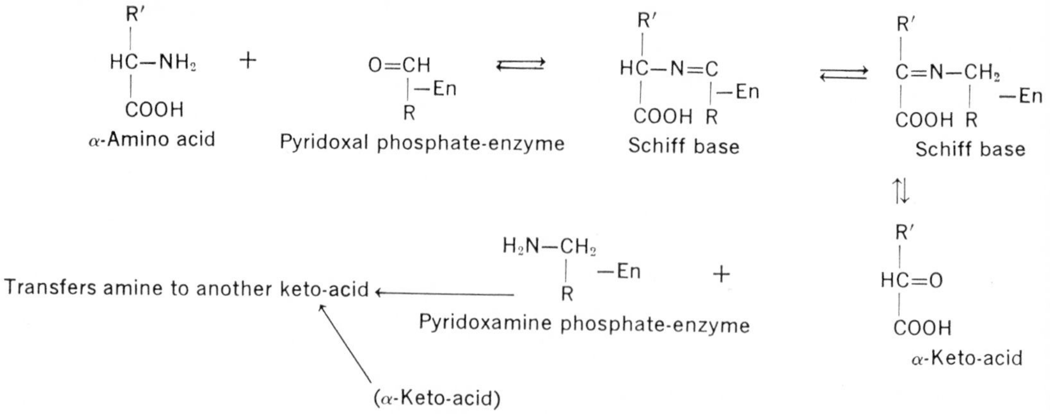

R′   R′   R′

HC—NH_2 +   O=CH   ⇌   HC—N=C   ⇌ C=N—CH_2

                               |—En |—En |—En

COOH   R   COOH R   COOH R

α-Amino acid   Pyridoxal phosphate-enzyme   Schiff base   Schiff base

⇅

R′

$\text{H}_2\text{N—CH}_2$

Transfers amine to another keto-acid ← |—En   +   HC=O

                                           R

                          Pyridoxamine phosphate-enzyme   COOH

                                                            α-Keto-acid

(α-Keto-acid)

Fig. 20-1. Mechanism of transamination. The conversion of an amino acid to its keto analog occurs through the formation of a Schiff base with a pyridoxal phosphate-enzyme complex.

In this reaction, the keto-acid picks up the amino group, forming a new amino acid; the keto-analog of the initial amino acid is formed also. The reaction has been found to have a specific requirement for a phosphorylated derivative of pyridoxine, vitamin B_6. The mechanism of action involves formation of a Schiff base between the amino acid, or keto-acid, and an enzyme-pyridoxal phosphate complex (Fig. 20-1).

The reaction occurs between paired α-keto-acids and an α-amino acid; that is, as the compound in the scheme is proceeding from the α-amino acid form to the α-keto form, another α-keto form, in parentheses, is proceeding to its α-amino form.

Since all cells can fix ammonia by forming glutamic acid from α-ketoglutaric acid, it would be expected that this amino acid is quite active in transamination in the nitrogen pool. This expectation is substantiated in the scheme given in Fig. 20-2, where some of the major transaminations are shown.

The glutamic-oxalacetic acid transamination sequence is very important for several reasons: Oxalacetic acid is an intermediate in the Krebs cycle and can thus be removed and transaminated to the amino acid, aspartic. Second, the aspartic acid is required for the urea cycle and is thus quite rapidly removed from the nitrogen pool. But because the aspartic acid is deaminated and dehydrogenated to fumaric acid in the urea cycle (p. 222), the oxalacetic acid is regenerated in order to make more aspartic acid.

The transaminase mechanism is a means of getting the amine group of glutamic acid on to other organic molecules, in this case the keto-analogs of the amino acids. This is the major limitation on the range of the mechanism— the keto-analog of the particular amino acid must be a normal component of the cell. Transamination can be the starting reaction for both synthetic and degradative sequences. As a tool for manipulation of nitrogen in the amino acid pool, this process is invaluable.

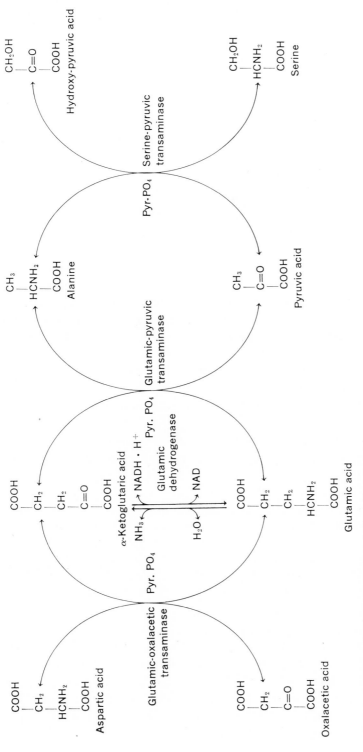

Fig. 20-2. Transamination conversions in the nitrogen pool.

Transmethylation and 1-carbon transfer

Often in the synthetic or degradative processes there is a need for a single carbon to be removed or added to the compound, and decarboxylation mechanisms are many times not acceptable for a number of reasons. The cell has at its disposal two other means by which a 1-carbon fragment can be transferred—transmethylation and the 1-carbon pool.

Methionine, with its terminal methyl group removed from the sulfur with relative ease, is one of several compounds involved in the transmethylation sequence. Perhaps it is a little too specific to go into this pathway, but the conversion of methionine to other constituents of the cell demonstrates so well the importance of interconversion that it merits outlining the steps involved.

Reaction 1. Methionine is at once complexed with the adenosine portion of ATP, with pyrophosphate and P_i being released. This cleavage of ATP into adenosine, pyrophosphate, and inorganic phosphate is a unique reaction. The normal hydrolysis of ATP yields AMP or ADP but not adenosine.

$$H_3CSCH_2CH_2CHNH_2COOH + ATP \rightarrow H_3CSCH_2CH_2CHNH_2COOH + PP_i + P_i$$

|
Adenosine
Methionine   S-Adenosyl methionine

The sulfur is attached to the 5′ carbon of the pentose sugar of adenosine.

Reaction 2. The methyl group is given off and is donated to guanidoacetate to form creatine or a precursor of choline to form the trimethylated choline.

Choline
or
creatine
↗
$$H_3CSCH_2CH_2CHNH_2COOH \rightleftarrows SCH_2CH_2CHNH_2COOH + CH_3$$
| |
Adenosine   Adenosine
S-Adenosyl methionine   S-Adenosyl homocysteine

Reaction 3. The adenosine is split off and feeds back into the adenylic acid system.

$$S—CH_2CH_2CHNH_2COOH \rightleftarrows Adenosine + HSCH_2CH_2CHNH_2COOH$$
|
Adenosine
S-Adenosyl homocysteine   Homocysteine

Reaction 4. Finally, in a reaction analogous to transamination, a Schiff base between serine and homocysteine is formed, with pyridoxal phosphate mediating the reaction. The point of attachment is the sulfur of the homocysteine and the amine group of the serine. The intermediate is believed to be cystathionine (see top of opposite page).

Other compounds of the pathways can participate in a methylation reaction. Choline ($OHCH_2CH_2N(CH_3)_3^+$) or betaine ($HOOCCH_2N(CH_3)_3^+$) have available methyl groups which can be donated to various compounds.

In addition to the transmethylation sequence, a folic acid derivative, tetrahydrofolic acid, can reversibly add a single carbon as $-CH_2OH$ to the nitrogen in position 10 to form the N^{10}-hydroxymethyltetrahydrofolic acid. The ability

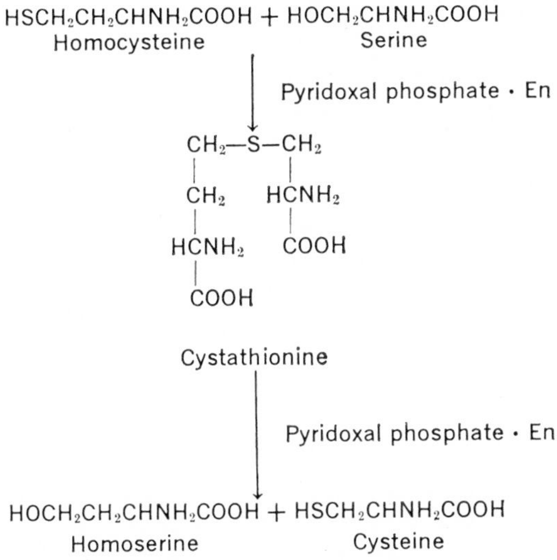

$$HSCH_2CH_2CHNH_2COOH + HOCH_2CHNH_2COOH$$

Homocysteine　　　　　　　　Serine

Pyridoxal phosphate · En

$$CH_2-S-CH_2$$
$$CH_2 \quad HCNH_2$$
$$HCNH_2 \quad COOH$$
$$COOH$$

Cystathionine

Pyridoxal phosphate · En

$$HOCH_2CH_2CHNH_2COOH + HSCH_2CHNH_2COOH$$

Homoserine　　　　　　　　Cysteine

of this folic acid derivative and others to yield or take up a single carbon is exploited as the 1-carbon pool. Single carbons as a formyl group or as the hydroxymethyl can be transported from one biosynthetic pathway to another.

Transulfuration

The mechanism of transulfuration quite often parallels that of transmethylation, particularly since methionine may be involved in both pathways. Sulfur is similar to nitrogen as far as nutrition to the cell is concerned. Very few cells can use sulfur in its molecular form. As a result, the cell depends on external sulfates and related forms to get sulfur to the inside medium. The possible limited supply necessitates a "hoarding" device such as transulfuration in order to limit the loss of this element. The importance of sulfur to the three-dimensional structure of proteins has already been discussed.

Decarboxylation

In amino acid degradative pathways, decarboxylation frequently is one of the processes which occurs. Although many of these decarboxylations occur in

Table 20-1. Decarboxylation products of some amino acids

Amino acid	Decarboxylation product
Arginine	Agmatine
Aspartic acid	α-Alanine or β-alanine
Glutamic acid	γ-Amino butyric acid
Histidine	Histamine
Lysine	Cadaverine
Ornithine	Putrescine
Phenylalanine	Phenylethylamine
Serine	Ethanolamine
Tryptophan	Tryptamine
Tyrosine	Tyramine

bacteria and other microorganisms, there are many which occur in higher forms as well. The one trait shared by all of them is that the decarboxylation product is usually toxic and has definite physiological effects on the cell. Thus, decarboxylation pathways must be coupled with sequences which can remove these harmful products.

The actual mechanism of decarboxylation often involves pyridoxal phosphate, which immediately suggests formation of the Schiff base. There are some decarboxylations, however, which do not seem to follow this pattern.

A list of some of the more common decarboxylations and their products is seen in Table 20-1.

Deamination

Much of the ammonia which is liberated in the cell comes from deamination of the amino acids. Although many times the end product of this α-amine removal is the keto-analog of the amino acid, there are four distinct pathways by which deamination may occur. The results of aspartic acid deamination (Fig. 20-3) serve as examples of these pathways.

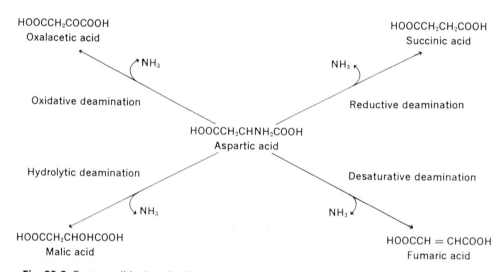

Fig. 20-3. Four possible deamination products of aspartic acid.

Oxidative deamination is perhaps the most common pathway of amine removal. All of the amino acid oxidases (deaminases) studied so far are flavoproteins which react in a two-step manner to complete the reaction.

(1) $RCHNH_2COOH + H_2O + FAD \cdot En \rightleftharpoons RCOCOOH + FADH_2 \cdot En + NH_3$

(2) $FADH_2 \cdot En + O_2 \rightarrow FAD + H_2O_2$

A third step, however, must occur to prevent toxic buildup of the peroxide:

(3) $H_2O_2 \xrightarrow[\text{Peroxidase}]{\text{Catalase or}} H_2O + \frac{1}{2} O_2$

The reverse of the ammonia fixation reaction catalyzed by glutamic acid dehydrogenase is, in fact, an oxidative deamination.

$$\text{Glutamic acid} + \text{NAD} + H_2O \rightleftarrows \alpha\text{-Ketoglutaric acid} + \text{NADH} \cdot H^+ + NH_3$$

This reaction has the added advantage in that the $\text{NADH} \cdot H^+$ can be shunted to the electron transport system where high-energy compounds in the form of ATP may be generated.

CARBAMYL PHOSPHATE

The production of ammonia by deamination of amino acids or the degradation of ring structures containing nitrogen may exceed the reutilization of this compound. A scheme must be present to secure this ammonia to an organic compound which can enter both synthetic and excretory pathways. Such a compound is carbamyl phosphate.

The synthesis of this substance (p. 214) is unique in several respects. First, there are two alternate pathways for producing it; one is reversible and requires 1 ATP, and the other is irreversible and requires 2 ATP. Second, the formation of carbamyl phosphate removes two by-products of degradation processes in that both carbon dioxide and ammonia are utilized in its formation.

Involvement in the urea cycle

One method of ridding the cell of nitrogenous wastes is to form urea through the steps of the sequence called the urea, or Krebs-Henseleit, cycle. The urea cycle, *in toto*, exists only in the cells of ureotelic organisms, but the individual steps appear throughout both kingdoms.

The starting point of the urea cycle is carbamyl phosphate, which, as it was previously pointed out, is formed from the two by-products of metabolism, CO_2 and NH_3. All of the other components of the cycle are α-amino acids, but their presence in the cell is fairly much restricted to participation in this cycle. As will become evident, the critical enzyme is arginase, since it catalyzes the final step which forms the urea.

The scheme for the urea cycle is seen in Fig. 20-4, and only some of the highlights and interrelationships will be pointed out here.

When ornithine, which can be formed from glutamic acid, combines with the carbamyl phosphate to form the citrulline, the terminal end of the latter acid has the urea fragment, $-NHCONH_2$. This cannot be split off at this point, however, because there would be no way to recycle the remaining fragment. The balance of the cycle is concerned with various additions and subtractions to return to the ornithine to allow for the recycling of the end product.

The addition of aspartic acid to the citrulline and the subsequent removal of fumaric acid is in essence a desaturative deamination. The fumaric acid can, of course, enter into the Krebs cycle, offering another pathway for getting an amino acid into the mainstream of the metabolic paths.

The final step in the cycle, the splitting off of urea from arginine, is the only

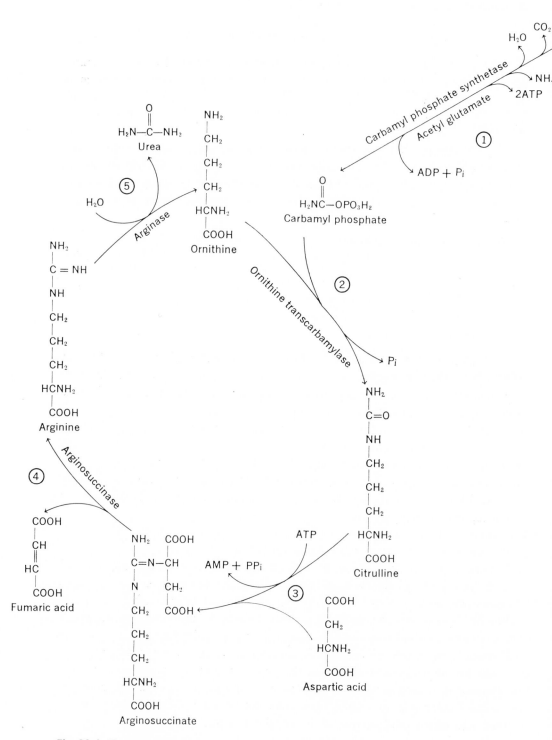

Fig. 20-4. The urea cycle.

step in the cycle which is exergonic in both the chemical and enzymatic synthesis of the urea.

The effect of enzymes on the overall standard free energy change is very evident in comparing the $\Delta F°$ of chemical synthesis of urea and the $\Delta F°$ of the enzymatic synthesis. Cohen and Brown[1] have calculated the $\Delta F°$ of the chemical synthesis to be approximately $+10,000$ calories; for the enzymatic synthesis, the $\Delta F°$ is approximately $-13,200$ calories. This difference of 23,000 calories is due to the fact that the high-energy bonds of ATP are utilized in the enzymatic scheme.

It is perhaps anthropocentric to include the urea cycle in a discussion of the general metabolism of the nitrogen-containing compounds. But of all of the sequences of amino acid involvement, this particular one demonstrates both the manipulations of the acids and the close relationship they have to the Krebs cycle.

Involvement in synthetic pathways

The urea cycle is not the only pathway in which carbamyl phosphate participates. It has already been mentioned that microorganisms, which do not have a urea cycle, can produce carbamyl phosphate. All of the roles of this compound have not been elucidated. Its involvement in synthesis of pyrimidines seems to be a certainty, but other pathways and uses have not been completely worked out.

AMINO ACID BIOSYNTHESIS

It would be overstepping the bounds of this text to go into any great detail on the biosynthesis of some twenty or thirty amino acids. Some basic rules can be set down, however, which will outline certain aspects of these pathways.

Biosynthesis of the amino acids ultimately depends on a nitrogen source. Once this source has been established, the cell must be able to fully exploit these compounds and to manipulate them in such a way as to get them into forms which can enter the specific synthetic pathways. Often this means continued involvement of the intermediates of the established cycles such as the Krebs and the Embden-Meyerhof. As in all other synthetic pathways of the cell, production of the amino acids requires a large input of energy from the various high-energy compounds of the cell. This almost guarantees irreversibility; that is, ATP input and subsequent hydrolysis to ADP and P_i essentially renders the reaction irreversible.

Finally, cells vary in the demands placed on them for biosynthesis. Exacting cells have very specific requirements for substances in the surrounding medium. As a result, their synthetic capacity is lowered since the cell does depend on the transport of preformed substances from the outside. Nonexacting cells, on the other hand, have few medium requirements. It follows that these cells must have an extremely high biosynthetic capacity.

The biosynthetic pathways of many of the aliphatic amino acids have been inferred from a discussion of some of the basic mechanisms of these acids. Many of the aliphatic amino acids, particularly the branched ones, have very specific pathways involving a peculiar set of intermediates.

The synthesis of aromatic acids involves many elaborate steps to build up the ring structure from the simpler aliphatic compounds. The unusual and unique intermediates (for example, shikimic acid) are just biochemical curiosities to one just passing through a discussion of the amino acids.

AMINO ACID DEGRADATION

There are two primary reasons for amino acid degradation in the living cell. One is the consequence of the normal, dynamic turnover which exists in all biological material—the balanced anabolic and catabolic pathways. The second is that degradation which is necessitated when the cell must call upon the proteins and, thus, the amino acids, for an energy source. Because of the latter, the end products of degradation should be some intermediate which can feed directly into the common metabolic pathways in order to obtain maximum energy yield. The breakdown products of many of the amino acids are summarized in Table 20-2. Some representative pathways are shown in Figs. 20-5 and 20-6.

PURINES AND PYRIMIDINES

The second major grouping of nitrogen-containing compounds which will be considered are the purines and pyrimidines. The fact that they are the bases of DNA and RNA generates interest in their formation and degradation. Again, it is beyond the scope of the book to deal in great detail with the individual pathways.

Table 20-2. Degradation products of some amino acids*

Amino acid		Products
Alanine	G	Pyruvic acid
Arginine	G	Glutamic acid $\rightleftarrows$ α-ketoglutaric acid
Aspartic acid	G	Oxalacetic acid; alanine
Cysteine	G	Pyruvic acid
Glutamic acid	G	α-Ketoglutaric acid
Glycine	G	Pyruvic acid
Histidine	G	Glutamic acid $\rightleftarrows$ α-ketoglutaric acid
Isoleucine	K;G	Acetyl-CoA; propionyl-CoA
Leucine	K;G	Acetoacetic acid; acetyl-CoA
Lysine	G	Glutamic acid; acetoacetyl-CoA
Phenylalanine	K;G	Acetoacetic acid; fumaric acid
Proline	G	Glutamic acid $\rightleftarrows$ α-ketoglutaric acid
Serine	G	Pyruvic acid
Threonine	G	Pyruvic acid
Tryptophan	G	Glutamic acid
Tyrosine	K;G	Acetoacetic acid; fumaric acid
Valine	G	Succinyl-CoA

*List restricted to those that form products which enter into the major pathways.
G, glycogenic; K, ketogenic.

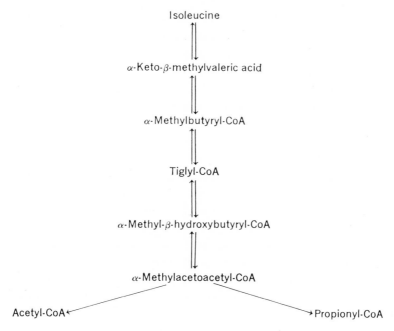

Fig. 20-5. Metabolic pathway of isoleucine.

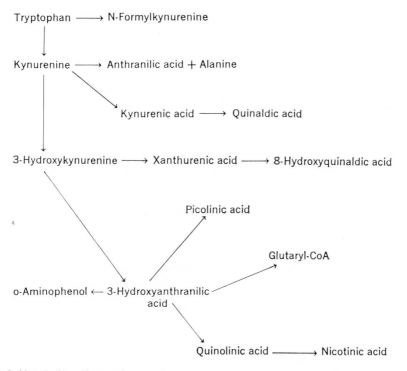

Fig. 20-6. Metabolic pathway of tryptophan.

Biosynthesis

Pyrimidine synthesis starts with carbamyl phosphate, to which is combined a mole of aspartic acid. The resulting complex is closed into the typical six-membered ring, this first ring structure being dihydroorotic acid which is subsequently converted to orotic acid. It is interesting to note that the phosphory-lated pentose is often added into the sequence before the orotic moiety is converted into one of the common pyrimidine nucleotides; that is, the pyrimidine is not formed first and then the pentose phosphate added.

The nine-membered purine ring derives its various atoms from glycine, the formyl group, aspartic acid, carbon dioxide, and glutamine. The individual steps are quite complex because of the closure of the two rings. Again, the pentose phosphate is added before the main structure becomes a purine nucleotide.

The preciseness of the pathways of both the purines and pyrimidines is critical in that they provide the coding mechanism for the genetic material. This means that the biosynthetic sequences of these compounds are extremely important and, as a result, are sensitive to antimetabolite activity. The production of abnormal purines or pyrimidines will often lead to permanent damage to the cell.

Degradation

The pyrimidine catabolic pathways generally lead to either β-alanine or β-amino isobutyric acid by opening of the ring and splitting off of carbon dioxide or ammonia, respectively. These two acids can be modified so that they can enter directly into the common metabolic pathways.

Purine catabolism, however, may not lead to such simple intermediates. In some instances, the cell will degrade the purine nucleus only as far as uric acid, which is then removed. In other circumstances, the rings are opened to allow further degradation (Fig. 20-7).

SUMMARY

The nitrogen-containing compounds include among their numbers some of the most important components of the cell. The amino acids, the purines, and the pyrimidines are all so critical to the survival and dynamics of the living cell that some consideration of their metabolic pathways should be made.

An immediate problem of most cells is the availability of nitrogen or a nitrogen derivative in an organic molecule which can then be used in the metabolic web. All cells have some capabilities of fixing ammonia into glutamic acid, glutamine, carbamyl phosphate, or several other compounds, and this serves as the major nitrogen source for many of these cells.

The amino acids undergo a series of basic reactions which are used in the various interconversions and manipulations necessary to maintain the correct levels of the different acids in the nitrogen pool. These reactions are as follows:

1. Transamination, where an exchange of an amine group is made between an amino acid and a keto-analog of an amino acid
2. Transmethylation and 1-carbon transfer, where a 1-carbon fragment is added to or subtracted from an amino acid being metabolized

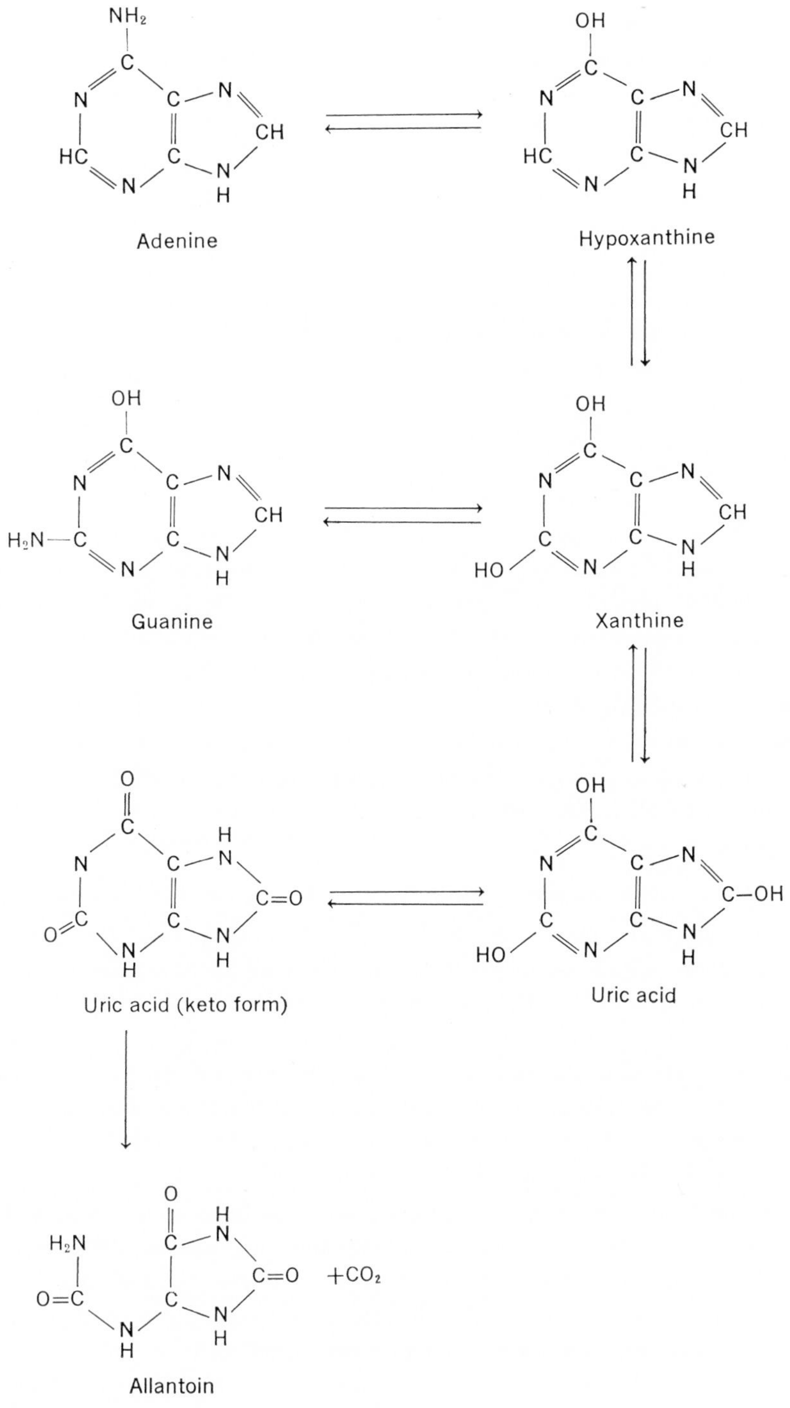

Fig. 20-7. Degradative pathway of the purines.

3. Transulfuration, in which sulfur is retained in the system by transferring it from one amino acid to another
4. Decarboxylation, which is usually involved in degradation
5. Deamination, which is removal of the amino group and which can be carried out in several different manners

All of these processes add to the flexibility of the amino acid pathways.

Carbamyl phosphate, which is formed from the by-products of metabolism —carbon dioxide and ammonia—has two metabolic roles. It is the input molecule of the urea, or Krebs-Henseleit, cycle. This molecule also is a precursor in some biosynthetic pathways such as the formation of pyrimidines.

The amino acid biosynthesis and degradation pathways are specific for each acid, but generally have their starting point (biosynthesis) or end product (degradation) in the intermediates of the common pathways.

Purine and pyrimidine pathways are relatively complex because of the ring structures involved. As in the other sequences, however, these compounds, and the other ring compounds, have their precursors as intermediates of the Krebs and Embden-Meyerhof cycles.

All in all, the nitrogen-containing compounds offer a variety of pathways and reactions which, on the surface at least, are more complex and interwoven than the specific sequences encountered in carbohydrates and lipids.

Literature cited

1. Cohen, P. G., and G. W. Brown, Jr. 1960. Ammonia metabolism and urea biosynthesis, vol. 6, p. 161. In Florkin, M., and H. S. Mason (editors): Comparative biochemistry. Academic Press, Inc., New York.

General references

Adams, E. 1962. Amino acid and metabolism. Ann. Rev. Biochem. 31:173.

Cohen, P. P., and M. Marshall. 1962. Carbamyl group transfer, vol. 6, p. 327. In Boyer, P. D., H. Lardy, and K. Myrbäck (editors): The enzymes. Academic Press, Inc., New York.

Dalgliesh, C. E. 1955. Metabolism of the aromatic amino acids. Advances Protein Chem. 10:31.

Gale, E. F. 1959. Synthesis and organisation in the bacterial cell. John Wiley & Sons, Inc., New York.

Greenberg, D. M. 1964. Amino acid metabolism. Ann. Rev. Biochem. 33:633.

Greenstein, J. P., and M. Winitz. 1961. Chemistry of the amino acids. John Wiley & Sons, Inc., New York. Vol. 1 and 3.

Karlson, P. 1963. Introduction to modern biochemistry. Academic Press, Inc., New York.

Kleiner, I. S., and J. M. Orten. 1962. Biochemistry. 6th ed. The C. V. Mosby Co., St. Louis.

Kosower, E. M. 1962. Molecular biochemistry. McGraw-Hill Book Co., New York.

McElroy, W. D., and B. Glass (editors). 1955. Amino acid metabolism. Johns Hopkins University Press, Baltimore.

Meister, A. 1962. Amino group transfer (survey), vol. 6, p. 193. In Boyer, P. D., H. Lardy, and K. Myrbäck (editors): The enzymes. Academic Press, Inc., New York.

Ratner, S. 1954. Synthesis and metabolism of arginine and citrulline. Advances Enzymol. 15:319.

Reichard, P. 1959. The enzymic synthesis of pyrimidines. Advances Enzymol. 21:263.

Sakami, W., and H. Harrington. 1963. Amino acid metabolism. Ann. Rev. Biochem. 32:355.

White, A., P. Handler, and E. L. Smith. 1964. Principles of biochemistry. 3rd ed. McGraw-Hill Book Co., New York.

21

Electron transport chains and oxidative phosphorylation

T **INTRODUCTION**

he pathways of intermediary metabolism are relatively well defined, and their value to the cell has been set forth. The Embden-Meyerhof cycle is a pathway which takes degraded starch and converts it to a 6-carbon sugar which is then further degraded to a triose. And in this process some ATP's are formed by direct phosphorylation of a member of the adenylic acid system. This pathway operates in anaerobic conditions and is therefore capable of high-energy bond production without the presence of oxygen.

The Krebs cycle is an aerobic pathway in which a 2-carbon fragment, carried on coenzyme A, is introduced into this cyclic mill and is oxidized, with the concomitant release of 4 molecules of reduced coenzymes—2 $NADH \cdot H^+$, 1 $NADPH \cdot H^+$, and 1 flavoprotein as $FADH_2$—and 1 mole of ATP which is produced by direct phosphorylation.

Lipid catabolism yields 1 mole of reduced $FADH_2$, 1 mole of $NADH \cdot H^+$, and 1 mole of acetyl-CoA per 2-carbon fragment split off from the fatty acids. No ATP is directly produced in this pathway.

With few exceptions, the various nitrogen-containing pathways do not produce ATP directly in their cycles.

It has been inferred that the *raison d'être* of the common pathways and the stepwise degradation of the carbohydrates, lipids, and proteins was to provide energy in the form of high-energy bonds to the cell. And yet, at this point, there are apparently no end products except a collection of reduced coenzymes. One would expect, *a priori*, that somehow energy can be produced in some manner, either from the coenzymes directly or from some phase of their metabolism.

Direct breakdown of the coenzymes does not seem a feasible way to get utilizable energy. The coenzymes, first off, are relatively scarce, particularly those with the pyrimidine ring since they can shuttle back and forth among the pathways. Second, and of prime importance, if the coenzymes are degraded, they must again be re-formed. Even efficiently coupled reactions for the synthesis could not afford much excess energy for the production of high-energy bonds, if, in fact, any at all.

The alternate, that of gleaning energy from further metabolism of the coenzymes, seems quite a real possibility. Shunting of the hydrogens and electrons through various electron transport chains has been shown to be coupled with the production of the high-energy ATP. The patterns in the respiratory chains from organisms of all levels show a consistency which infers a common mode of action in those chains; perhaps, the sequence in the chain is also a common denominator in aerobic systems.

It is one thing to say that hydrogen and electrons moving across a respiratory chain are coupled with the production of ATP. It is another, however, to explain what the mechanism is. How the stepwise electron transport, which has as one of its driving forces the difference in oxidation-reduction potential, can be coupled to the creation of high-energy phosphates is one of many pressing questions facing cell physiologists and biochemists.

It is tempting to consider this entire subject under the topic of biological oxidation since the process does, in fact, entail oxidation-reduction reactions. But, after the various metabolic pathways and the by-products of these cycles are discussed, the overall integration of metabolism and electron transport can be better appreciated.

At the risk of some redundancy, the discussion will be developed along four distinct lines. First, the components of the electron chain will be reviewed, and, in addition, the order that has been established or postulated will be presented. Second, oxidative phosphorylation will be defined and discussed. These two topics will be meshed together by presenting the energetics involved in the chain and the more accepted mechanisms of ATP production. Finally, alternate mechanisms will be reviewed as well as other respiratory chains pointed out.

COMPONENTS AND COMPOSITION OF THE ELECTRON TRANSPORT SYSTEM

The final common pathway of the respiratory chain, or electron transport system, is a multienzyme system which has as its prime function the transference of hydrogens and electrons to oxygen. The major components have been established as being the pyridine nucleotides, the flavoproteins, and the assorted cytochromes. Another possible contributor in the chain may be coenzyme Q, or ubiquinone. It is evident from experimental data that some of this chain, located in the mitochondrion, is particulate and thus membrane-bound. Other members, again the NAD and NADP, are probably not a permanent part of the particulate material, but on the other hand there may be some NAD which is bound and not free to move in and out of the membrane.

Since the final members of the electron chain are the cytochromes, the electron transport chain is often referred to as the cytochrome chain. The ability of the cytochromes to transfer the hydrogen to the oxygen necessitates their being at the end of the chain. On an *a priori* basis, however, that is essentially all that can be postulated about the order in the chain. The remainder of the data must come from experimental evidence.

Identification of the individual components

Electron carriers are very difficult to assay for, and their structure is even more difficult to determine. The subtle similarities among the flavin group and among the cytochromes add to the difficulty of determining not only which components are present but also in what order they occur.

Pyrimidine nucleotides

The by-products of many enzymatic steps in the metabolic pathways are the reduced NADH·H$^+$ and NADPH·H$^+$. As starting points in the respiratory chain, these reduced coenzymes must feed off their hydrogens to some other member of the chain in order to return in the oxidized state to participate in the oxidative steps of the cycles. NADPH·H$^+$ probably does not give up its hydrogen directly to the other components of the chain. Evidence suggests that the NADPH·H$^+$ is oxidized by NAD, the latter feeding the hydrogen into the electron transport system.

$$NADPH \cdot H^+ + NAD \rightleftharpoons NADP + NADH \cdot H^+$$
$$\downarrow$$
$$ETS$$

The pyrimidine nucleotide, NADH·H$^+$, can be considered to be one of the major links between the pathways and the other components of the electron transport chain.

Flavoproteins

Early work suggested that flavoproteins form a bridge between the pyridine nucleotides and the cytochromes, but the more work performed in this area, the more the confusion grew. At one time, King,[1] in a search of the literature, found sixteen flavoproteins which were considered to be the link between the NADH·H$^+$ and the cytochromes.

Part of the problem arose from the fact that flavoproteins are direct acceptors of the hydrogens generated from the oxidative steps in the pathways. Succinic dehydrogenase, for example, is a flavoprotein which removes the hydrogen from succinic acid to form fumaric acid. Yet another factor is the easily triggered conversion of FAD → FMN, which can lead to apparently different compounds that may in reality be the same substance.

The enzyme NADH·H$^+$-dehydrogenase, a flavoprotein, is the catalyst for the transfer of hydrogen and electrons to the cytochromes, and it is this enzyme with which several compounds seemed to be synonymous. However, Singer and associates[2] report a compound which has most of the characteristics claimed for NADH·H$^+$ dehydrogenase. Nevertheless, there is a flavoprotein which is a firm component of the electron chain which functions to oxidize NADH·H$^+$.

Coenzyme Q (ubiquinone)

More and more evidence is accumulating which places coenzyme Q in the electron transport system. Both its ubiquitousness and structure hinted at its use as an electron or hydrogen carrier, but more sophisticated experiments (for example, its being reduced by NADH·H[+] and oxidized by the cytochrome oxidase system) were needed to indicate that coenzyme Q may be a firm component of this final common pathway of the respiratory chain.

Coenzyme Q is not the only quinone which apparently participates in the electron transport system. Other quinones, such as a naphthoquinone and vitamin K_9H,[3] may have the ability to transport hydrogens and electrons.

The cytochromes

The presence of cytochromes is a criterion that infers electron transport, and their occurrence usually connotes a specific respiratory chain. The presence of cytochromes also implies that there is the possibility of coupling the transport with ATP production. Although this criterion is not always valid (that is, their presence indicates the occurrence of an electron transport system as it is usually known), when electron transport does occur with the oxygen as the final receptor and ATP produced, the cytochromes are an integral part of the pathway.

The cytochromes transport only electrons, with the free protons released into the medium. Cytochrome oxidase, the terminal member of the chain, transfers its electrons (and thereby the hydrogen proton) to oxygen. This oxidase, composed of cytochromes a and a_3, is first reduced by other cytochromes in the system. Cytochromes b, c_1, and c are some of those which precede a and a_3 in the chain.

Reconstruction of the order

The electron transport chain is no misnomer. It has been established that the individual members of the system are assembled together as components of the inner membrane folds of the mitochondria (Plate 15, A, p. 317). Furthermore, these respiratory assemblies have been shown to have the components appearing in distinct ratios to one another, which hints that they may act as a macromolecule of definite composition.

Reconstruction of the order of the individual members of this chain is no mean task. Purification of the components often leads to faulty assumptions because purified extracts may not act the same as the component when it occurs in the cell in a three-dimensional structure. The fact that the respiratory assembly can accept hydrogens and electrons from five different NAD-linked dehydrogenase enzymes (pyruvic, isocitric, α-ketoglutaric, malic, and β-hydroxyacyl-CoA) and from two flavoproteins (succinic and acyl-CoA dehydrogenases) does not clarify the situation. By pooling of experimental data and observations, a sequence has been suggested. Most of the data came from the inhibitor and spectrographic techniques, while confirmatory data were derived from potential differences among the components.

Inhibitor and spectrographic data

If an aerobic cell is maintained for some time in anaerobic conditions, the individual components of the electron transport chain become reduced because of inability to transfer the hydrogens and electrons to a final carrier. Coupling this fact with the spectographic data which indicate a different absorption peak in the reduced and oxidized cytochrome, Chance and Williams essentially worked out the order of the cytochromes in the chain. Exposing these afore-mentioned cells to oxygen, which caused the respiratory assemblies again to function, they discovered that cytochromes a were oxidized first, and were immediately followed by c and b. This suggested the following sequence: $b \rightarrow c \rightarrow a \rightarrow a_3 \rightarrow O_2$.

Utilizing the fact that different inhibitors of electron transport work at different points in the chain, other workers began to add data to help elucidate the sequence. Antimycin A, for example, was found to allow c, a, and a_3 to become oxidized, whereas all other components were in the reduced form. This indicated that probably intermediates were not interspersed among these three cytochromes. Amytal, on the other hand, allowed all members but $NADH \cdot H^+$ to reach their oxidative states. With the assumption that there is no additional carrier between cytochromes c and b, a tentative sequence was suggested:

$$MH_2 \longrightarrow NAD \longrightarrow FAD\text{-protein}$$
$$\downarrow$$
$$Cytochromes\ b \longrightarrow c \longrightarrow a \longrightarrow a_3 \longrightarrow O_2$$

Oxidation-reduction potentials

Oxidation-reduction data can be useful in helping to establish the pathway of electrons. The data often have to be qualified because of several factors. The isolation techniques used on the various components of the chain will affect the recorded potential of its oxidized/reduced pair. In the discussion on coupled reactions, it was seen that reactions with a small positive ΔF could still proceed. Thus, the order of the oxidation-reduction potential may not necessarily be the order of sequence of the components. The data, however, are valuable for comparison with evidence from other areas. The oxidation-reduction potentials of some systems normally found in the mitochondria were seen in Table 16-1 in Chapter 16.

Carrier complexes

Many reconstructions of biological processes suffer from early inaccuracies, for the prime reason that isolated compounds do not act the same as in vivo compounds. The electron transport system in the mitochondria is an excellent example.

In spite of tedious and painstaking searches for more components of the chain, few possibilities have arisen. And yet, there are certain reactions that are not accounted for, or appear aberrant, when only the known components are considered. This has suggested the possibility that some of the carriers must occur together as a macromolecular complex in order to function as they do in the cell. This postulate, coupled with the electron photomicrographic evidence of distinct electron transport particles (ETP), has spurred some investigators to pursue the complex idea further. To date, four major complexes have been suggested:

1. NADH·H$^+$-coenzyme Q reductase—contains NADH·H$^+$ dehydrogenase and coenzyme Q
2. Succinate-coenzyme Q reductase—contains the flavoprotein succinic dehydrogenase and coenzyme Q
3. Coenzyme Q-cytochrome c reductase—contains cytochromes b and c and coenzyme Q
4. The cytochrome oxidase system

The occurrence of these complexes, as suggested by Green's laboratory at the University of Wisconsin, immediately infers that not all the reduced coenzymes from the metabolic pathways enter at the same point; coenzyme Q may be a relay station for electrons fed into the system. As shown in Fig. 21-1, the available evidence is summed up in a scheme which is compatible with most of the data.

In retrospect

There are many areas of doubt, disagreement, and dearth of knowledge about the composition and physical arrangement of the electron transport system. Several facts seem to stand out at this point:

1. Whatever the arrangement turns out to be, there is a strong possibility that it will be fairly universal, with only minor modifications occurring among the phyla.
2. The recurrent plague of biological reconstruction, that isolated products act differently from combined compounds, has forced reconsideration of these components in a form more closely related to their natural complexes.
3. The physical makeup of the electron transport particles (assuming they occur as such) gives little hint of the mechanism of the transport itself, let alone of the mechanism of coupling this transport with high-energy bond production—that is, oxidative phosphorylation.

OXIDATIVE PHOSPHORYLATION

The production of high-energy phosphate bonds is an endothermic reaction which requires the input of up to 12,000 calories. When the energy to drive this phosphorylation comes from the oxidation-reduction energy of electron transport, the process is called oxidative phosphorylation.

As would be suspected from the discussion on the carrier complexes, oxidative phosphorylation requires at least some intact mitochondrial membrane in order to be carried out. Thus, the process is apparently a membrane phe-

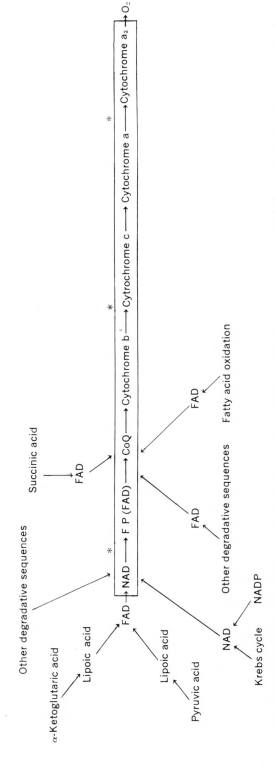

Fig. 21-1. Schematic representation of the respiratory chain, showing the feed-in of coenzymes from the pathways. Asterisks (*) indicate probable sites of oxidative phosphorylation.

nomenon, or at least requires the membrane in order to function properly.

Early investigators found that a relatively constant ratio of high-energy phosphates was produced for each two hydrogens and electrons that passed across the electron transport chain to oxygen, provided that the starting point was NADH·H⁺. The P/O ratio (phosphate to oxygen) approaches 3.0 in most systems studied. This means that there are 3 ATP produced at the expense of the oxidation-reduction energy generated when 1 mole of NADH·H⁺ is oxidized to NAD and the electrons and hydrogens are passed through the chain to oxygen. This also infers that there are probably three distinct sites for the production of these ATP.

The search for the three sites of oxidative phosphorylation has yielded some good possibilities. With the use of inhibitor information and the observed fact that the P/O ratio from cytochrome c to oxygen is 1.0 and from the flavo-protein succinic dehydrogenase to hydrogen is 2.0, the following sites have been proposed, as shown on Fig. 21-1.

The ATP reactions

After the ATP is produced in the mitochondria, it can undergo a series of reactions which are independent of oxidative phosphorylation and electron transport. These types of reactions are typical of a dynamic system.

1. *ATPase.* As the name suggests, this reaction is the reversible breakdown of the formed ATP. As in many phosphorylation reactions, a kinase and a phosphatase may be involved.
2. *ATP-P_i exchange.* Labeled inorganic phosphate has been found to occur in the terminal phosphate of ATP.
3. *H_2O-P_i and H_2O-ATP exchange of oxygen.* Oxygen can exchange between the water and the oxygen of the inorganic phosphate and the water and ATP.
4. *ATP-ADP exchange.* Labeled ADP can be spotted in ATP.

The importance of these reactions in oxidative phosphorylation is not known. Whether they occur at each of the phosphorylating sites and, if so, to what extent are still unresolved questions. Certainly, all of the steps for the production of ATP are in these four reactions. The enzymes which catalyze these reactions may, in fact, be the substance which couples the electron transport chain to the phosphorylation process.

Inhibitors of oxidative phosphorylation

The literature is being filled with the effect of various inhibitors on oxidative phosphorylation. These compounds fall into three general classes:

1. Those which inhibit electron transport and as a result prevent production of ATP
2. Those which uncouple the phosphorylating process from electron transport: that is, compounds that allow electron transport to continue, but production of ATP is stopped
3. Those which inhibit the electron transport which is involved with

oxidative phosphorylation but not that transport which is independent of this process

Examples of Class 1 are cyanide, Amytal, and Antimycin A. Of the compounds in Class 2, dinitrophenol is the most widely known. However, Dicumarol and certain antibiotics also act in this capacity. Finally, oligomycin is a representative example of a Class 3 inhibitor.

The exact mode or specific site of action of these inhibitors is not known, but they have become excellent tools for the study of both electron transport and oxidative phosphorylation.

ENERGETICS OF ELECTRON TRANSPORT

From the data given in Table 16-1, the free energy change from the various points can be calculated. The oxidation-reduction potential between the $NAD/NADH \cdot H^+$ system and the oxygen system is

$$\Delta F = - nF\Delta E$$
$$= - 2 \cdot 23000 \, (0.82 - (-0.32))$$
$$\approx - 52,000 \text{ calories}$$

This is more than adequate to produce 3 ATP with a ΔF of -8000 calories. With an efficiency of over 50%, the energetics are not out of line with other processes.

The energetics data support the three sites which are postulated. The free energy change for each site is as follows:

$$\text{I} \quad \Delta F = -2 \cdot 23000 \, (0.04 - (-.32))$$
$$\approx -16,600 \text{ calories}$$

$$\text{II} \quad \Delta F = -2 \cdot 23000 \, (0.26 - 0.04)$$
$$\approx -10,000 \text{ calories}$$

$$\text{III} \quad \Delta F = -2 \cdot 23000 \, (0.82 - 0.29)$$
$$\approx -24,000 \text{ calories}$$

From thermodynamic data, the three sites which are postulated seem to be the only ones where the free energy difference would be large enough to drive the endergonic reaction of $ADP \rightarrow ATP$ which has a ΔF of at least 8000 calories.

MECHANISMS OF OXIDATIVE PHOSPHORYLATION

In postulating a chemical mechanism for the generation of a high-energy compound, one almost has to include a coupled reaction in which there is a common intermediate. From a thermodynamic standpoint, this seems the most feasible method for an exothermic reaction to drive the endothermic one, although there are other means by which energy could be generated to drive endergonic reactions.

Energy-rich intermediate

Most of the mechanisms which have been proposed suggest the existence of some compound, X, which will complex with the component of the respiratory chain and/or P_i to form a high-energy intermediate. Thus the sequence of reactions might go as follows, where A and B are electron carriers in the chain and X the complexing compound:

$$
\begin{array}{ll}
AH_2 + X \rightarrow & AH_2 - X \\
AH_2 - X + B \rightarrow & A \sim X + BH_2 \text{ (electron transfer)} \\
A \sim X + P_i \rightarrow & A + X \sim P \quad (H_2O-PO_4 \text{ exchange)} \\
X \sim P + ADP \rightarrow ATP + X & \quad (ATP-P_i \text{ exchange)}
\end{array}
$$

overall $AH_2 + B + P_i + ADP \rightarrow A + BH_2 + ATP$

This type of scheme is quite attractive, but no high-energy intermediates have been isolated from the mitochondrial systems. One would expect that some evidence of $X \sim P$ or $A \sim X$ should appear. This does not preclude the possibility of a scheme such as this being representative of what does occur at these sites. However, before these postulates are fully accepted, more conclusive evidence is needed.

Chemiosmotic coupling and the electron pump

Some of the energy generated from the electron transport system goes to drive other reactions in the mitochondrion in addition to ATP production. Contraction and ion movement are the two prime processes which require energy from oxidation. The ion movement is capable of generating energy as well, and there are some workers who believe that a vectorial separation of charges across the membrane may create enough charge difference to generate enough energy to drive the ADP → ATP reaction.

Mitchell [4,5] suggested that other schemes to explain oxidative phosphorylation did not take into account the effects of the three-dimensional structure on the phosphorylating mechanism. He proposed that a vectorial system may exist in the mitochondrial membrane which is so directed that the hydrogen and hydroxyl ions are separated in the membrane, causing an electrochemical gradient across the membrane. This, then, would be coupled with the phosphorylation of ADP to form the necessary $\sim P$.

A recent work of Urry and Eyring [6] proposes a more definite scheme which still incorporates some of Mitchell's early ideas. Their model involves use of the quinones as the electron-transferring agents and further proposes that each quinone is placed between two imidazole rings, the latter being attached to the iron porphyrin system in a covalent bonding. Their postulated theory is based on the following observations:

1. Quinol phosphates have a high-energy bond which is enough to drive the ADP → ATP reaction.
2. With the quinones involved in the electron transfers, quinol phosphate formation and phosphate exchange could occur without the presence of ADP; that is, they can be independent.
3. The phosphoryl-imidazole bond is a high-energy linkage.
4. The quinone-imidazole electron shift can allow univalent changes while still effectively transferring two electrons.

The scheme would have the following steps: The membrane is delimited by the upright bars | |, with the electrons released from the coenzymes feeding into the left.

The electrons, as they pass across the imidazole-quinone bridge, set up a quinol $\sim$ imidazole bond, which is a high-energy link.

(a) |Fe-imidazole quinone imidazole-Fe| $\longrightarrow$ (1)
(b) |Fe-imidazole $\sim$ quinol imidazole-Fe| $\longrightarrow$
(c) |Fe-imidazole quinol $\sim$ imidazole-Fe|

Inorganic phosphate, P_i, is added, the quinol returns to the quinone form, the hydroxyl is split off, and a high-energy phosphoryl-imidazole bond is formed.

P_i + |Fe-imidazole quinol $\sim$ imidazole-Fe| $\longrightarrow$ (2)
|Fe-imidazole quinone P $\sim$ imidazole-Fe| + OH^-

The high-energy phosphate is transferred to the ADP to form ATP.

|Fe-imidazole quinone P $\sim$ imidazole-Fe| + ADP $\longrightarrow$ (3)
|Fe-imidazole quinone imidazole-Fe| + ATP

This scheme offers many solutions to existing problems and fits quite a lot of the experimental data. First off, no high-energy intermediate is necessary in this proposal. The fact that none has been isolated to this point makes the Urry and Eyring idea more attractive. Second, the observed vectorial release of OH^- on one side of the membrane can be handled by this scheme in step (2). The hydroxyl could be pumped out one side of the membrane because of the arrangement of the quinone-imidazole bridge. Finally, uncoupling can be easily explained. If orthophosphate is blocked from entering the system, the electron in step (1c) could be passed off and the system could be returned to the original structural relationship in step (1a). If P_i does enter the system and ADP is either blocked or absent, the phosphate could be passed off to other acceptors —for example, quinol phosphate.

OTHER ELECTRON TRANSPORT CHAINS

The mitochondrion does not have a monopoly on electron transport chains. Bacterial systems contain respiratory chains which resemble the mammalian mitochondrial membranes, but which do have distinct differences.[7] These assemblies are also capable of coupling phosphorylation with electron transport.

The endoplasmic reticulum membranes associated with the microsomal fraction has been shown to have electron transport ability. Utilization of the electron flow energy is still unresolved. The membranes involved do have a cytochrome, termed b_5, which undergoes oxidation-reduction reactions with $NADH \cdot H^+$ and $NADPH \cdot H^+$, but the pathway of electrons after cytochrome b_5 is merely supposition.

SUMMARY

The aerobic cell depends on the metabolic pathways to produce high-energy compounds for the purpose of driving other physiological processes. And yet, very few of the high-energy phosphates, such as ATP, are produced directly in these degradative sequences. The burden of ATP production falls on the electron transport systems which are capable of coupling the energy of electron flow through a gradient to phosphorylation of ADP to ATP.

The components of the respiratory chain, or respiratory assembly, are the pyridine nucleotides, flavoproteins, cytochromes, and probably coenzyme Q (ubiquinone). Inhibitor data and oxidation-reduction potentials have been used as two of the techniques to determine the order of these components in the chain. The generally agreed upon order is as follows:

$$MH_2 \longrightarrow NAD \longrightarrow FP \longrightarrow CoQ \longrightarrow (cytochromes\ b \longrightarrow c \longrightarrow a \longrightarrow a_3) \longrightarrow O_2$$

These components may occur in a series of macromolecular complexes. Coenzyme Q seems to act as a relay center for electron movement into the cytochromes in that it receives electrons from a number of flavoproteins, including succinic dehydrogenase, $NADH \cdot H^+$-dehydrogenase, and acyl-CoA dehydrogenase.

Endergonic production of ATP from ADP and P_i requires coupling with a reaction which is exergonic in nature. Such a sequence is the electron flow through the respiratory chain where a ΔF of $-52,000$ calories is available. The coupling of ATP production with this oxidation-reduction energy is called oxidative phosphorylation.

Available data suggest that there are at least three sites on the chain where this phosphorylation occurs. Inhibitor data and calculation of the free energy available between the components of the respiratory chain place the three sites as follows:

1. At the NAD-FP junction
2. At the cytochrome b to cytochrome c junction
3. At the cytochrome oxidase $(a + a_3)$ to oxygen junction

The mechanism for oxidative phosphorylation is still uncertain. Many workers favor the formation of a high-energy intermediate as the possible answer. Others suggest that the energy comes from chemiosmotic energy or as a result of an electron pump vectorially applied across a membrane. The various models which have been proposed should stimulate more experimentation and comparison.

Finally, the mitochondrial membranes which have a respiratory assembly do not have a monopoly on electron transport chains. Such systems have been found in cells without recognizable mitochondria as well as on the endoplasmic reticulum membranes associated with the microsomal fraction.

Literature cited

1. King, T. E. 1962. Reconstitution of respiratory enzyme systems. VI. Biochem. Biophys. Acta 59:492.
2. Singer, T. P. 1963. Flavoprotein dehydrogenases of the electron transport chain, vol. 7, p. 345. In Boyer, P. D., H. Lardy, and K. Myrbäck (editors): The enzymes. Academic Press, Inc., New York.
3. Gale, P. H., B. H. Auson, N. R. Trenner, A. C. Page, Jr., and K. Folkes. 1963. Coenzyme Q. XXXVI. Isolation and characterization of coenzyme Q_{10}. Biochemistry 2:196.
4. Mitchell, P. 1961. Coupling of phosphorylation to electron and hydrogen transfer by a chemi-osmotic type of mechanism. Nature 191:144.
5. Mitchell, P. 1963. Molecule, group and electron translocation through natural membranes,

p. 142. In Bell, D. J., and J. K. Grant (editors): Membranes and surfaces of cells. Biochemical Society Symposia. Cambridge University Press, London.

6. Urry, D. W., and H. Eyring. 1965. Biological Electron Transport. II. A variation of the imidazole pump model to include coupling. J. Theoret. Biol. 8:214.

7. Brodie, A. F., and J. Adelson. 1965. Respiratory chains and sites of coupled phosphorylation. Science 149:265.

General references

Boyer, P. D., H. Lardy, and K. Myrbäck (editors). 1963. The enzymes. Academic Press, Inc., New York. Vol. 7 and 8.

Chance, B. (editor). 1963. Energy-linked functions of mitochondria. Academic Press, Inc., New York.

Conn, E. E. 1960. Comparative biochemistry of electron transport and oxidative phosphorylation, vol. 1, p. 441. In Florkin, M., and H. S. Mason (editors): Comparative biochemistry. Academic Press, Inc., New York.

Green, D. E. 1964. The mitochondrion. Sci. Am. (Jan.), p. 63.

Ingraham, L. L. 1962. Biochemical mechanisms. John Wiley & Sons, Inc., New York.

Karlson, P. 1963. Introduction to modern biochemistry. Academic Press, Inc., New York.

Kleiner, I. S., and J. M. Orten. 1962. Biochemistry. 6th ed. The C. V. Mosby Co., St. Louis.

Kosower, E. M. 1962. Molecular biochemistry. McGraw-Hill Book Co., New York.

Lehninger, A. L. 1964. The mitochondrion. W. A. Benjamin, Inc., New York.

Stewart, R. 1964. Oxidation mechanisms. W. A. Benjamin, Inc., New York.

White, A., P. Handler, and E. L. Smith. 1964. Principles of biochemistry. 3rd ed. McGraw-Hill Book Co., New York.

Wolstenholme, G. E. W., and C. M. O'Connor (editors). 1961. Quinones in electron transport. Little, Brown & Co., Boston.

22

Bioluminescence

INTRODUCTION

Many cells have specialized uses for the energy and metabolites extracted from the various biochemical pathways. The metabolism in these specialized cells shifts according to the type of process which is being performed. Many bacteria produce fantastic numbers of by-products which are of little use to the organism itself (for example, acetone- or alcohol-producing bacteria). Some plant cells adjust their pathways for the production of anthocyanin and other pigments. The cells which produce hormones in animals are specialized as far as their metabolism is concerned. In fact, all cells which are differentiated are "specialized" metabolically for their microecological niche.

Some metabolic specializations, however, are not limited to particular cell types. Bioluminescence, the production of light through biological processes, is one of these.

LUMINESCENCE—PRODUCTION OF LIGHT WITHOUT HEAT

Incident energy falling on a biological molecule offers a potential source of added energy to that compound. Like other radiations, the photon energy from incident visible light is capable of affecting the atomic configuration of this molecule.

The electrons spinning in predetermined orbits around the atomic center have a certain energy requirement which is necessary to maintain them at their particular orbital level. Electrons can, however, be forced into an outer orbit by getting an energy boost from some source; this source may be the energy in the photon of light. The molecule is then said to be excited.

For an electron change to occur, the molecule in which the electron resides must preferentially absorb photon energy from light. In other words, a molecule, in order to become excited, has to be absorbing a large percentage of a certain incident wavelength of light. Photon packets of energy cannot be split. As a result, the number of quanta used in a reaction is always the next highest integer to the actual amount of energy required. For example, if a process requires 11,000 calories of energy and the quantum energy involved is 8000 calories, 2 quanta, or 16,000 calories, would be necessary to make the reaction go. Thus, a certain number of quanta are necessary to displace an electron to set up an excited state. The wavelength at which the molecule absorbs and this final reaction of the electron once it reaches the excited state determine the overt phenomenon which will occur.

The excited electron may return to its original orbit, which is at the lower energy level, and as it does so, the quantum of light originally absorbed is released. This phenomenon is known as photoluminescence. There are two ways by which light can be emitted as the energy is released from the molecule. This return to the lower energy level may bring about luminescence which continues long after the excited state of the molecule is reached—a glow known as phosphorescence. The other possibility is that the quantum release as the electron returns to its original orbit will occur almost immediately after the molecule has been irradiated; this shorter flash of light is called fluorescence.

Electroluminescence occurs in the same manner as photoluminescence except that the energy supplying the force necessary to move the electrons out of orbit is electrical. Electrical excitation of molecules and atoms causes light release when the excitation current is removed.

All of the preceding events have little application to the cell as such. Luminescence is sometimes used as a diagnostic criterion of some phenomena and can be used in biophysical and biochemical investigations of compounds that are known to luminesce under certain conditions. The phenomenon of electron agitation or excitation due to incident light and luminescence must be kept separate. Luminescence is only one result of electron excitation and has little application to the physiological dynamics of the cell; electron excitation per se can have marked effect on the cell and is directly involved in some of its major processes (for example, photosynthesis). The aforementioned types of luminescence, for the most part, remain as curiosities, and their only value to the physiology of the cell is to aid in explaining the phenomenon of chemiluminescence, commonly referred to as bioluminescence when it is applied to living systems.

BIOLUMINESCENCE

The metabolic pathways produce the energy compounds of the cell in order that these high-energy substances can further the physiological processes. The synthetic phenomena require great amounts of energy, as do membrane transport, secretion, and many other similar dynamic events of the cell. The energy produced, however, can also be transformed into special forms of other energy, one of these being light emission.

Emission of light by a living organism derives the energy for its occurrence from the chemical energy stored in the cell. Thus, bioluminescence is a form of chemiluminescence and is one result of harnessing of high-energy bonds for a particular physiological purpose.

Bioluminescence poses several problems which at this point are unsolved. Unlike many other processes, the chemical mechanism for the light-emitting reaction does not seem to be universal. A clear-cut set of reactions has not yet been elaborated. The importance of this process, which occurs in approximately one half of the animal phyla in addition to the bacteria and fungi, is unknown. Why some of the cell's energy should be shunted toward the production of light is just one of the unanswered questions.

Historical background

Observations that rotting organic material often becomes luminous have been made for centuries, but it was not until the advent of the microscope that light emission was determined as coming from living bacteria.

That the process was an enzymatic one was not considered until Dubois, in 1887, isolated a heat stable substance which he called *luciférine* and a heat labile enzyme named *luciférase*. This nomenclature, which has persisted, infers that there is some enzyme, luciferase, which reacts on some naturally occurring substrate, luciferin, to produce light emission.

Many other workers have made great advances in elucidation of this process but the name of E. Newton Harvey was, for years, synonymous with bioluminescence. Two excellent works by him[1,2] summarize the background and specifics of biological light emission.

Requirements for light emission

There is no universal mechanism for bioluminescence, and therefore the requirements differ, depending on the particular mode of action of light emission. It is possible, however, to generalize and name some of the requirements which are most common.

Luciferin is a generic term for those substrates which are acted upon to bring about an excited state. The compounds which are, or make up, the luciferin molecule are quite varied in nature. Flavin complexes, proteoses, and albumins are only three of the substances which have been considered to be luciferin.

Luciferase is also a generic term in that no one enzyme would be able to use the variety of luciferins as a substrate. Those luciferases which have been isolated behave as enzymes and have the typical characteristics of the high-weight biocatalysts.

Oxygen, unfortunately, is not always required for bioluminescence. It is unfortunate because a requirement such as this would give some ground upon which to base a mechanism. It was originally postulated that the energy from the oxidation-reduction reactions of the cell supplies the driving force for electron displacement. The lack of oxygen in some forms does not preclude this, but it does mean that the process is not always associated with a respiratory chain, although an oxidative process is probably necessary either for the reaction itself or for generation of some other necessary compound.

A high-energy compound such as ATP is not always required either, although in the common firefly it is a prerequisite for the reaction. A large amount of energy is necessary, however, for light emission. The calorie requirement for emissions in the red, yellow, green, and blue portions of the spectrum are 41,000, 50,000, 55,000 and 62,000, respectively. This is a very high-energy requirement corresponding to 5 to 6 ATP of 8000 calories each.

Some postulated mechanisms

The mechanisms of light emission of a number of organisms have been postulated, some of which have much more experimental evidence than others. However, there are several schemes which are sufficiently worked out in detail that it seems worth the risk to present them. The two mechanisms selected represent distinct modes of action and thus give an idea of the range of schemes that must occur to yield essentially the same outcome.

Firefly

Of all of the bioluminescent systems, the one in the common firefly has had the most experimentation. The ready availability and some peculiar quirks in the mechanism stimulated much research.

The now-classical experiment of Dubois in which he found that a hot-water extract after cooling would luminesce if a cold-water extract made from the same tissue were added gave the first clues to the mechanism of emission. The logical interpretation would be that the boiled extract contained luciferin, but the luciferase was destroyed. The cold-water extract, on the other hand, had both components and would luminesce, using up the luciferin. Thus, it was postulated that the luciferin was the limiting factor and was replaced when the hot-water extract was added. This proves that a biologist's interpretation of data is limited by the depth of knowledge at his disposal, for after work in other areas demonstrated the occurrence of a high-energy compound, ATP, it was found that it was the compound, and not the luciferin, which was the limiting factor.

Further investigation indicated that the reaction for light emission in the firefly required luciferin, luciferase, ATP, Mg^{++}, and oxygen. The similarity to the requirements of a phosphorylating system was noted.

The ATP is apparently necessary to form a complex with the luciferin, in this case a luciferin-AMP (LH_2AMP).

$$ATP + LH_2 \longrightarrow LH_2 \cdot AMP + PP_i \tag{1}$$

One of the few processes which can add enough energy to the system in order to create the needed excited state is peroxidation.

$$LH_2 \cdot AMP + {}^-O_2 \longrightarrow LOOH_2 \cdot AMP \tag{2}$$

$$LOOH_2 \cdot AMP + LH_2 \longrightarrow L \cdot AMP^* + 2\ H_2O + L \tag{3}$$

The end product of equation (2) is unstable and is quickly converted into the adenyloxyluciferin ($L \cdot AMP^*$), the excited molecule, which is standardly noted with an asterisk. Equation (3) can occur in the presence of another molecule of oxyluciferin (L) or AMP.

Bioluminescence in fireflies is truly an oxidative process. The luciferin is oxidized by having two hydrogens removed, the removal mediated by the peroxidation of LH_2 to $LOOH_2$. Under anaerobic circumstances, the adenylluciferin (LH_2AMP) is broken down to luciferin and AMP. Biochemical and biophysical analyses of luciferin and luciferase indicate that the enzyme is an euglobulin of moderate molecular weight ($\sim 100{,}000$). Luciferin, the substrate, is of smaller molecular weight (~ 310), but its structure has not been completely worked out.

The photogenic cells of the organ in the firefly which produce the bioluminescence are well innervated and have the end cells of the tracheae in close contact with these light-emitting cells. Nervous stimulation of the cell can set off the luminescent mechanisms, and the oxygen coming through the tracheae is necessary to continue or repeat the process.

One striking feature of the firefly flash is that the entire process can be mimicked in the test tube. The addition and control of all of the components invariably will produce light. The cell itself does not seem to do much more than supply an area in which the reaction can occur and to regulate the components necessary for light emission. Control of emission, however, is a function of the living system, and accumulated data indicate that the neurohumoral substance released at nerve endings (acetylcholine in most forms) may be the compound which triggers the luminescence.

Bacteria

The size of the bacteria at once hindered experimental attempts to extract the compounds necessary for luminescence in these organisms. By collating and correlating of data, the following scheme was proposed in which the critical factors are luciferin-luciferase, reduced flavinmononucleotide ($FMNH_2$), a long chain aldehyde, $NADH \cdot H^+$, and oxygen.

Bacterial luciferin is a complex of the reduced coenzyme and the aldehyde.

$$FMNH_2 + RCHO \longrightarrow FMNH_2 \cdot RCHO \tag{1}$$

This complex undergoes oxidation catalyzed by luciferase,

$$FMNH_2 \cdot RCHO + O_2 \xrightarrow{\text{Luciferase}} FMN \cdot RCOOH^* + O_2 \tag{2}$$

which can emit the energy as quanta of light in the blue part of the spectrum.

$$FMN \cdot RCOOH^* \longrightarrow FMN + RCOOH + \text{light} \tag{3}$$

In order to recycle the coenzyme, the reduced form of the flavinmononucleotide is regenerated by $NADH \cdot H^+$.

$$FMN + NADH \cdot H^+ \rightleftarrows FMNH_2 + NAD \tag{4}$$

The composition of the luciferin may not be constant. Several aldehydes have been demonstrated to be able to complex with the $FMNH_2$ and continue completely through the sequence, including light emission. Whether more than one of these aldehydes participate in the reaction in the bacterial cell is not known. Again, like the firefly system, the entire sequence can be carried out in vitro in a water medium. This infers that the enzyme does not have to be membrane-bound in order to function.

ROLE OF LUMINESCENCE IN BIOLOGY

The large number of different phyla that demonstrate light emission and the apparently distinct mechanisms for this bioluminescence make generalizations about the role of the process in biology quite improbable. An attempt will be made to relay some ideas which have been proposed.

Differences between plants and animals

The basic difference between the light-emitting properties of animals and plants is that the animal luminescence occurs only when stimulation occurs, whereas in bacteria and fungi the emission is continual, varying only with the physiological state of the organism. This observation is not unexpected in that in at least higher animals nervous control of this process has been demonstrated. These animals, then, have the potential for controlling the emission, using it in such behavioral situations as feeding, aggression, protection, and mating rituals.

The cells in which the chemical reactions occur do not share much more in common than any other cells which might be compared among the phyla. They are generally larger than surrounding cells, are innervated, and have some granular material. In association with those cells clustered in an organ is a reflector layer which helps to magnify the appearance of the light (Fig. 22-1).

The luciferases in most systems studied are low to moderate weight proteins which are capable of functioning outside of the cell environment. The luciferins do not have any particular chemical nature. The only trait they all show is the ability to undergo peroxidation (or oxidation). It is in the oxidized state where the electrons become excited, eventually giving up the quantum energy as light.

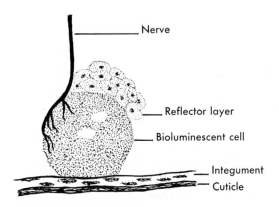

Fig. 22-1. Diagrammatic representation of the light-emitting cells of animals, showing the presence of an innervating system and a reflector layer.

The other requirements for each of the sequences do not show any pattern. Many cofactors, coenzymes, and other enzymes may be involved, the specific ones varying from organism to organism.

Evolutionary importance or significance

Early cells had experience with molecules or electrons in the excited state because many of these underwent photosynthesis, a process whose success depends on excitement of special molecules. The shift to almost the reverse of photosynthesis in bioluminescence is not too hard to imagine. In the lower forms, the energy gleaned from metabolic pathways had to be utilized in some manner, and it is possible that the excess energy was channeled into luminescent processes.

When the high-energy bond was exploited, much of this energy went into ATP production, and the number of luminescent organisms may have decreased. In the higher forms bioluminescence may have redeveloped, but now with behavioral patterns for survival as the evolutionary pressure. The cycle, then, seems to have swung completely around because in some of these higher forms ATP is now required for bioluminescence.

SUMMARY

The production of light without heat by living organisms is a peculiar phenomenon in that its mechanism and purpose are varied and unresolved in most cases.

The basis of bioluminescence is that energy produced from the metabolic pathways is channeled into the excitement of certain molecules by electron displacement. As these electrons return to a normal orbit, quanta of light are given off as the energy level returns to normal. The components of the reaction are rarely the same from organism to organism, but the generic groups of luciferin—the substrate which will become excited—and luciferase—the enzyme catalyzing the reactions leading to the excited state—are always present. The other reactants vary, depending on the specific mechanisms involved.

The mechanisms of light production in the firefly and in luminous bacteria are quite different. The first sequence involves ATP as one of the energy sources for the reaction, an AMP-luciferin complex being formed. The energy for electron displacement comes from peroxidation.

In the bacteria, the luciferin is a $FMNH_2$—long chain aldehyde complex which undergoes peroxidation to attain the excited state. No high-energy compound is involved in the reaction.

The role of luminescence in biology is unclear. There are some basic differences between light emission in animals and plants, and is primarily due to innervation of the cells in the animal kingdom. The purpose of shunting of energy into the luminescence process may be a means of ridding the cell of excess energy. The overt effect in higher animals is establishment of behavioral patterns based on the light-emitting properties.

Literature cited

1. Harvey, E. N. 1952. Bioluminescence. Academic Press, Inc., New York.
2. Harvey, E. N. 1960. Bioluminescence, vol. 2, p. 545. In Florkin, M., and H. S. Mason (editors): Comparative biochemistry. Academic Press, Inc., New York.

General references

Cormier, M. J., and J. R. Totter. 1964. Bioluminescence. Ann. Rev. Biochem. 33:431.

Giese, A. C. (editor). 1964. Photophysiology. Academic Press, Inc., New York. Vol. 2.

Hastings, J. W., and Q. H. Gibson. 1963. Intermediate in the bioluminescent oxidation of reduced flavin mononucleotide. J. Biol. Chem. 238:2537.

McElroy, W. D., and B. Glass (editors). 1961. Light and life. Johns Hopkins University Press, Baltimore.

23

Photosynthesis

INTRODUCTION

The biochemical processes of the cell which have been discussed thus far have had to do with synthesis and degradation of metabolites, with utilization of the energy gain directed toward various goals. All of these pathways and sequences have presupposed an external source of carbon in an organic form. Ultimately, somewhere in the living world some cells must create organic carbon-carbon bonds for other cells to use. The process most used to accomplish this end is photosynthesis.

Photosynthesis, then, is a process in which simple, inorganic substances with strong bonding are converted to the weaker bonded organic compounds, with a resulting decrease in entropy, and at the same time the electromagnetic energy of incident light is transformed to chemical energy. Stated another way, photosynthesis is reduction of carbon dioxide to organic materials by a photochemical mechanism with the concomitant release of gaseous oxygen.

These two definitions infer the following:

1. That carbon dioxide is the inorganic compound to which the photochemical energy is directed
2. That there must be an input of energy if there is to be an overall decrease of entropy
3. That light must supply at least some of the energy

Thus, the overall reaction can be written

$$CO_2 + H_2O + Cal_{light} \longrightarrow (CH_2O) + O_2 \uparrow + Cal_{chem} + Cal_{lost} \qquad (1)$$

where Cal_{light}, Cal_{chem}, and Cal_{lost} represent the energy (in calories) which comes from the light, which is bound as chemical bonds, and which is lost as heat and other forms of energy, respectively. The energy involved here is quite sizable, running in excess of 112,000 calories.

250

From the various energies described, a set of definitions can be derived which aid in quantitative discussion of the reaction. The ratio of the calories trapped as chemical bonds to the calories input from the light (Cal_{chem}/Cal_{light}) is the energy efficiency of the overall process.

The amount of energy necessary to produce the 6-carbon glucose is the positive value of its standard free energy, which is approximately 686,000 calories. One CO_2 would then require one sixth of this value for its reduction to a formed organic compound. To find the quantum number, that is, the number of quanta necessary to provide that amount of energy, the ratio of $X \, hv/114,000$ is used, where X is the number of quanta, hv the calories per mole quantum at a particular wavelength, and 114,000 the energy necessary to reduce 1 Co_2(1/6 of 686,000). The reciprocal of this ratio is termed the quantum efficiency.

Photosynthesis is an involved process in which the following occur:

1. Oxidation-reduction [$CO_2 \rightarrow (CH_2O)$]
2. Photochemical reaction where the energy of light is harnessed
3. Series of biochemical or thermochemical reactions where the energy applied to the oxidation-reduction produces an organic compound which can enter the metabolic pathways of the cell

In general, the factors which primarily affect the photosynthetic process are the light intensity, wavelength of the incident light, carbon dioxide concentration, and physiochemical variables involved in the ecological environment such as temperature and pH. These factors will not be elaborated on at this point, but that they do have an effect on the process should be kept in mind as the various stages of photosynthesis are developed.

The importance of photosynthesis can only be understated. A mere introduction to ecology stresses the significance of the primary producer to the total food chain of the living world. That cells have the capability of autotrophic existence either individually or collectively as an organism is certainly the most single important physiological adaptation which occurs. Any process having the far-reaching consequences that photosynthesis has demands a detailed discussion of its mechanism and of its relationship to the overall physiology of the cells which carry out the process.

STAGES OF PHOTOSYNTHESIS

The overall reaction (1) hints at three major phases of the photosynthetic process (Fig. 23-1). They will be listed here and will be discussed in full, one at a time in following sections.

The first stage is removal of hydrogens from one of the reactants in order to use them to reduce the carbon dioxide. This must occur with the production of oxygen on the product side of the reaction. The removal of hydrogen necessitates energy input since the hydrogen-oxygen bond is more stable than the hydrogen-organic molecular bond; that is, there is a decrease in entropy.

Second, the hydrogens and electrons which are removed must be picked up by some intermediate and transferred against an oxidation-reduction potential gradient to another intermediate which is involved in the last stage. The

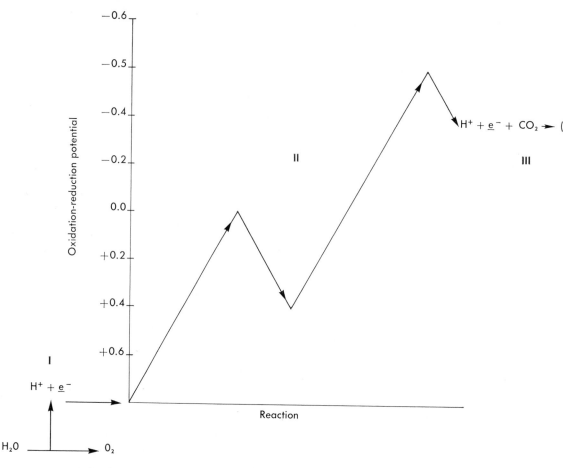

Fig. 23-1. Schematic representation of the three major phases of photosynthesis. The first stage, I, is the effective removal of hydrogen from water, with the concomitant release of oxygen. The hydrogen must then be transported against an oxidation-reduction potential to the level where it can be used to reduce carbon dioxide. Because of the large energy difference, stage II cannot occur in one jump. Finally, the third stage, III, is the use of the hydrogens to reduce carbon dioxide to an organic molecule.

great difference in this oxidation-reduction potential between CO_2 and any organic molecule again demands an energy input to overcome the difference.

The final phase is the use of these hydrogens and electrons to convert carbon dioxide into an organic constituent, presumably a carbohydrate. Once this organic constituent reaches the mainstream of metabolism, the process has reached an end point.

The first two stages are photochemical, deriving their energy from light. The series of reactions which use light energy, require chlorophyll, and evolve oxygen are known as the Hill reaction. The final stage does not depend on light energy and is thus called the dark, or Blackman, reaction of photosynthesis. The distinction should become clear as the individual mechanisms are discussed.

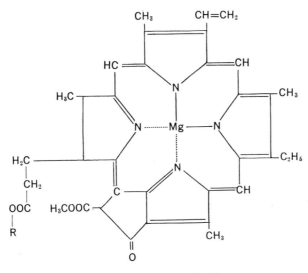

Fig. 23-2. Chlorophyll a. R in left-hand structure is a phytyl group.

THE PIGMENTS OF PHOTOSYNTHESIS

The primary pigments of photosynthesis are the chlorophylls. These compounds are substitution derivatives of protoporphyrin IX and are thereby related to heme, catalase, and cytochromes. Different from the other porphyrins is the presence of the magnesium ion and the long phytol chain (Fig. 23-2).

Five chlorophylls (a through e) have been found in algae and higher plants, but chlorophylls a and b are the most common and apparently the most active. Two bacterial pigments which are classified as chlorophylls have also been isolated. These green pigments absorb primarily in the red and far-red regions, although other wavelengths can also be absorbed. Synthesis of the chlorophyll pigments parallels that of formation of heme and other protoporphyrin IX derivatives. Succinyl-CoA and glycine are the building blocks, with pyridoxal phosphate a requirement for the reaction.

Accessory pigments have also been demonstrated in a variety of forms. There is a large series of xanthophylls, or yellow pigments, which have been found in almost all groups that undergo photosynthesis. In the higher plants alone, six xanthophylls are known to occur. In addition, five carotenes are present in these groups, but only the more common α-carotenes and β-carotenes occur in the higher plants. Finally, the phycobilins are specialized pigments restricted to some algae and possibly some bacteria.

The plant pigments function in the cell to take up energy from light. The energy thus trapped has to be transferred from the pigments to other molecules.

THE PRIMARY PHOTOCHEMICAL REACTION

Of all of the stages in photosynthesis, the one least understood is the primary photochemical reaction. At one time it was thought that the oxygen evolved in the primary reaction came from the CO_2, but with analogies made with the

Table 23-1. Representative plant pigments*

Pigment	Occurrence and remarks
Phycoerythrin	Various algae; very high molecular weight ($\sim$300,000)
Phycocyanin	Various algae; high molecular weight ($\sim$250,000)
α- and β-Carotene	Widely distributed; low molecular weight (536)
Xanthophyll	Widely distributed; carotenoid
Leghemoglobin	Root nodules of leguminous plants; pyrrole-globin complex
Chlorophyll a	All photosynthetic organisms except bacteria; molecular weight 901
Chlorophyll b	Most photosynthetic organisms
Chlorophyll c	Diatoms, dinoflagellates, and brown algae
Chlorophyll d	Primarily in red algae; (sulfur and nonsulfur)
Bacteriochlorophyll	All purple photosynthetic bacteria

*Data from Spector, W. S. (editor). 1956. Handbook of biological data. W. B. Saunders Co., Philadelphia

sulfur bacteria and with the use of isotopes, it was demonstrated that the oxygen came from the water. This is not surprising in one respect because the energy necessary for separation of the hydrogen from the oxygen is of the correct magnitude. The "photolysis" of water was then suggested to be the mechanism of this first reaction.

$$h\nu + H_2O \rightarrow 2[H] + [O] \tag{2}$$

Other work demonstrated that the light quanta probably cause the chlorophyll molecule to become excited. Other investigators postulated that, from an efficiency standpoint, the chlorophyll is probably assembled into "photosynthetic units" in which the individual chlorophyll molecules cooperate in trapping and directing the quantum energy to some center which has as its prime purpose photochemical reaction. Semiconductance may enter the picture as a very important concept in the energy trap of chlorophyll complexes.

Park and Biggins[1] have called the cooperating units the quantasomes, and calculations on the number of chlorophyll molecules in each quantasome range from 230[1] to 400.[2] Associated with these quantasomes, or perhaps as an integral part of these units, are several cytochromes and a special photosensitive pigment. The presence of these compounds, along with a high concentration of reductants and oxidants found associated with electron transport, has led to elaborate theories about the second stage of the photosynthetic process. These hypotheses can help to explain the first stage.

HYDROGEN TRANSFER AND ELECTRON TRANSPORT IN PHOTOSYNTHESIS

Photolysis is an overt reaction in which the bonds of hydrogen and oxygen are split, forming hydrogen and hydroxyl radicals. The hydrogen is then removed to reduce CO_2 to (CH_2O). In the metabolic pathways are many instances where water is a reactant in an enzyme reaction in which either the hydrogen, hydroxyl, or oxygen is removed in a coupled series of steps which acts as the driving force to pull the water apart.

In photosynthesis, the following reaction probably occurs

$$H_2O + U \longrightarrow UH_2 + [O] \tag{3}$$

where U is some unknown acceptor. If this acceptor is assumed to be a member of an electron chain or some substance which can pass the hydrogens and electrons to this chain, the reaction can be forced to the right.

The energy to drive the transfer of hydrogen must come from the chlorophyll, which acts as a photocatalyst; that is, when the chlorophyll is in the excited or energized state, an energy-storing photochemical reaction occurs.

If the hydrogens and electrons are moved along a particular chain in this second stage of photosynthesis, the movement will be against the electromotive potential. In the respiratory assembly, however, the potentials become more positive as the hydrogens move down the chain; that is, each member of the chain can easily reduce the next component, and the electrons move with the potential. In photosynthesis, this is not the case, and thus the energy trapped in the chlorophyll must somehow supply the energy to pump the hydrogens against the gradient.

Energetics

A look at the energetics of the reaction indicates the massive amount of energy which must be put into this phase of photosynthesis. Using the formula

$$\Delta F = -nF \Delta E$$

the free energy change can be calculated. The starting point for the photosynthetic process is the H_2O/O_2 oxidation-reduction system. This has a calculated potential of approximately 0.8 volts. The end product of the process is the $(CH_2O)/CO_2$ system, which has a calculated potential of -0.4 volts.

$$\Delta F = 23060 \, (0.8 - (-0.4))$$
$$= 28{,}000 \text{ calories per 1 electron shift}$$

The conversion from CO_2 to (CH_2O) requires four hydrogens, and the free energy change is thereby increased to about 112,000 calories. This is indeed a large amount of energy to supply to an oxidation-reduction system in order to carry out this second stage of photosynthesis.

It has been established that the electron chain must take the electrons (hydrogens) from the primary donor, water, to the final acceptor, CO_2. Some of the pieces in the path have been put in place, but much is still in the realm of speculation.

Components of the chain

The identity of the primary acceptor in reaction (3) has not been determined. Although it would help edify the total picture, the identification of this substance is not critical to the presentation of some of the schemes which are in the literature for getting the hydrogen uphill to the $CO_2 \rightarrow (CH_2O)$ reaction. Some of the more recent work on the electron chain and some interesting models will be discussed.

The $CO_2 \rightarrow (CH_2O)$ reaction has an oxidation-reduction potential of -0.4 volts. Of the common electron carriers, the NADP $\rightleftarrows$ NADPH·H$^+$ system has a potential of -0.32 volts, not quite of the magnitude necessary to couple with the first reaction to complete the reduction of CO_2. There is the possibility that an input of energy through ATP could help drive the reaction, however.

An iron-containing protein, ferredoxin, has been found in the chloroplasts. This compound has an oxidation-reduction potential of —0.42. This protein would logically be placed along side of NADP in the electron chain, thus reducing the NADP, which could then in turn reduce carbon dioxide. At least one other substance has been suggested as preceding the ferredoxin in the chain. This compound supposedly has a potential of —0.6, which would place it before ferredoxin in the chain. In addition, two cytochromes have been discovered to be associated with the chlorophyll in the quantasomes. Both cytochrome b_6 and cytochrome f have been described as occurring in the chloroplasts.

The two-step electron pump

Any proposed scheme for the energy flow in photosynthesis must take the following into consideration:

1. $NADPH \cdot H^+$ is one product of the second stage of photosynthesis.
2. ATP is also a product of this second stage. To be thermodynamically feasible, the production of this high-energy compound must occur on a downhill portion of the energy flow.
3. A series of electron carriers have to be postulated which can raise the oxidation-reduction potential from 0.8 to —0.4.
4. The energy input has to be in the order of magnitude of at least 112,000 calories.

Rabinowitch and Govindjee[3] have presented one of the more recent schemes in a stimulating article published in 1965. The high points of this scheme are presented here.

Much evidence has accumulated recently which suggests that the movement of electrons against the oxidation-reduction gradient in photosynthesis is a two-step process. One striking piece of datum was the calculation that eight quanta of light are required to move the four hydrogens (and thus electrons) from the water to the carbon dioxide. It follows that two quanta are required to move each electron if the assumption is made that no large amount of energy is lost in fluorescence or some similar waste. It is true that chlorophyll is known to fluoresce, but the calculated energy lost is not great enough to require two quanta of light for maintaining the molecule at the excited state.

The first hint of a scheme which could incorporate this two quanta per electron relationship came on reexamination of the so-called Emerson effect. The primary chlorophylls in green plants, a and b, differentially absorb the incident light. Chlorophyll a can absorb light from a broad band of wavelength, with a peak near 6700 Å in the red range and other peaks above 6800 Å, or in the far-red range. Chlorophyll b, on the other hand, absorbs only in the red portion of the spectrum, having a peak near 6500 Å, followed by a sharp drop with minimal or no absorption in the far-red range.

Emerson demonstrated that the photosynthetic quantum yield of plants is not the algebraic sum of the stimulation of chlorophyll a and b. Using red and far-red light, he found that exposure to the two lights separately gave a much lower photosynthetic yield than if the plants were exposed to the two beams simultaneously. That is, with the incident energy from the two wavelengths the same in both experiments, the exposure to both lights at the same time had a synergistic effect which could not be explained as a simple addition phenomenon.

The question was then raised as to whether chlorophyll b and the other pigments had a separate role in the photosynthetic process or whether they were merely accessories of chlorophyll a. Further work showed that regardless of which pigment does the primary absorbing of the incident light the energy is transferred to chlorophyll a by some resonance process. A final piece of evidence indicated that in the living cell chlorophyll a probably occurs in two distinct forms, one which absorbs primarily in the 6700 Å range (red) and one which absorbs primarily above 6800 Å, or in the far-red range.

From these and other data, the following scheme, which involves two separate systems of chlorophyll complexes, has been proposed for the electron

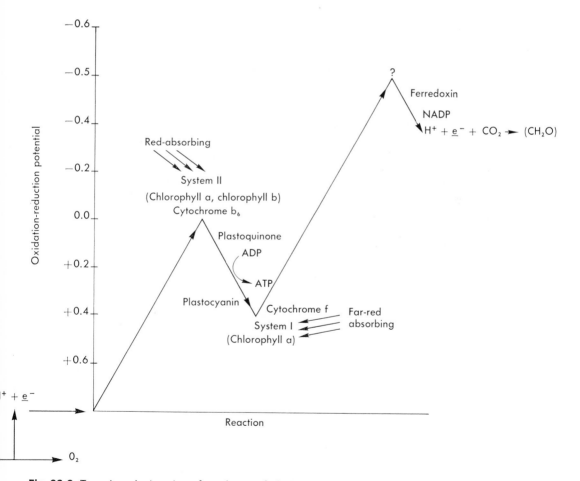

Fig. 23-3. Two-step electron transfer scheme of photosynthesis. (See text.)

movement. According to the proposal, System I of chlorophyll contains primarily chlorophyll a which absorbs in the far-red range associated with some accessory pigments. System II contains chlorophyll a or chlorophyll b with the pigment specific for red absorption. Chlorophyll a is also associated with chlorophyll b and the other accessory pigments. Finally, cytochrome b_6, with an oxidation-reduction potential of 0.0 volts, is associated with System II, whereas cytochrome f, with a potential of 0.4 volts, is aligned with System I.

The two-step electron transfer scheme is seen in Fig. 23-3. The salient features of the process are as follows: Incident light on the System II complex agitates the electrons of chlorophyll a or chlorophyll b until the molecule reaches an energized state. The energy thus trapped is the driving force which causes an electron to pass from some primary donor to cytochrome b_6. The voltage difference is 0.8, which means that the energy input must be 20,500 calories, an energy value lower than that which can be found in a quantum of light. The electron then passes from cytochrome b_6 to cytochrome f in a step which is extremely important in that it is an exergonic reaction and can yield energy, in this case some 10,000 calories. This would be enough to generate the ATP which will be needed later in the scheme. Some proposed mechanisms for the generation of the high-energy bond in this step will be considered later.

The next step is raising of the electron from the oxidation-reduction potential of cytochrome f to at least the level of the $CO_2 \rightarrow (CH_2O)$ potential of -0.4. According to the proposed scheme, incident light is again required, but here it is chlorophyll a of System I which is energized. The energy required to go from 0.4 to -0.6 is 23,060 calories, again a value compatible with the energy in a quantum of light.

Then, in a downhill transport, the electron is passed to ferredoxin (-0.42 volts) and NADP (-0.32 volts). As NADPH·H^+, the hydrogens are passed to a carbohydrate intermediate, which reduces this compound. The reaction between NADPH·H^+ and the carbohydrate is partially driven by the breakdown of ATP $\rightarrow$ ADP.

PHOTOPHOSPHORYLATION

The process of photophosphorylation is the production of ATP from the energy produced in electron movement during photosynthesis; that is, energy from incident light which is trapped in the chlorophyll is utilized to produce ATP.

On the surface, the process is analogous to oxidative phosphorylation, with the overt difference being the source of the energy. Various schemes have been proposed for this process, and although they are different on the surface, they still have some basic similarities.

On the pathway between cytochrome b_6 and cytochrome f several other electron carriers are probably interspersed. Plastoquinone, the quinone found in chloroplasts, and plastocyanin, a copper-containing protein, are the best guesses as to the identity of the other compounds involved. It is not any great stretch of the imagination to presuppose an electron transport particle similar

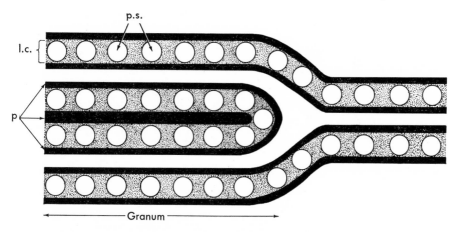

Fig. 23-4. Lamellar structure of chloroplasts showing possible location of photophosphory lating aggregates. **p,** Protein. **l.c.,** Lipoid-chlorophyll layer. **p.s.,** Photophosphorylating sites

to the respiratory assembly found in mitochondria. The lamellar structure of chloroplasts, with layered protein and lipid, is the ideal location for these particles (Fig. 23-4).

In the diagrammatic scheme of Fig. 23-4, sandwiching of the electron carriers between two layers of chlorophyll, one containing the red absorber and one the far-red absorber, makes for interesting speculation. The quinone involvement tempts one to look at the models of oxidative phosphorylation as proposed by Urry and Eyring and Mitchell a little more carefully.

PATHWAY OF CARBON IN THE PHOTOSYNTHETIC PROCESS

The pathway of carbon in photosynthesis has been fairly well resolved. The use of isotopes and other such techniques has afforded enough evidence to have a scheme proposed which seems to fit almost all of the available information.

The ATP and the NADPH·H⁺ which are produced by the electron transfer stage are used initially in reduction of carbon dioxide. The CO_2 acceptor apparently is ribulose-1,5-diphosphate which forms a 6-carbon addition compound. From this two 3-phosphoglyceric acids are split off.

$$CO_2 + \text{Ribulose-1,5-diphosphate} \longrightarrow \text{6-Carbon addition compound} \qquad (1)$$

$$\text{6-Carbon addition compound} \longrightarrow (2) \text{ 3-Phosphoglyceric acids} \qquad (2)$$

The 3-phosphoglyceric acid is then reduced to 3-phosphogylceraldehyde in a two-step sequence involving ATP and NADPH·H⁺.

$$\text{3-Phosphoglyceric acid} + \text{ATP} \longrightarrow \text{1,3-Diphosphoglyceric acid} + \text{ADP} \qquad (3)$$

$$\text{1,3-Diphosphoglyceric acid} + \text{NADPH·H}^+ \longrightarrow \text{3-Phosphoglyceraldehyde} + \text{P}_i \qquad (4)$$

Equation (4) probably involves many more cofactors besides NADPH·H⁺.

By an elaborate recycling mechanism (Fig. 23-5), there is a net gain of one 3-phosphoglyceric acid for every six initially formed from the CO_2 addition

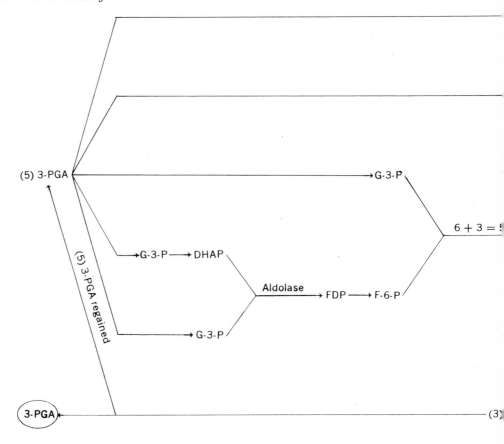

Fig. 23-5. Pathway of carbon compounds in photosynthesis. The elaborate recycling 3-phosphoglyceric acid. G-3-P, glyceraldehyde 3-phosphate. DHAP, dihydroxyaceton phate. E-4-P, erythrose 4-phosphate. SDP, sedoheptulose 1,7-diphosphate. S-7-P ribulose 1,5-diphosphate. HDP, hexose 1,6-diphosphate. ③-PGA, 3-phosphoglycer

to ribulose-1,5-diphosphate to form the 6-carbon addition compounds, each of which splits into two of the 3-phosphoglyceric acids. The overall reactions could be summed up as follows, using the number of carbons only.

(1) $5 + 1 \longrightarrow 6$ (repeat three times)

(2) $6 \longrightarrow 2\,(3)$ (repeat three times to give 6 (3))

(3) $6\,(3) \overset{12\ H^+}{\longrightarrow} 6\,(3)$

(4) $2\,(3) \longrightarrow 6$

(5) $6 + 3 \longrightarrow 4 + 5$

(6) $4 + 3 \longrightarrow 7$

(7) $7 + 3 \longrightarrow 2\,(5)$

There are several points which should be noted about the pathway shown in Fig. 23-5.

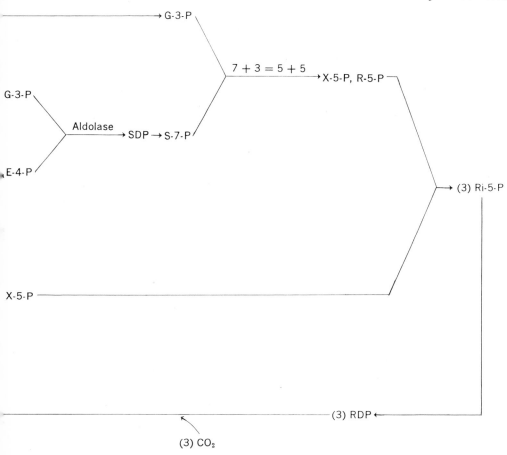

ows a gain of one 3-phosphoglyceric acid for every six initially formed. Key: 3-PGA, FDP, fructose 1,6-diphosphate. F-6-P, fructose 6-phosphate. X-5-P, xylulose 5-phos- se 7-phosphate. R-5-P, ribose 5-phosphate. Ri-5-P, ribulose 5-phosphate. RDP, nting the net gain from one completed cycle.

1. Each of the 3-phosphoglyceric acids must be converted to 3-phosphoglyceraldehyde at the expense of one ATP and one NADPH·H⁺ per molecule of the acid.
2. The enzymes and paths parallel the sedoheptulose monophosphate (pentose) shunt.
3. The intermediates in the pathway are of such a nature as to unite the other major pathways of the cell.

The pathway as proposed is not without dissenters. Some investigators in a series of papers have reported different compounds as early products of photosynthesis, and other workers have suggested some unstable intermediates. Most physiologists concur with the preceding scheme as presented.

Bassham[4] has suggested that the dark reaction, or carbon dioxide reduction cycle, is catalyzed by a multifunctional organized enzyme system, which fits quite handily the scheme of Rabinowitch with the chlorophyll-quinone-cyto-chrome-plastocyanin electron "particle."

INTERRELATIONSHIPS BETWEEN PHOTOSYNTHESIS AND THE OTHER MAJOR PATHWAYS

If a plant cell is to depend on the photosynthetic process for all of its organic carbon source, then it implicitly follows that there must be a close relationship with the other metabolic pathways of the cell. Considering just the intermediates of the carbon pathway of the dark cycle, it can be seen that fructose-1,6-diphosphate can be pulled out or added to the system going to and coming from other sugars and the synthesis or breakdown of starch via the Embden-Meyerhof pathway.

The 3-phosphoglyceric acid could be further changed by continuing down the Embden-Meyerhof pathway, eventually forming pyruvic acid and acetyl-CoA, which have been discussed previously as the hub of the metabolic wheel. The reduction of 3-phosphoglyceric acid to 3-phosphoglyceraldehyde can continue to 3-dihydroxyacetone phosphate. The latter compound can then be converted to glycerol phosphate to participate in the lipid pathways.

The early appearance of labeled amino acids and Krebs cycle intermediates such as malic acid after exposure of photosynthesizing plants to labeled 14-carbon dioxide is not surprising in light of our more complete knowledge of the overall pathways.

Malic acid, for example, is easily formed from pyruvic acid and CO_2 through the Wood-Werkman reaction, as follows:

$$\text{NADPH·H}^+ + \text{Pyruvic acid} + CO_2 \underset{\xleftarrow{\hspace{5cm}}}{\xrightarrow{\text{NADP-linked malic dehydrogenase}}} \text{Malic acid} + \text{NADP}$$

Not only can this reaction fix CO_2, but it also requires the reduced form of the pyridine coenzyme. Labeling in the malic acid could come from two distinct sources—the CO_2 itself and the pyruvic acid which may have been labeled from a 3-phosphoglyceric acid formed during the dark reaction.

In addition to the established mechanisms for biochemically manipulating the intermediates of the photosynthetic carbon cycle, there may be processes and mechanisms which have not been determined. Nevertheless, it is apparent experimentally and from an *a priori* approach that there must be close contact and coordination between the carbon pathways of photosynthesis and the other major metabolic cycles of the cell.

SUMMARY

The autotrophic organisms by their very nature must overcome biochemical problems which do not face the heterotrophs. Since preformed metabolites are not available physiologically as the primary energy source, the autotrophs must find some other method for gleaning energy from the environment and trapping it in a utilizable form.

The most exploited means of trapping energy is the absorption of incident solar energy. This process, photosynthesis, is the use of the energy of incident light to bring about reduction of inorganic carbon dioxide to an organic compound, with the release of oxygen; that is, biochemically it is the reverse of oxidative degradation.

The central importance which the photosynthetic process has in maintenance of balance in the biotic world necessitates careful inspection of the mechanisms which bring about the phenomenon.

It has been established that many pigments are capable of trapping the energy of light, but the trapped energy is normally passed on to chlorophyll a. This compound reaches an excited state, having a higher energy content. Chlorophyll a, the accessory pigments including chlorophyll b, two cytochromes, NADP, and ferredoxin act as an electron chain to move the electrons, which are moved one at a time, from the oxidation-reduction potential of 0.8 volts for water/oxygen to the -0.4 volts for $CO_2/(CH_2O)$ system. The electrons and/or hydrogens moved against the oxidation-reduction gradient come from the water which must give up its hydrogen, forming gaseous oxygen. These processes are dependent on light energy and are called the light or Hill reaction.

The products of the system for electron movement are NADPH·H⁺ and ATP, the latter formed in the one portion of the electron chain which has a downhill gradient. These two products react on the 3-carbon compound formed from the splitting of a 6-carbon intermediate which was the result of the fixing of CO_2 to the 5-carbon ribulose-1,5-diphosphate. The NADPH·H⁺ and ATP are then used to reduce the 3-phosphoglyceric acid to 3-phosphoglyceraldehyde. The aldehyde then cycles through the dark reaction of photosynthesis, which parallels the pentose shunt, so that the final gain is one 3-carbon fragment for every three carbon dioxides which are fixed. The carbon pathway of photosynthesis is interrelated to the metabolic cycles in such a way to afford easy access in both directions.

The experimental data continue to accumulate concerning the various phases of photosynthesis, and for this reason any presentation is probably out of date before it is published. However, it is important to present those ideas which are prevalent at the time of discussion.

Literature cited

1. Park, R. B., and J. Biggins. 1964. Quantasome: Size and composition. Science 144:1009.
2. Clayton, R. K. 1963. Photosynthesis: Primary physical and chemical processes. Ann. Rev. Plant Physiol. 14:159.
3. Rabinowitch, E. I. and Govindjee. 1965. The role of chlorophyll in photosynthesis. Sci. Am. (July), p. 74.
4. Bassham, J. A. 1964. Kinetic studies of the photosynthetic carbon reduction cycle. Ann. Rev. Plant Physiol. 15:101.

General references

Arnon, D. I. 1960. The role of light in photosynthesis. Sci. Am. (November), p. 104.
Bassham, J. A. 1963. Photosynthesis: Energetics and related topics. Advances Enzymol. 25:39.
Bassham, J. A. 1962. The path of carbon in photosynthesis. Sci. Am. (June), p. 89.
Bayliss, L. E. 1959. Principles of general physiology. 5th ed. John Wiley & Sons, Inc., New York.

Calvin, M. 1963. Evolution of photosynthetic mechanisms. In Allen, J. (editor): The nature of biological diversity. McGraw-Hill Book Co., New York.

Duysens, L. N. M. 1964. Photosynthesis. Prog. Biophys. 14:1.

Giese, A. C. (editor). 1964. Photophysiology. Academic Press, Inc., New York. Vol. 2.

Hoch, G., and B. Kok. 1961. Photosynthesis. Ann. Rev. Plant Physiol. 12:155.

McElroy, W. D., and B. Glass (editors). 1961. Light and life. Johns Hopkins University Press, Baltimore.

Meyer, B. S., D. B. Anderson, and R. H. Böhning. 1960. Introduction to plant physiology. D. Van Nostrand Co., Inc., Princeton, N. J.

Smith, J. H. C., and C. S. French. 1963. The major and accessory pigments in photosynthesis. Ann. Rev. Plant Physiol. 14:181.

Wassink, E. C. 1963. Photosynthesis, vol. 5, p. 347. In Florkin, M., and H. S. Mason (editors): Comparative biochemistry. Academic Press, Inc., New York.

Function implies the unification of structure with the biochemical processes and concepts developed in previous sections. The functional cell is a dynamic, exciting machine, with each and every part an important entity for its survival. The regulation of influx and efflux of material into and out from the cell falls to the plasma membrane. The internal membranes regulate passage of material within the cell and also offer a surface on which many accessory functions occur. The basic phenomena of the membrane as a structural and physiological barrier are discussed in Chapter 24.

Each subcellular structure has a precise function in the cell (Chapter 25). However, because of the need for coordination of activity, the separate functions are integrated within the cell. Part of this integration is due to the activity of DNA and RNA, the macromolecules with a purpose (Chapter 26). The mechanism of protein synthesis and how these nucleic acids effect and regulate the process are an amazing story and are a tribute to the confluence of molecular biology and biochemistry.

24

The cell membrane and membrane transport

INTRODUCTION

The living cell has only one major contact with the outer environment, and that is the cell or plasma membrane. It has been established that the composition inside and outside of the cell differs with respect to ions, but the same facts hold true for both large and small organic molecules. And yet, these molecules can be moved into and out from the cell. This implies that the outer, limiting membrane is a functional entity of the cell. The task of regulation of the influx and efflux must fall to this interface. Maintenance of a steady state system where there is this difference between the internal environment and the surrounding medium necessitates some selective control of concentration, passage, or exclusion of various materials from the cell, and this essential property of control is relegated to the excrutiatingly thin tissue enveloping the cell. Considerable attention has been given the structure of this membrane, but the extreme thinness at once hinders study. However, great strides have been made in unmasking the membrane as a protoplasmic structure; concurrently, important disclosures about the membrane as a physiological barrier have been made.

No one chapter can really do justice to the cell membrane and the phenomena associated with transport through it. Only the highlights of the topics will be covered since various books and review articles (see references) discuss in detail the various phases of study. The role of the cell membrane in the overall physiology of the cell will be stressed here. The nature of the membrane, phenomena associated with it (osmosis, charge, and permeability), and active transport will be covered, the latter in some detail since it is an example of directed utilization of the energy gleaned from metabolism. The concepts developed for the phenomena of the cell membrane can be applied to any active membrane in the cell. In summary, the discussion will be divided into two separate but interrelated, topics—the membrane as a protoplasmic structure and the membrane as a physiological barrier.

NATURE OF THE MEMBRANE

The focus of attention for many years has been on the basic structure of the plasma membrane, and despite the electron microscope and other new techniques, the ideas of the basic structure have not been modified significantly from those proposed by earlier workers. The exact physiological composition, however, has not been resolved, particularly as far as the role and organization of the macromolecules in the membrane are concerned. This concept of macromolecular structure has modified many of the ideas of transport, as will be seen in succeeding sections. Before macromolecular dimensions can be considered, the basic structure of this membrane should be discussed.

Components

The evidences for the structure have been gleaned largely from investigations on erythrocyte ghosts and bacterial shells. In both of these preparations, it is relatively easy to get the membrane material free from cytoplasmic contamination.

All accumulated evidence has pointed to the fact that there is lipoidal material in this membrane. The solubility of various compounds into the surface which are characteristically dissolved in lipoids, high electrical resistance, and lysis by lypolytic agents all substantiate the inclusion of lipoidal compounds. However, when the plasma membrane is considered as a colloidal interface, the calculated dynes per centimeter of surface tension for a lipoid-water contact are much higher than those actually measured on the membrane. This can only infer that some other material is adsorbed at this interface, since this accumulation is known to lower the surface tension. The logical material would be protein, and all evidence bears this out. Not only is protein known to act as a biological detergent, but also the fact that enzymes must be present in this outer membrane confirm the presence of the lipoprotein complex. This complex is believed by many investigators to be a universal biological entity.

The lipoids found associated with the membrane are primarily the lecithins, cholesterol, cerebrosides, and sphingomyelin, although other compounds are occasionally present. One would not expect to be able to classify the protein of the membrane because of the diversity in enzyme structure. In addition to these two basic components, other materials have been found to be associated with the plasma membrane. Nucleoproteins, among others, have occasionally been found in membrane fractions.

The basic structure (Plate 4, p. 306)

Early evidence pointed to the fact that the lipoprotein layer may be double. Birefringence data and indirect measurements corroborate this. The plasma membrane has a thickness of approximately 100 Å (although this may vary), which allows for two layers of lipids and two of protein to be oriented in this

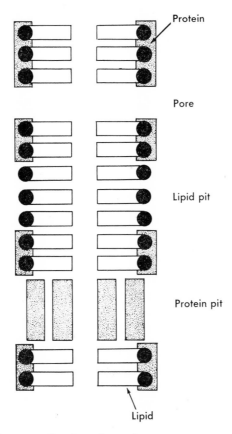

Fig. 24-1. Diagrammatic composite of a cell membrane.

space. Robertson,[1,2] working with myelin membranes, has proposed what he calls the "unit membrane" in which he postulates the universal presence of a triple-layered arrangement on the membrane with a bimolecular leaflet of oriented lipids sandwiched between two protein layers. He allows that there is a variation in thickness, but contends that this basic structure can normally vary within certain limits, depending on the lipids and proteins involved. Some controversy has arisen as a result of this proposal, and Sjöstrand,[3] for one, feels that the membrane arrangement which Robertson proposes may not hold for all membranes. Sjöstrand suggests that there may be protein strands going *through* the membrane as well as being present on the surface. In fact, he has gone so far as to suggest that perhaps the structure of some membranes may be globular pits of lipids separated by a honeycomb of protein lattice work. A composite illustration is seen in Fig. 24-1.

It does seem feasible that there would be protein cross-links bridging the two outer protein layers, particularly if there are macromolecular enzyme complexes which are going to participate in various kinds of transport.

The membrane, then, is probably not a continuous entity, being interrupted by various lipid and protein pits as well as by physical pores. These pores have an average size of 3 to 4 Å in the plasma membrane, in contrast to those in internal membranes which may be much larger.

Accessory structures

There are a number of special structures which are differentiations at the cell surface, at contact surfaces between cells, and at the cell base; they occur primarily on cells of multicellular forms. Most of these specializations have physiological importance and thus carry out the structure-function tenet.

Microvilli are extensions of the cell surface which increase effective areas for absorption and cell transport. They are particularly common on kidney cells and cells of the intestine where the clusters of villi are called the brush border and the striated border, respectively.

Cells in contact with other similar cells in a tissue arrangement often have specialized structures on the contact surfaces. The desmosomes are thickened areas where communication may occur between the cells. Terminal bars, another thickening on contact surfaces, are believed to be for support and strength only. Interdigitating membranes are also a means of increasing the contact surface area between cells (see Plate 4, p. 306).

At the base of cells, inpocketings from the basement membrane area allow for more effective transport between that particular cell and others. These modifications of the membrane can be seen in Fig. 24-2.

The delimiting outer membrane of all cells rarely occurs alone, but is usually found in conjunction with accessory membranes, jelly layers, or cell walls. This series of extraneous coats is peculiar to each cell type. Many of the accessory coats are glycoproteins. The mucin is a protective coating necessary in eggs of marine animals and amphibians and in the cells lining digestive tracts. The plant cells have the cell wall as a protective and structural characteristic. Cellulose and pectin are two main constituents of the wall, although many other compounds may be found as well. Hyaluronic acid surrounds most mammalian cells.

The extraneous coats and coverings do not participate "actively" in control of influx into and efflux out from the cell, although their presence does have an effect on exchange. The accessory membranes and coatings may filter out some

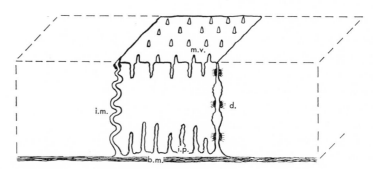

Fig. 24-2. Modifications of the cell surface. **i.m.,** Interdigitating membranes; **d.,** desmosomes; **m.v.,** microvilli; **i.p.,** inpocketing of the base of cell; **b.m.,** basement membrane.

of the components of the external environment before they reach the plasma membrane. This may effectively create a microecological environment near the cell membrane which is different from the general external environment.

Other apparent modifications of the membrane such as cilia and flagella are not exclusively membrane derivatives. These projections are protoplasmic extensions, and the membrane covering them is not much different from the membranes lining any other area of cytoplasm (Plate 6, p. 308).

• • •

The nature of the membrane is going to determine its physiological role (Plate 5, A, p. 307). Its components and orientation of the macromolecules will dictate the phenomena and kinds of transport which will be undertaken. It must be realized that there is no single structure for a membrane because the plasma membrane of any two cell types will be as different as the functional differences of the cells themselves. Only a generalization, then, can be made, and the same applies to membrane function. There are, however, some basic membrane phenomena which most cells undergo.

MEMBRANE PHENOMENA

The structure of a membrane is ideally suited for certain phenomena to occur. These events are associated with the unimpeded movement of materials back and forth across the membrane or for maintenance of a status quo once a disequilibrium exists. It is true that biological transport, or movement mediated by biological entities, may create the basis for these phenomena. This aspect will be covered later.

Diffusion

In this section, diffusion will be discussed in pure physical terms, ignoring the presence of a membrane interposed between two areas of different concentration. Thus, diffusion may be defined as the movement of dissolved substances from an area of higher concentration to an area of lower concentration until an equilibrium is reached where there is no concentration difference. It is a spontaneous process, and because of the attainment of an equilibrium, there is a decrease in the free energy of the system.

In such a system where there is an initial concentration difference, two forces will be set up which depend on the degree of difference between two points in the system. The net movement of the particles from the area of greater concentration to the area of less concentration is called the flux and is given the symbol M. Corollary to the flux movement is a force vector, the concentration gradient [grad], which is defined in terms of being more positive in going from regions of lesser to greater concentration; that is, the sign is negative in going with the flux. For any substance, X, the relationship between flux and concentration is given as

$$Mx = - [grad, (X)] \tag{1}$$

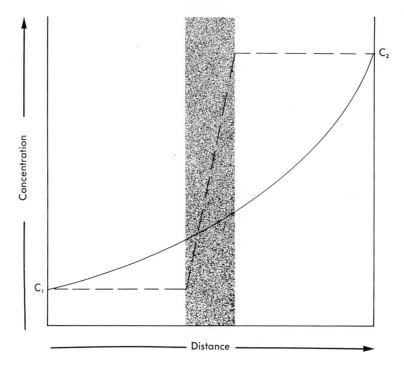

Fig. 24-3. Effect of an interposed membrane on the flux and concentration gradient. With no membrane, the gradient curve between the two concentrations (C_1 and C_2) is smooth and gradual. When a membrane is interposed, the jump from one concentration to the other must occur over a small distance (broken line).

Since the diffusion of material depends on a variety of factors such as particle size, viscosity of fluid, and interaction between particle and solvent, the diffusion constant, D, which is based on these factors, is added to the equation. Equation (1) can then be written as

$$Mx = -D\,[\text{grad},\,(X)] \qquad (2)$$

If a cell membrane is interposed between the areas of concentration, and the movement of the particles is essentially unimpeded, the effective diffusion is not altered. The only difference may be that the initial concentration gradient may be across the thin membrane and not across a large distance, as in a system without the membrane (Fig. 24-3).

Diffusion plays an important role in the transport of biological materials. Diffusion force not only causes some materials to be sent through the membrane but also brings other larger diffusible molecules into contact with the membrane in order to allow other transport mechanisms to occur.

Osmosis

Osmosis is the movement of water from an area of lesser *solute* concentration to an area of greater *solute* concentration. The fact that there is a differential solute concentration infers that there is some interposed membrane which is semipermeable—that is, it is permeable to solvent and some solute molecules but not permeable to others. In other words, a membrane helps maintain the concentration difference which is necessary for osmosis to effectively occur. The term *semipermeable* is sometimes restricted to systems in which the solvent only can move through the membrane; the term *selectively permeable* is reserved for those membranes which allow the passage of molecules other than the solvent. The difference in terminology is semantic because in an aqueous medium, as is found in biological systems, the *semipermeable* term could not apply. There are few, if any, cases in which water movement is not associated with the movement of at least some ions.

With few exceptions, cells are permeable to water, which may create problems for the steady state mechanism of the cell. The movement of water in osmosis is determined by the difference in osmotic pressure between any two points, and again entropy balance is of considerable importance. If one area, delimited by a membrane, has a solute concentration greater than some other region, the chemical potential is higher in that area where the concentration is higher. As a result, in an attempt to reach an equilibrium of forces, water is driven toward the area of greater chemical potential. This potential is essentially proportional to the number of molecules of solute present, assuming a solution rather than a colloid. Thus, the osmotic drive, force or pressure, is given by the formula

$$\pi V = nRT$$

where π is the osmotic pressure, V the volume, n the number of moles, and R and T the gas constant (0.032 l-atm/deg/mole) and absolute temperature, respectively. When the terms are rearranged, the effect of concentration can be seen:

$$\pi = \frac{n}{V} RT$$

The ratio $\frac{n}{V}$ is moles per volume, or concentration. This formulation demonstrates one of the colligative properties of a solution. The colligative properties are those which are dependent on the number of molecules present in a solution and not on the kind of molecules. Two factors could modify osmotic pressure. The first of these is the concentration itself. If a solution is very concentrated, the activity of each molecule is generally decreased because of interaction among the particles in solution. The $\frac{n}{V}$ should be equated to the *effective* concentration, which cannot easily be determined directly; measurement of the osmotic pressure by other means would give the effective concentration.

The second factor is the species of molecule in solution. In biological systems, many molecules do not exhibit those properties characteristic for particles in solution; that is, proteins and the macromolecules are in a colloidal system to which colligative properties cannot correctly be applied.

Nevertheless, each cell has an effective osmotic pressure which is often quite different from the external environment. This infers that there will be water movement into and out from the cell, and this must be controlled in order to maintain the steady state. Osmosis can be redefined in terms of pressure by stating that osmosis is the movement of water from an area of lesser osmotic pressure to a region where the osmotic pressure is greater.

Freshwater, single-celled organisms exert control by forming contractile vacuoles which excrete the excess water which has moved into the cell. These cells have a higher osmotic pressure than the surrounding medium, and as a result, there is an influx of water into the internal milieu. Very few single-celled organisms have osmotic pressures less than the outer environment and therefore the active uptake of water is unnecessary. In multicellular forms, control is primarily in the fluid bathing the cells rather than in the cells themselves.

Cells of both animals and plants, when placed in a hypertonic medium, exhibit a predictable reaction to this higher concentration. The plant cell wall prevents the entire cell from undergoing any visible reaction, but the cytoplasm, inside the wall, with the surrounding plasma membrane, loses water to the outside and shrinks, the reaction being called plasmolysis. In animal cells, where the outer membrane is flexible, the whole cell shrinks, a process called crenation. Conversely, if cells are placed in a very hypotonic medium, there is a general influx of water, causing swelling and eventually bursting of animal cells not having a mechanism such as the contractile vacuole to control the excess water. In plant cells, the cell wall again prevents large configurational changes, but the cytoplasmic mass inside swells against the cell wall in a process called plasmoptysis. The pressure exerted against the cell wall is a result of the turgid pressure of the cell.

Permeability

If permeability is defined as the rate of movement of a substance through a permeable layer under a given driving force, it seems implicit that there are three major conditions which affect and effect this movement:

1. The characteristic of the membrane as to its chemical nature and enzymes present
2. The molecule being moved
3. The driving force of the molecules, a force which may be totally independent of any property of the membrane

Permeability is of fundamental importance for the functioning of the living cell and the maintenance of satisfactory intracellular physiological conditions. This function determines which substances can enter and leave the cell and, to some degree, the rate at which this movement occurs. Thus, permeability is a prerequisite to steady state control in the open system. Further, cell permeability undergoes continual changes which are determined by the physiological state of the cell and/or a change in the external environment.

The characteristics of the molecule being moved which are of prime importance to the permeability are the following:

1. Species of molecule

2. Size
3. Lipid solubility
4. Charge
5. Polarity
6. Degree of ionization

The effect of these factors will become apparent as the chemical nature of the membrane which is responsible for the permeability characteristics is discussed.

Pore size in the membrane is, of course, a determining factor in permeability. A molecule which is larger than the pore normally will not move across the membrane in a passive process. However, the fact that a molecule is of smaller size than the pore does not guarantee its being allowed to move across the membrane. Often, pores have an inherent charge associated with them due to orientation of the molecules around them. As a result, if the pore and the molecule have the same charge, repulsion will occur. Even if a molecule is smaller than the pore and has an opposite charge, it may not be able to penetrate the membrane. Many ions and molecules are surrounded by a heavy layer of the water of hydration. This adsorbed layer makes the effective size of the ion or molecule larger than the pore, and as a result, passive movement cannot easily occur.

The lipid content of the membrane is also an important factor in permeability. Those compounds which are fat soluble, such as many polar molecules, are more likely to be passed through the membrane than those compounds which are not easily attracted to the lipids. In other words, the membrane will be more permeable to the compounds with the highest partition coefficient (in this case, the ratio of solubility in lipids to its solubility in water). Some permeability characteristics of membranes have been attributed to nucleoproteins,[4] although these cases seem to be rare.

The proteins in the membrane, acting as enzymes in active transport, determine which species of ions and molecules will be carried across the membrane. The individual factors in the process are discussed in the section on active transport.

Gibbs-Donnan equilibrium

The presence of a molecular species to which the membrane is not permeable sets up a condition which affects the normal diffusion and permeability of other molecules. If it is assumed that K^+ and Cl^- ions are free to pass through a membrane, then any concentration difference set up between the two sides of the membrane will be met by a diffusion of the ions until an equilibrium is reached. At equilibrium, according to the Gibbs-Donnan rule, the product of the diffusible ions on both sides of a membrane are equal, or

$$[K^+]_1 \times [Cl^-]_1 = [K^+]_2 \times [Cl^-]_2 \tag{3}$$

Often, in a biological system, however, the charge on the inner side of the membrane is supplied by a nondiffusible molecule (for example, the second carboxyl group of a dicarboxylic amino acid residue of a protein). When complete ionization and no binding of the ions are assumed, a sequence of calculations can be made. Assume that the initial condition on the two sides of the membrane is

$$(a) \ K^+; \ P^- \quad \Big| \quad K^+; \ Cl^- \ (b) \qquad (4)$$

If the Gibbs-Donnan rule applies, then (3) must hold true at equilibrium. But at equilibrium, the following condition exists:

$$(a) \ K^+; \ P^-; \ Cl^- \quad \Big| \quad K^+; \ Cl^- \ (b) \qquad (5)$$

Compartment (b) contains only the potassium and chloride ions since the protein, P^-, cannot diffuse across the membrane. Therefore, in addition to the products of the diffusible ions being equal at the final equilibrium, the number of positive and negative charges must be balanced. The following set of equations describes the final condition in these terms.

It is implicit that the amount of K^+ on the inside (a) of the membrane will have a higher final concentration than the K^+ on the outside (b) because of the need to balance both the P^- and Cl^- negative species. If X is considered to be the final concentration of the Cl^- on the inside (a), then at equilibrium the concentration of each component is

	Initial		Final	
	(a)	(b)	(a)	(b)
K^+	C_1	C_2	$C_1 + X$	$C_2 - X$
Cl^-	0	C_2	X	$C_2 - X$
P^-	C_1	0	C_1	0

with C_1 and C_2 being the initial molar concentrations in (a) and (b). Applying the law of mass action to the final state of the diffusible ions

$$(C_1 + X)(X) = (C_2 - X)(C_2 - X)$$

or

$$(X^2) + (C_1 X) = (C_2)^2 - 2(C_2 X) + X^2$$

Solving for X

$$X = \frac{(C_2)^2}{C_1 + 2C_2}$$

This relationship is called the Gibbs-Donnan equilibrium as applied to a single pair of diffusible ions. It can, however, be extended to any number of pairs. The effects of the distribution of K^+ and Cl^- on the two sides of the membrane can be seen in Tables 24-1 and 24-2. The Gibbs-Donnan equilibrium can only be applied generally to a living cell because of the active processes involved which disrupt the passive diffusiveness of the ions. Nevertheless, the equilibrium and its concepts offer an explanation of the effect that nondiffusible cellular constituents have on the overall movement of diffusible molecules. Furthermore, the Gibbs-Donnan relationship demonstrates how a disequilibrium of an ion

Table 24-1. Distribution of KCl on two sides of a membrane which is impermeable to one charged species (P⁻)

Initial state				Equilibrium state*				
C_1		C_2		$C_1 + X$	C_1	X	$C_2 - X$	$C_2 - X$
K⁺	P⁻	K⁺	Cl⁻	K⁺	P⁻	Cl⁻	K⁺	Cl⁻
1000	1000	1000	1000	1333	1000	333	666	666
1000	1000	100	100	1008	1000	8.3	91.7	91.7
100	100	1000	1000	576	100	476	524	524

*Notice that at the equilibrium state in each set of conditions, the number of positive and negative charges on any one side of the membrane is equal, but the concentrations are not equal when the inside (C_1) is compared with the outside (C_2).

Table 24-2. Distribution ratios of KCl on two sides of a membrane which is impermeable to one charged species (P⁻)

Initial ratio of KP to KCl $\dfrac{C_1}{C_2}$	Percent KCl going from C_2 to C_1 $\dfrac{100X}{C}$	Equilibrium ratio of KCl between C_2 and C_1 $\dfrac{C_2 - X}{X}$
1.00	33.0	2.00
10.00	8.3	11.10
0.10	47.6	1.10

pair can be created across a membrane by passive forces. This is important in maintenance of the membrane potential.

Membrane potential

In most instances, the cell membrane can be considered to be an electrical membrane. Interposition of a nonaqueous membrane as a boundary between the aqueous intracellular fluid and aqueous external medium sets up two striking characteristics of living membranes:

1. An ion concentration difference is set up between the two sides of the membrane.
2. As a result, there is a difference in electric potential between the inside of the cell and the external environment.

These differences are created by such phenomena as the Gibbs-Donnan equilibrium and active transport of ionic species. Even if the charges are balanced in each side of the membrane, there may be a concentration differential of any one ionic species (Table 24-1). This differential, or ionic gradient, can be expressed as an electrochemical potential by applying the Nernst equation.

This equation states that the electrochemical potential of an ion across a membrane is proportional to the ratio of the concentration on the two sides of the membrane. Mathematically,

$$E_{ion} = \frac{RT}{FZ} \ln \frac{C_2}{C_1}$$

where E_{ion} is the electropotential in millivolts, C_2 and C_1 are the concentrations outside and inside the membrane, R is the gas constant, 8.2 joules/mole-degree,

T is the absolute temperature, F is the faraday (96,500 coulombs/mole), and Z is the valence of the ion. At 37° C., and converting to log to the base 10, this equation simplifies to

$$E_{ion} = 60 \log_{10} \frac{C_2}{C_1}$$

for an ion such as potassium with a valence of +1.

Each ion, then, has its own electrochemical equation, but some have a greater effect on the membrane than others because of their being present in greater concentrations. For many membranes, the resting potential or steady state membrane potential is determined primarily by sodium and potassium. As we will see later, these two ions have different permeability coefficients, and thus the Nernst equation would have to be modified to account for this in that the effective concentration is altered by the ratio of the permeability coefficients.

The measured resting membrane potential is about 90 mv, which is a large voltage, considering that it is across a membrane only 100 Å thick. The calculated potential from the measured ion difference values plugged into the Nernst equation is very close to the observed electrochemical potential. The active mechanism to maintain this resting potential and the sequence of events which change this potential are discussed in both the section on active transport and the chapter on conductivity (Chapter 27).

•   •   •

The membrane phenomena are dependent upon the physical principles of osmosis, diffusion, and effect on concentration differences as modified by the interposing of a membrane of selective permeability. These events which are peculiar to the living membrane form the basis for a discussion of biological transport.

BIOLOGICAL TRANSPORT

According to Csaky,[5] there are four basic means by which a substance may move across a membrane:
1. Free diffusion
2. Diffusion through pores
3. Pinocytosis
4. Carrier-mediated transport

The first two do not require energy input by the cell, the force being supplied by diffusion and osmotic pressures. Some small solvent-soluble particles, though, may also be pulled through the membrane even if the membrane does not normally allow their passage by passive means. This phenomenon is called solvent drag. Pinocytosis, which is the phagocytic-like capture of materials to be brought into the cell, and the carrier-mediated transport may involve expenditure of energy by the cell. The latter classification can be further broken down in order to differentiate between those processes involving energy input and those which use a carrier, but apparently without requiring energy. Some investigators have long proposed that the term *facilitated diffusion* be applied to those transports which occur when a carrier or mediator is involved but in which the substance (or complex) is not able to proceed uphill against the concentration gradient. The observed fact that some cells can apparently accumulate some substances without the expenditure of energy necessitates, perhaps, modification of the definition to read "against the *effective* concentration gradient."

Active transport implies that there is utilization of energy to move the substance through the membrane, and this poses the question as to how the energy of the cell can be converted to osmotic energy. Whereas diffusion and osmosis follow the second law of thermodynamics, active transport does not. There is a decrease in the entropy of the system when active transport occurs, and the only means by which this can occur in an isothermal condition is the addition of some cellular energy to the process.

Energy sources and applications to transport phenomena

There is probably no energy form in the cell which does not participate in active transport in some way. The increase in free energy which occurs when a metabolite is moved across the membrane against the gradient is a worthwhile investment. Energies which are available for the process can come from the following:

1. High-energy ATP
2. Mechanical energy due to contraction
3. Oxidation-reduction reactions (electron flow)
4. Electrical field
5. Vectorial metabolism
6. Any combination of the above sources

ATPase in the membrane

In order for the membrane to harness the energy of ATP, there must reside in the membrane a specific enzyme which will hydrolyze the ATP to glean the energy from its $\sim$P. The highly ionized phosphate grouping apparently facilitates the use of the adenylic acid system in moving ions and electrolytes across the membrane. They are not the only substances to which the ATP energy is directed. Inhibitor studies show that the movement of amino acids, sugars, and other organic compounds is depressed when the ATPase system is blocked. This would indicate that the energy from ATP is necessary for active transport of these compounds.

Mechanical energy due to contraction

There has been some evidence that the contraction of a protein molecule around which a membrane has formed causes expression of water from the membrane and concentration of the ions within this small vesicle. If the vesicle is then extruded, or breaks at the cell surface, the ions will move out from the cell. How general this phenomenon is has not been suggested.

Energy from electropotential differences (the redox pump)

This mechanism implies a biological pump in which there is an anisotropic alignment of electron or ion carriers across the membrane. Urry and Eyring's[6] imidazole pump is an example of this type of utilization. In this case, the energy is used to generate an ATP, but it could be applied to movement of materials across a membrane just as well. There are other examples where the coupling of a pathway involves a large difference in electropotential with the movement of substances through a membrane. The direct use of metabolic energy is attractive as a theory, but conflicting data indicate that it is not applicable to all systems.

Free radicals and transport

The release of free radicals on either side of a membrane sets up an electric field which facilitates the movement of charged particles through the membrane. Free radicals are known to exist in biological systems, but whether their concentration reaches levels high enough to exert a definite effect on membrane transport is not known.

Vectorial metabolism

Mitchell[7] has suggested that metabolic energy can be directed toward transport by simply enzymatically catalyzing a change in the material being transported in such a way that the reaction will pull more of the same material to be changed by applying the mass action law. If the change is a splitting of the molecule, and if the enzyme is asymmetrically oriented so as to release the split halves of the molecule in different directions, there could be an effective transfer of a substance (Fig. 24-4).

There seems to be no one mechanism for energy input which is universal for all cases of active transport. The means of harnessing the energy are just as different as the mechanism for the transport requires. In all instances, though, it must be kept in mind that active transport, by definition, requires energy in some form. What the form is and how it is converted to osmotic energy may not be clear.

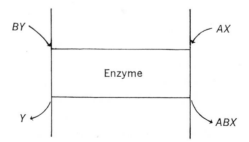

Fig. 24-4. Transport through asymmetrically oriented enzymes. BY is split by the enzyme, with each half being released on different sides of the membrane.

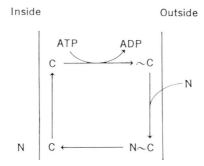

Fig. 24-5. Diagram of a possible scheme for active transport. Carrier, *C*, is "activated" by the ATP. The "activated" *C* continues with material to be transported, *N*. The *N* is released at the inside of the membrane at the expense of energy. Carrier, *C*, is then ready for reactivation.

Nature of the carrier

Although most evidence implies that active transport involves some type of carrier, the nature of the carrier is uncertain. There are several distinct possibilities, two of which will be discussed here.

The possibility that the energy-requiring step in active transport is production through the metabolic paths of a substance which is produced for the specific purpose of combining with and moving a substance across the membrane is not remote. This necessitates that the membrane have enzymes in it for the production of the carrier molecule, or that the pathways be contiguous with the membrane, with the carrier penetrating the membrane in order to carry out its function. Such a system could be visualized as shown in Fig. 24-5.

The second possibility, which looms stronger as evidence accumulates, is that there are present as components of the membrane, stereospecific compounds which can bind with or alter the substance to be transported and then, by expending metabolic energy, can transfer the molecule to the other side of the membrane (Fig. 24-6). The carrier molecule could actually undergo a 180° change in orientation in order to bring about this transport. This 180° reversal permits coupled transport in the other direction when the original orientation is regained.

Permeases

The permeases are stereospecific transport systems which are operative in at least bacterial systems, according to their proponents. The fact that the description and action parallel the stereospecific carriers just discussed has caused some consternation and confusion among membrane physiologists. One striking fact about some permease systems in bacteria is that the system for transporting a substance across the membrane may be induced. That is, there is no mechanism present for getting a particular metabolite across the cell membrane until the cell comes in contact with the substance itself. This does not mean that the metabolic pathway for handling the metabolite is not present, because more often than not, the pathway is already established. It simply means that the

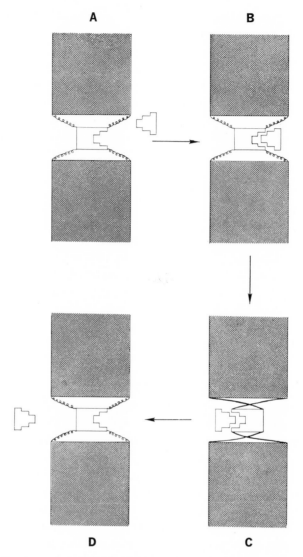

Fig. 24-6. An active transport model in which carrier molecule undergoes 180° reversal in orientation, resulting in transport. *A,* Carrier is in "active" state, facing the outside of the membrane. *B,* Molecule to be transported attaches to carrier, and then undergoes a 180° turn. *C,* The turn results in the molecules being transported to the inside. *D,* The carrier returns to its original orientation. Energy would probably be required to bring about both reversal and return to the original orientation.

active transport mechanism, whatever it might be, is not present and is only produced or activated when the membrane comes in contact with the substance to be transported.

The fact that the permease systems as described may operate without apparent energy input also adds to the nomenclature confusion, for this, on the surface, mimics facilitated diffusion. There is good likelihood that the nomenclature disagreement will not be resolved until more evidence accumulates as to what the characteristics of the system are and how much they overlap with other transport mechanisms.

Examples of active transport

It is difficult to select examples of active transport because there might be a tendency to generalize. The distinct possibility that each transport mechanism may be different from all others must be kept in mind, and thus the examples discussed here must not be construed as necessarily being typical.

Intestinal transport

One of the systems which possesses a mechanism for actively moving sugars and amino acids across a membrane is the one in the epithelium of the gut. The energy source is apparently ATP, as is borne out by most evidence. The phosphorylation, or hexokinase, step in glucose uptake is well known, and there is an excellent possibility that amino acids are charged in the same manner. This system also demonstrates one other phenomenon which is becoming more and more prevalent, and that is the link between the active transport of an electrolyte and the movement of nonelectrolytes.

Whether by vectorial metabolism, carrier transport, or some other means, the glucose when it moves across the membrane of the gut is phosphorylated at the expense of the energy in ATP.

$$Glucose + ATP \longrightarrow Glucose\text{-}6\text{-}phosphate + ADP$$

This mechanism must not be this simple because, in addition to phosphorylating inhibitors, low sodium decreases the rate of transport. Csaky[8] proposes that this dependence may be the necessity of maintaining a critical intracellular sodium concentration. This internal level of sodium, he postulates, is required for conversion of chemical energy into osmotic energy for pumping glucose through the membrane. Such evidence as listed below are corroborating data.

1. The inhibition due to low sodium is reversible if the ion is replaced.
2. The facilitated diffusion systems do not require a specific sodium level.
3. The sodium requirement in active transport is nonspecific.

The sodium pump

In most cells there is a differential between the internal milieu and the external environment so far as the concentrations of potassium and sodium are concerned. Sodium tends to be present in very small amounts in the cell, at levels much below the concentration outside the cell. Conversely, the potassium concentration is quite high within the cell and significantly lower in the external medium.

For any theory proposed for an active transport of sodium and potassium through a membrane, the following criteria must be met.[9]

1. The mechanism must be located in the membrane.
2. The inside of the membrane should have a site which more specifically binds sodium than it does potassium.

3. By the same token, there should be a site on the outside of the membrane which more specifically binds potassium than it does sodium.

4. There should be an ATPase mechanism present in the membrane, that is, some system which can release the energy from the $\sim$P of ATP.

5. The utilization of the energy from the $\sim$P should be proportional to the concentrations of both the potassium and the sodium.

6. The proposed mechanism should be found in all cells where this universal, linked transport of Na$^+$ and K$^+$ occurs.

In one scheme which accounts for much of the evidence, the Na$^+$-K$^+$ balance is maintained by a combination diffusion—active transport mechanism. The pore size of most membranes is such that K$^+$ can penetrate relatively easily. Sodium, on the other hand, has a large layer of hydration and cannot enter the pore with any great ease. Both ions, then, can move through the membrane, but the sodium only with great difficulty. Because of the relative permeability, the sodium balance must be maintained by an active transport mechanism pumping out of the cell, whereas there must be a corollary mechanism for actively accumulating K$^+$ within the cell. This type of system is known as the pump-leak mechanism where there is active transport of a substance in one direction, with passive diffusion of the compound in the opposite direction. Disequilibrium can be maintained only as long as the pump is working.

Skou[10] postulates that the transport system for sodium and potassium is located in a distinct, submicroscopic particle in the membrane. The idea is not incompatible with data, but the existence of a structural, macromolecular unit has not been firmly established.

•   •   •

Many other transport systems have been worked out to the point where hypothetical schemes have been postulated. Most of them, however, have to do with smaller organic molecules or inorganic electrolytes. The important area of large molecule movement has not been developed, although the next topic suggests some ideas.

Pinocytosis

It may be that all transport into the cell is not through the plasma membrane per se. Quite a large amount of accumulated evidence suggests that a process once described as a curiosity may in fact be widespread. This process, pinocytosis, is the transport of materials within a membrane structure. The process parallels phagocytosis in that the membrane closes about the substance to be transported, forming a membrane-lined vacuole. This vacuole is then pulled to the inner surface of the membrane, and the contents are extruded to the internal milieu. Or conversely, the vacuole will open to the outside in an excretory or secretory function (Plate 8, p. 310).

The cell surface is not smooth and rigid as many diagrammatic representations depict it. Instead, there are many channels, infoldings, and outpocketings along the entire membrane. Experimental evidence for the process is irrefutable, but the extent of occurrence is still uncertain. There is good evidence that the process occurs in ameba and ameboid cells, kidney tubule cells, cells of the reticuloendothelial system, cells of root hairs, and many other cells which are known to have a flexible and pliable membrane. The occurrence in many other cell types, however, has not been demonstrated, but this may be due to difficulties in technique.

An important clue to the mechanism of pinocytosis is the fact that the presence of various compounds and ions in the medium induces formation of pinocytotic vesicles. Various salts induce this process, particularly the cations. A surprising finding associated with ion-induced pinocytosis is that if a certain concentration level is reached the process diminishes in rate. Then, if the cell is washed free of the inducer and is then placed in fresh medium, the induced pinocytosis again occurs. This might imply that there are specific sites for pinocytotic transport of each particular compound, and that under high concentrations these sites become saturated, decreasing the pinocytotic activity. The alternate possibility is that there is a general control mechanism which is nonspecific. The former suggestion is more attractive.

Various proteins induce pinocytosis, and this fact hints of the great importance that this process may have. It has often been demonstrated that large proteins and other macromolecules can penetrate the cell membrane, but few mechanisms have been suggested. Pinocytosis may very well supply the answer to this perplexing question. If a specific site is assumed for transport of molecules characteristically moved across the membrane of a cell, a plausible mechanism is apparent. As the macromolecule comes in contact with this specific site, pinocytosis could be induced, resulting in transport of the substance across the membrane. This hypothesis is attractive in many ways in that it explains away many of the difficulties of other transport mechanisms so far as large molecule movement is concerned. Small pore size and movement through the membrane of a substance probably larger than most postulated carriers have been perplexing impasses to suggesting an accepted mechanism of transport. If pinocytosis is demonstrated to be a universal, as well as a specific, phenomenon, it may turn out to be an important facet of active transport.

MEMBRANE FUNCTION

The function of the membrane is not only the movement of materials into and out from the cell. The mechanisms of transport are in themselves only the tools which allow transport processes to participate in certain specific functions which are critical to the living cell. Specialized membrane phenomena are associated with such cellular processes as conduction and contraction or movement. These will be dealt with separately. There are other roles, however, which are more general and can be applied to most cell types. These membrane functions are regulation of cell volume, regulation and control of various cell processes, and secretion.

Cell volume regulation

The regulation of cell volume pertains particularly to the regulation of the water content of the cell. But as the axiom "As sodium goes, so goes water" states, the problem of control is regulation of the sodium, and thus potassium, level in the cell.

The pump-leak mechanism of Na^+-K^+ transport is essentially a one-for-one exchange of sodium and potassium. That is, for each potassium brought in there is one sodium pumped out. Much of the work on the effect of these two ions on the cell volume has been done on HK and LK sheep red blood cells. Apparently, the potassium level of these cells is inherited as a single mendelian character. It has been found that both of these cell types will swell if the pump mechanism is blocked by an inhibitor. In other words, if leakage of the ions increases or active transport decreases, swelling occurs.

Tosteson[11] has commented on the evolutionary importance of the sodium control mechanism. He suggests that there are three ways to prevent swelling of cells:

1. By making the outer membrane essentially impermeable to sodium
2. By having a tough extraneous coat around the cell
3. By having an active transport mechanism designed as a pump-leak system

Plant cells do use the second alternative, but the first is untenable, at least if cells are going to be at all excitable. The pump-leak, then, is the best solution, particularly for animal cells where rigidity is not desired. The underlying factor in controlling the swelling is that the macromolecules of the cell must be in close contact in order to function effectively. An increase in cell volume would bring about the physical separation of these macromolecules, causing a more inefficient physiology of the cell.

Regulation of cell processes

The various cell processes are regulated by the transport mechanism, but the relationship is often reciprocal.

The ATP-ATPase system has already been established as a possible energy source for transport of various cations. The tie between ATP production and metabolism is apparent. In addition to the overt relationship between ATP production by the metabolic pathways and the use of the high-energy bond for transport, there is some evidence, at least in mitochondria, that the enzyme system which produces ATP in the membrane may be the same system which is involved in cation transfer. When the mitochondrion accumulates calcium, the production of ATP by the membrane is significantly decreased.

If the permeases are considered to be specific proteins with catalytic activity for transport, then these compounds are involved in regulation of cell function. Their presence would determine the rate at which the metabolites would be brought into the cell. The fact that some can be, or must be, induced is an added control factor of internal metabolite level.

Finally, the level of certain critical ions determines the level of enzyme activity within the cell. The series of ionic cofactors are obviously needed to complete the electrostatic configuration of the enzyme-substrate complex. More subtly, other ions such as monovalent K^+ exert direct influence on the level of certain activities. More than twenty enzymes have been listed by Lubin[12] as being activated by potassium. Potassium depletion in the cell prevents protein synthesis but allows nucleic acid synthesis to continue. This dependence may have been evolutionary pressure for high intracellular potassium. This, coupled with the need for low internal sodium to control cell volume, partially explains the type of kinetics found in the Na^+-K^+ pump-leak mechanisms.

The membrane in secretion

Secretion in its final stages is almost invariably a membrane phenomenon. The products to be secreted may be formed in internal structures of the cell, but the final elaboration of the secretion falls to the membrane.

The membrane itself may perform the actual secretion. Examples are the formation of hydrochloric acid by the parietal cells of the gastric mucosa and the ion exchange mechanism of the kidney tubule cells. The necessity for these secretions to be a surface phenomenon is due to the high toxicity of the compounds involved. The transport of these substances within the cell organelles to the outer membrane could result in damage.

That portion of the secretory mechanism which involves removal of the secretion to the outer environment is almost exclusively a membrane function. The transport of ions and small organic molecules fits into the accepted modes of transport; the secretion of such substances as hormones and other large molecules causes one to reflect on a pinocytotic-like release of these materials by the membrane.

Without belaboring the point, it should be apparent that the membrane is like any other organelle. It has its specific functions and mechanisms peculiar to these functions, but it does not operate totally as a separate entity from the rest of the physiological cell. Thus, the membrane has cellular functions which are derived from its transport mechanisms.

SUMMARY

The cell membrane is the only organelle of the cell which is in constant contact with the outer environment. As a result, precise control of the internal milieu with respect to the outer medium is the primary role of this outer delimiting membrane. The plasma membrane is more than a structural unit; it is a physiological barrier.

The structure of the membrane has not been determined to any great satisfaction, although it is implicit that the nature of the membrane will determine its physiological role. Its extreme thinness makes it very difficult to analyze, and this fact, along with the evidence that there may be variations among different types of cells, allows only generalizations to be made as to structure. All evidence suggests the presence of both lipoid and protein material, probably arranged in some lipoprotein complex; the exact orientation is still under debate. Other compounds, however, may also be present.

The membrane is not a smooth, outer coating but instead has characteristic folds as well as accessory structures. Some of these latter modifications are microvilli, desmosomes, terminal bars, and a variety of extraneous membranes and coats.

Any membrane has associated with it a series of phenomena which are independent of any active mechanism by the cell. The physiological processes may enhance or depress these characteristic phenomena, but they still play an important part in the overall functioning of the membrane.

The movement of water and solute particles in response to concentration pressures is dictated by the laws of diffusion and osmosis. The difference between these two is that osmosis implies a membrane through which material must travel. What gets through the membrane, and thus affects the osmotic pressure, is determined by the permeability of the membrane itself. There are three major conditions which affect permeability and thus movement through a membrane.

1. The nature of the membrane
2. The molecule being moved
3. The driving force of the molecules

In osmosis and diffusion, the force follows the second law of thermodynamics, thereby increasing entropy. Only active transport causes an increase in free energy, with concomitant decrease of entropy.

Selective permeability brings about two phenomena based on this property. The first is the Gibbs-Donnan equilibrium, which describes the concentration of diffusible ions on two sides of the membrane in the presence of a charged group on one side to which the membrane is impermeable. The result of any imbalance of concentration of an ion leads to the creation of a membrane potential which is proportional to the ratio of concentrations on the two sides.

The actual transport of material across the membrane is encompassed in the subject of biological transport. This transport can be passive where the driving force is effective concentration only. This includes movement by diffusion, facilitated diffusion with a carrier, and osmosis. Active transport, on the other hand, implies utilization of some cellular energy to move material through the membrane. There are several possible sources of this energy, among them ATP, electropotential differences, contractile forces, and vectorial metabolism.

Harnessing of the energy by the membrane almost necessitates the presence of specific enzymes. Whether these enzymes are a part of the carrier system or supply the energy for the carrier is not resolved. Nonetheless, there is good evidence that the carrier is specific for a particular transport mechanism. A type of specific carrier or site of attachment of the molecule to be moved is the permease system. This stereospecific system is a transport mechanism capable of being induced by the presence of the substance to be transported.

An example of an active transport mechanism in which the electrolytes may affect nonelectrolyte movement is in the epithelium of the gut which pumps sugars and amino acids into the bloodstream against a gradient. This process is apparently sodium-dependent.

The Na$^+$-K$^+$ pump-leak mechanism is a transport system in which potassium and sodium are exchanged one for one in order to maintain a definite ratio of ions inside to ions outside. As the name implies, there is active pumping of the ion in one direction and a permitted amount of leakage in the other.

Pinocytosis, a process of envacuolating material to be transported, is a mechanism which may explain the movement of large molecules into and out from the cell.

Finally, the membrane is involved in other functions besides transport per se. Some of these are the following:

1. Control of cell volume
2. Activation of internal enzymes by controlling ion levels
3. Participation both primarily and secondarily in the secretion process of the cell

Literature cited

1. Robertson, J. D. 1959. The ultrastructure of cell membranes and their derivatives, p. 3. In Crook, E. M. (editor): Structure and function of subcellular components. Biochemical Society Symposium No. 16. Cambridge University Press, London.
2. Robertson, J. D. 1964. Unit membranes: A review with recent new studies of experimental alterations and a new subunit structure in synaptic membranes, p. 1. In M. Locke (editor): Cellular membranes in development. Academic Press, Inc., New York.
3. Sjöstrand, F. S., and L. Elfin. 1964. The granular structure of mitochondrial membranes and of cytomembranes as demonstrated in frozen-dried tissue. J. Ultrastruct. Res. 10:263.
4. Mazia, D. 1940. The binding of ions by the cell surface. Cold Spring Harbor Symposia on Quantitative Biology. Vol. 8, p. 195.
5. Csaky, T. Z. 1965. Transport through biological membranes. Ann. Rev. Physiol. 27:415.
6. Urry, D. W., and H. Eyring. 1965. Biological electron transport. II. A variation of the imidazole pump model to include coupling. J. Theor. Biol. 8:214.
7. Mitchell, P. 1963. Molecule, group and electron translocation through natural membranes, p. 142. In Bell, D. J., and J. K. Grant (editors): The structure and function of the membranes and surfaces of cells. Biochemical Society Symposium No. 22. Cambridge University Press, London.
8. Csaky, T. Z. 1963. A possible link between active transport of electrolytes and non-electrolytes. Fed. Proc. 22:3.
9. Skou, J. C. 1964. Enzymatic aspects of active linked transport of Na$^+$ and K$^+$ through the cell membrane. Prog. Biophys. 14:131.
10. Skou, J. C. 1957. The influence of some cations on the adenosine triphosphate from peripheral nerves. Biochim. Biophys. Acta. 23:394.
11. Tosteson, D. C. 1963. Active transport, genetics, and cellular evolution. Fed. Proc. 22:19.
12. Lubin, M. 1964. Cell potassium and the regulation of protein synthesis, p. 193. In Hoffman, J. F. (editor): The cellular functions of membrane transport. Prentice-Hall, Inc., Englewood Cliffs, N. J.

General references

Anderson, B., and Ussing, H. H. 1960. Active transport, vol. 2, p. 371. In Florkin, M., and H. S. Mason (editors): Comparative biochemistry. Academic Press, Inc., New York.

Bayliss, L. E. 1960. Principles of general physiology. 5th ed. John Wiley & Sons, Inc., New York. Vol. 2.

Bayliss, L. E. 1959. Principles of general physiology. 5th ed. John Wiley & Sons, Inc., New York. Vol. 1.

Bell, D. J., and J. K. Grant (editors). 1963. The structure and function of the membranes and surfaces of the cell. Biochemical Society Symposium No. 22. Cambridge University Press, London.

Casey, E. J. 1962. Biophysics. Concepts and mechanisms. Reinhold Publishing Corp., New York.

Christensen, H. N. 1962. Biological transport. W. A. Benjamin, Inc., New York.

Danielli, J. F. 1954. Morphological and molecular aspects of active transport, vol. 8, p. 502. Symposium, Society of Experimental Biology. In Bourne, G. H., and J. F. Danielli (editors): International review of cytology. Academic Press, Inc., New York.

Davson, H. 1959. A textbook of general physiology. 2nd ed. Little, Brown & Co., Boston.

Giese, A. C. 1962. Cell physiology. 2nd ed. W. B. Saunders Co., Philadelphia.

Hoffman, J. F. (editor). 1964. The cellular functions of membrane transport. Prentice-Hall, Inc., Englewood Cliffs, N. J.

Hokin, L. E., and M. R. Hokin. 1963. Biological transport. Ann. Rev. Biochem. 32:553.

Holter, H. 1961. How things get into cells. Sci. Am. (Sept.), p. 167.

Holter, H. 1960. Pinocytosis. Internat. Rev. Cytol. 8:481.

Kuyper, Ch. M. A. 1962. The organization of cellular activity. Elsevier Publishing Co., New York.

Lehninger, A. L. 1964. The mitochondrion. W. A. Benjamin, Inc., New York.

Ling, G. N. 1962. A physical theory of the living state: The association-induction hypothesis. Blaisdell Publishing Co., New York.

Mazia, D. 1940. The binding of ions by the cell surface. Cold Spring Harbor Symposia on Quantitative Biology. Vol. 8, p. 195.

Mommaerts, F. H. M. 1963. Introductory remarks to symposium on borderline problems around the field of active transport. Fed. Proc. 22:1.

Ponder, E. 1961. The cell membrane and its properties, vol. 2, p. 1. In Brachet, J., and A. E. Mirsky (editors): The cell. Academic Press, Inc., New York.

Robertson, J. D. 1962. The membrane of the living cell. Sci. Am. (April), p. 65.

Robertson, J. D. 1960. The molecular structure and contact relationships of cell membranes. Prog. Biophys. 10:343.

Rustad, R. C. 1961. Pinocytosis. Sci. Am. (April), p. 120.

Schoffeniels, E. 1964. Cellular aspects of active transport, vol. 7, p. 137. In Florkin, M., and H. S. Mason (editors): Comparative biochemistry. Academic Press, Inc., New York.

Shaw, J. 1960. The mechanism of osmoregulation, vol. 2, p. 471. In Florkin, M., and H. S. Mason (editors): Comparative biochemistry. Academic Press, Inc., New York.

Tamarin, A., and L. M. Sreebny. 1963. An analysis of desmosome shape, size, and orientation by the use of histometric and densitometric methods with electron microscopy. J. Cell Biol. 18:125.

25

The cell organelles as functional entities

INTRODUCTION

The discussion of the cell membrane and its overall relationship to the dynamics of the living cell suggests that all such cellular organelles, or subcellular particles, operate in a discrete manner, performing a series of functions which are necessary for normal maintenance of the cell. The structure-function tenet applies well to these organelles, for each is modified for its characteristic roles. (Plate 9, p. 311.)

A single-celled organism must contain all those functional entities which are present in the multicellular forms. Circulation, digestion, control, secretion, reproduction, and metabolism are physiological functions which must be met by living forms. Every independent cell contains organelles which can perform these requirements, but many cells in the multicellular forms may have lost some activity during evolution to a dependent existence.

ENDOPLASMIC RETICULUM

The endoplasmic reticulum is the series of internal membranes which course the area between the cell membrane and the nuclear membrane. The functions attributed to this subcellular unit are many, and the structure lends itself to the functions which are assigned.

The endoplasmic reticular membranes in many cells appear to be a continuation of interlacing membranes which run from the nuclear membrane to the outer surface. There is some evidence that there is direct contact between the nuclear and plasma membrane systems and that of the endoplasmic reticulum. The membranes are not always parallel, and as a result, a series of sacs, vesicles, and spaces are formed. The saclike areas in the system are called cisternae and are really a part of the internal lumen. The fluid cytoplasm outside the mem-

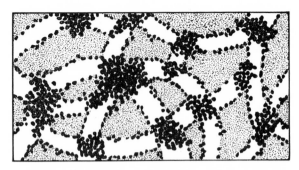

Fig. 25-1. Diagrammatic representation of the endoplasmic reticulum and the ribosomal particles. Channels of endoplasmic reticulum (*light bands*) are lined by ribosomal particles (*dark dots*). The particles appear to cluster, particularly where the channels intersect.

branes is called the hyaloplasm. These subdivisions are represented diagrammatically in Fig. 25-1.

The functions of the membranes of the endoplasmic reticulum are apparently many. Like other membranes, the system responds osmotically to the local presence of hypertonic or hypotonic concentration of salts and metabolites. This, however, is not the only membrane phenomenon attributed to the endoplasmic reticulum system. In muscle cells, in particular, these intracellular membranes are believed to conduct an excitation potential generated on the outer membrane to the internal portion of the cell. The mechanism of conduction seems to parallel that of the plasma membrane of muscle and of nerve. Portions of these membranes are also capable of electron transport, containing cytochrome b_5, flavoprotein, a transport sequence involving NAD, and another in which NADP participates. There is evidence that some pigment may also take part in the electron transport scheme. Finally, there is an indication that the sodium pump mechanism and an ATPase system are both present in these membranes. These observed facts set up the possibility of a system which may mimic the mitochondrial function.

These membrane systems are also involved in the metabolic pathways. The membranes proper apparently contain the enzymes for triglyceride synthesis; other phases of lipid metabolism may also be located there. The enzymes for the Embden-Meyerhof cycle are located in the hyaloplasm, or the nonparticulate portion of the cell.

The membranes of the endoplasmic reticulum are of two types. The first class consists of membranes which are smooth upon microscopic examination. The second class, or rough type, has distinct particles associated with the membranes which are the ribosomes, or RNP (ribonucleoprotein), the particles of a ribonucleic acid–protein complex involved in protein synthesis (Chapter 26). These particles are attached to the outer surface of the membranes.

It does not take any great stretch of the imagination to envision the endoplasmic reticulum as an intracellular circulatory system. Its membranes communicate with essentially every other organelle in the cell, and the importance of the nuclear membrane–plasma membrane link cannot be overlooked. There have been theories that the membranes of the endoplasmic reticulum may actually have their origin from one or both of these other membranes. It is very difficult to ascribe this general function of circulation of metabolite and information particles without confirming evidence, but the material flow around the cell is probably controlled, and from a structure-function point of view, the endoplasmic reticulum would appear to be the subcellular particle which could function best in this capacity.

Many enzymatic functions have been assigned to the microsomal fraction, but what proportions are really in the membranes is uncertain. Some of the more common enzymes which have been found are deaminase, cholesterol synthetase, iodine-uptake enzyme, and the enzymes of fatty acid synthesis.

RIBOSOMES

Invariably associated with the endoplasmic reticulum, the ribosomes are submicroscopic particles containing ribonucleic acid and protein. Their function is primarily in protein synthesis, a subject which will be dealt with at length in Chapter 26.

Because of the high-level importance of their role in the cell, the ribosomes are ubiquitous in all cell types, occurring in both the plant and animal kingdoms. These particles are very constant from cell to cell in their size, shape, and chemical composition. The RNA content is approximately 50 percent. The other half is protein, with possibly some lipoid material. The RNA which is present contains purine and pyrimidine base ratios which are not in the typical complementary pairing as in DNA. Furthermore, the ratio of bases which is present varies from cell to cell, and perhaps from ribosome to ribosome. The protein which is contained in these particles is similar to that associated with the DNA. It is very basic, as would be expected with the highly acid nucleotides contributing an overall negative charge to the particle. Found in association with the ribosome is the enzyme ribonuclease, which is present in the latent form. What triggers its activity is not certain.

One fascinating aspect of ribosomes is that the individual particles have no protein synthesis ability, but are apparently distinct subunits of a physiological particle called a polysome. The polysome is an aggregation of individual ribosomes which function together to catalyze the protein synthesis. The combination of ribsomes to form a polysome is a reversible reaction, and in the cell all stages of ribosome aggregation are seen from single particles to large polysomes. The critical physiochemical factor for the combination seems to be the magnesium ion which is necessary for binding. Physiological control of polysome formation would be the synthetic demands of the cell.

The ribosome and its properties have allowed speculation as to a further role of the endoplasmic reticulum. It has been suggested that the membranes associated with ribosomes do, in fact, transport the protein formed in the particles to that portion of the cell requiring the material.

In nerve cells, the endoplasmic reticulum is believed to transport the material for new axoplasm synthesis down the processes. This has not been completely confirmed, but it does suggest the use of the endoplasmic reticulum as a microcirculatory system.

THE MITOCHONDRION

A discussion of the mitochondrion has to overlap the section on biochemistry because this subcellular particle *is* the biochemical powerhouse producing most of the ATP of the cell, and its structure and function should reflect its roles. As a cell organelle, the mitochondrion has many unique properties, not the least of which are its independence and mode of biogenesis. The mitochondrion is discussed at some length primarily because of its significant role in the dynamics of the cell. Secondarily, its structure, which has been worked out in fine detail, demonstrates again that the functional aspect of a biological entity is determined by its structural characteristics. (Plate 11, *A*, p. 313.)

The structure of the mitochondrion

Despite the enormous amount of experimentation and examination of this organelle, the precise ultrastructure is not completely agreed upon. The general structure, however, has been worked out to the satisfaction of most investigators, and although there are many variations in shape and size, some generalizations can be made concerning a typical mitochondrion.

General structure and characteristics

An average mitochondrion, having the approximate external dimensions of 1.5 to 3.0 μ long × 0.5 to 1.0 μ in diameter, is really a sac within a sac (Fig. 25-2). The outer membrane is relatively smooth (see discussion of ultra-structure, p. 296), and is separated from the inner sac by a fluid matrix. The inner sac, having the characteristic folds, or cristae, contains another matrix which, apparently, is not in contact with that fluid between the two membranes. The inner matrix contains some protein and lipid material and, as a result, may be semirigid.

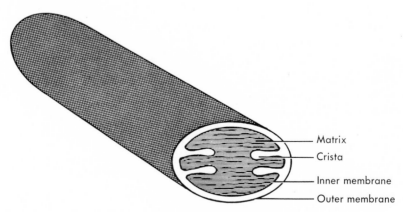

Fig. 25-2. Diagrammatic view of a mitochondrion, sliced to show double sac structure.

Although the average mitochondrion has the dimensions just listed, there is quite a variation in the size and shape of these organelles in any one cell, but the size-weight distribution curve is quite similar from cell to cell. There are cells, however, which have characteristically shaped mitochondria and even an intercellular distribution which is constant.

Another variation in structure is the arrangement of the cristae which project in from the inner membrane. In some mitochondria, the cristae are small nubs which barely project into the central matrix; on the other hand, there are some mitochondria in which these cristae seem to project all the way across the matrix to the inner membrane on the opposite side. These cristae may be arranged in a pattern in which they are all parallel to each other, or they may present an interlaced pattern by projecting in all directions. Finally, the membranes which make up the cristae may flatten to form sheets which are fenestrated by pores, and at the other extreme, the membranes may take the peculiar prismatic shape of those in the muscle of the bat.[1]

The purpose of the cristae is twofold. They first offer a larger surface area to this active internal membrane. Second, they house the respiratory assemblies which produce ATP (Plate 15, *A*, p. 317). The correlation between number and size of the cristae and the recorded activity of the cell bears this out. In the liver cell, for example, the area of the inner membrane may be as high as four times that of the outer membrane, and the total membrane area from all the mitochondria may be higher than the total surface area of the plasma membrane.

The number of mitochondria per cell varies, depending on the cell type, but remains fairly constant in any particular kind of cell. Numbers range from 500 in some liver cells to over 100,000 in some single-celled organisms. The location of these bodies is also a variable, but, again, they are typically placed in any one cell type. Three generalizations about the location can be observed:

1. The mitochondria are often polarized, that is, oriented in one direction. This anisotropic placement is typical of cells which are very active, as in the wings of a blowfly.
2. The mitochondria are more likely to be localized on the side of the cell in which metabolites enter. In single-celled organisms, this would result in a random pattern. However, in cells of the higher animals and plants, usually one end of the cell is nearest the source of substrate.
3. Mitochondria are found associated with the area of the cell known to be the active portion. For example, one would expect them to be near the contractile protein of muscle cells and the secretory portion of gland cells.

The mitochondria are not rigid bodies. They have a plasticity which allows some movement and variation in shape to occur. The presence of contractile protein in the membranes has been suggested as the force which causes the movement. In addition to change of shape, the mitochondria of some cells are freely moved about, mostly passively; in other cells the mitochondria are fixed in a particular position.

Thus, the mitochondria can vary in shape, size, number, location and type, and number of cristae. However, the major variation is among cell types and not among cells of the same type. It becomes difficult on the basis of this to generalize the gross structure, although some basic characteristics are shared by all mitochondria.

The fine structure of the mitochondrion

Some controversy exists over the exact fine structure of the mitochondrion, but several postulated ideas about its microanatomy are quite prevalent and are supported by most of the evidence. They will be discussed, but it must be kept in mind that the entire problem of ultrastructure has not been resolved.

Membrane structure.   The two membranes must have the properties which allow the various changes to occur, as pointed out previously. This means that these membranes must be strong enough to hold a structural shape, stable enough to allow membrane phenomena to occur, and flexible enough to allow movement. It turns out that the same basic structure attributed to the cell membrane probably exists in the mitochondrial membranes as well. Up to 70 percent by weight of the membrane material is protein, with the remainder of the material being lipoid, primarily phospholipid. The ratio, in addition to other evidence, again suggests the triple-layered lipoprotein complex.

The protein may be of two types. There is a structural protein which has an amino acid content high in those acids with a paraffin side chain. This protein is a polymer, composed of basic subunits of a small protein. Second, actomyosin, or a protein similar to this contractile substance, has also been found in the mitochondrial membrane. On the basis of plasticity observations, the finding of a contractile protein is not unexpected.

The lipid portion of the molecule is almost exclusively phospholipids, with cardiolipin, lecithin, cephalin, and inositol phosphatides forming the bulk of the material. These lipids are necessary for the integrity of membrane structure, but specific functions have also been attributed to them in that certain ones may be involved in the transport mechanisms and contraction process of the mito-chondrion.

How these two major components, the lipids and the proteins, are oriented in the membrane is one of the areas of disagreement. The two ideas which are prevalent are that they are arranged in a unit membrane organization with a lipid bilayer in between two protein layers. However, Sjöstrand[2] suggests that the mitochondrial membrane, in contrast to the plasma membrane, has essentially a seven-layered structure with two of the triple-layer arrangements separated by another lipoid or nonprotein layer (Fig. 25-3). Sjöstrand further contends that there is a granular fine structure in these layers which does not exist in the plasma membrane.

Mitochondrial particles.   Electron micrograph studies of the membranes have shown distinct particles distributed on the inner side of the inner membrane and on the outer side of the outer membrane. The particle located on the cristae, termed the elementary particle or electron transport particle (ETP), is believed to be the electron chain. This particle, then, is the site of the ATP production resulting from oxidative phosphorylation. Mild separation techniques

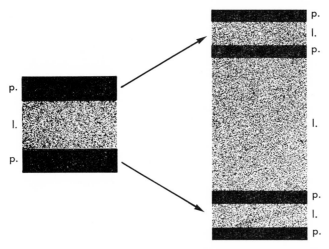

Fig. 25-3. Schematic drawings of the two membrane structures attributed to the mitochondrial membrane. Difference in measured thickness is probably due to fixation techniques. *p*, Protein. *l*, Lipid.

and electron micrographs of separated material from the mitochondrion have shown that these particles have a tripartite arrangement consisting of a head, a stalk, and a base piece.[3] Biophysical calculations show striking agreement between the sum of the known molecular weight of the components of the electron transport chain and the weight of the elementary particle. The scheme for the arrangement of the components in these three pieces will be discussed in the section on mitochondrial function.

Acceptance of the presence of outer particles is not universal. Although energetics necessitate that the pathways feeding into electron chains be contiguous to the elementary particles, there is not general agreement that the enzymes of these pathways—the Krebs and the fatty acid cycles—are localized in discrete particles on the outer membrane. Logistics suggest, however, that these enzymes must be located in the outer membrane since they receive the metabolites from the rest of the cell from this direction.

In summary, the presence of inner particles has widespread acceptance. The dynamics of electron flow and the resulting water formation, along with the possibility of ATP production, require an anisotropic system with vectorial parameters. From both space-saving and energy-saving standpoints, the aggregation of the components of electron transport into an organized particle seems a plausible, if not a requisite solution. The outer particles may or may not exist, but the fact remains that the Krebs and fatty acid enzymes should be on the outer membrane of the mitochondrion.

Functions of the mitochondrion

A discussion of the functions of the mitochondrion will be, for the most part, a review of basic biochemical pathways. Therefore, these will be handled generally and without detail, the particulars having been related in Section V.

Metabolic functions

Apparently two distinct forms of metabolism occur in the mitochondrion. There is that metabolism which involves oxidation of metabolites for the purpose of energy gain to the cell and synthetic reactions for the cell using this ATP as the driving force. Second, there is that special metabolism which is involved in biogenesis of the mitochondrion itself. Only the former class will be considered at this time.

The biochemical pathways which are present in the mitochondrion are the Krebs cycle, the fatty acid oxidation sequence, and the enzymes responsible for ketone body oxidation and formation. These cycles are those which yield the great number of reduced coenzymes, the hydrogens of which can be shunted into the electron transport chain. All of these cycles have acetyl-CoA as an end product or starting product. This minimizes the number of compounds which have to be exchanged between the mitochondrion and the other portions of the cell. (Plate 10, A, p. 312.)

Electron transport chain

The components of the electron chain are arranged into four complexes:

I. NADH·H+-coenzyme Q reductase complex
II. Succinic acid-coenzyme Q reductase complex
III. Coenzyme Q-cytochrome c reductase complex
IV. Cytochrome oxidase systems

Green and associates[4] at Wisconsin suggest a hypothetical arrangement of these complexes in the elementary particles in which complex I and complex II are in the base of the particle, complex III in the stalk, and complex IV in the head. Since complex I and complex II both receive hydrogens from two different sources and then feed them to coenzyme Q, it seems logical that these two would be separated in the base. A second logistic factor is that complexes I and II should be near the outer membrane to better facilitate the hydrogen-accepting function.

Assuming the possibility of particles on the outer membrane, these macromolecular complexes must then get the hydrogen across the membrane to either complex I or II.

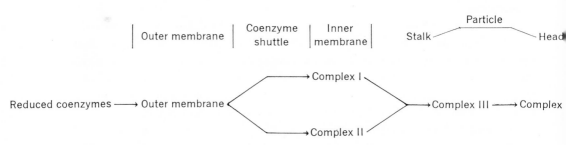

Fig. 25-4. Scheme showing flow of electrons through the outer and inner membranes of the mitochondrion.

It is thought that this electron movement is brought about by a shuttling by the reduced coenzymes formed in the cycle. The shuttle does not necessarily imply mobility of these enzymes, as there is good evidence that the phospholipids in the center of the membrane may participate in this electron and hydrogen transfer. More work is necessary before any conclusions can be drawn (Fig. 25-4).

Oxidative phosphorylation was discussed previously (Chapter 21), and nothing about the structure of the mitochondrion reveals any more. Alignment of the electron components could fit into any of the schemes suggested for the mechanism of ATP production.

Ion translocation

The mitochondrial processes are not restricted to oxidation, synthesis, and high-energy bond production, although these are certainly the *raison d'être* of the mitochondrion to the cell. The mitochondrial membrane must transport many substances through it in order for the organelle to function. Among these substances are those ions which are necessary for carrying out these functions. Magnesium and manganese are required in the adenylic acid system, and calcium is probably used for the contractile process. It is possible that these divalent ions, particularly Ca^{++}, may be accumulated beyond the needs of individual mitochondrion (for example, muscle cells), and the movement of these ions is called translocation.

The calcium ion goes across the membrane in combination with phosphate ions, and, surprisingly enough, this uptake apparently may use the same set of enzymes which produce ATP or one of the critical intermediates. Under normal physiological conditions, ATP production, of course, takes precedence over any massive calcium movement, but under certain conditions, for example, the presence of the parathyroid gland secretion, parathormone, the mitochondrion accumulates calcium actively at the expense of ATP production. Just as the ratio of high-energy phosphate produced for each pair of electrons transported across the chain is a definite ratio (P/O) approaching 3:1, there is a definite stoichiometry in calcium uptake. For every two electrons transported, five calcium ions are moved across the membrane, giving a Ca/O ratio of 5:1. Evidence indicates that Mg^{++} and Mn^{++} also move across the membrane as a phosphate complex, but whether the action is the same as that of the calcium is uncertain.

Movement of ions through the membrane is mediated by an enzyme called translocase. The exact mode of action is not certain, but there is some evidence which suggests that a contractile protein is involved which attaches the Ca^{++} (or Mg^{++}, Mn^{++})-phosphate crystals to one end and then, by a contraction process, flips 180° to the other side of the membrane and releases the ions. This process requires conversion of ATP to ADP, thus draining the ATP from oxidative phosphorylation.

The ion movement in mitochondria may hold the key to ion transfer in other membrane systems. This necessitates postulating a contractile protein bridge across the membrane and an energy source to trigger the contraction. Although this 180° flip seems fanciful, other transfer systems are postulated as employing some similar device (Chapter 24).

The significance of ion translocation in mitochondria is in the realm of speculation. It may help maintain microecological control within the cell, or it may be a means of sequestering ions until the need for them arises. Finally, it is not beyond the realm of possibility that the mitochondria may participate in a transcellular transport mechanism whereby ions are moved from one cell surface through the cell to be released at the other side.

Changes in structure related to function

The mitochondrion is capable of changing its dimensions because of two factors. First, as has been mentioned, there is a contractile protein in the membrane. The presence of a large amount of sulfur-containing amino acids in this protein suggests that some of the shortening may be due to induced disulfide bridging between protein segments. Second, mitochondria by the nature of their membranes can act as osmometers, swelling and shrinking as the tonicity of their matrix changes.

The physiological state also affects the structure of the mitochondria. During cell division, they undergo a series of characteristic changes, and during embryological development of cells, mitochondria may follow a typical pattern of structural changes. Hormones also affect the structure. Thyroxine causes swelling or formation of unusual forms. Parathormone can cause swelling by inducing massive ion accumulation. Finally, X-irradiation and disease cause mitochondria to assume atypical shapes and structures.

Phenomenon of crypticity and compartmentation

Mitochondrial structure and function illustrate the type of control that can occur at the organelle and molecular levels. The precise biochemical controls will be dealt with in Chapter 31, but the concepts of crypticity and compartmentation should be introduced since they offer an insight into the type of subtle control exhibited by a functional cell.

Crypticity infers that some component of a reaction is "hidden" or unavailable to the remainder of the reactants. For example, if acetyl-CoA were outside of the mitochondria and could not get to the enzymes of the Krebs cycle because the acetyl-CoA was tied up or unavailable to the Krebs cycle, the situation is called cryptic. Another more probable example is coenzyme NADH·H⁺. This reduced coenzyme is oxidized within the mitochondria through the electron chain. However, external NADH·H⁺ is not acted upon even though the enzymes for catalyzing it are present within the organelle. This is another example of crypticity. Generally, any time a substance cannot participate in a reaction in which the enzymes are there to bring about the reaction, the situation is called cryptic. The capacity for metabolizing is there, but the metabolite is unavailable for reaction.

Compartmentation is a broader term which implies that biochemical entities may be kept apart so far as participating in the various cellular reactions is concerned. An example would be the ATP of the mitochondrion. These ATP do not get out from the mitochondrion to take part in the Embden-Meyerhof and other cytoplasmic pathways. Compartmentalization requires the mitochondrial ATP to transfer its high-energy bond to an ADP outside of the organelle. The various membrane systems impose a physical compartmentation, although a substance may be compartmentalized within the same structure or even within the same membrane.

There is some overlap between compartmentation and crypticity. The concepts embodied in these terms are important in explaining some of the factors in control at the organelle level.

Biogenesis

One fascinating aspect of the mitochondrion is the biogenesis of new organelles. Three major theories have been proposed.

The theory of *de nova* synthesis of mitochondria states that the structure is formed in situ from precursors which exist in the hyaloplasm of the cell. Most modern evidence indicates that this type of biogenesis does not occur.

The proposal that mitochondria are formed from preexisting membrane material or from other organelles is the second theory for mitochondrial origin. The endoplasmic reticulum, pinocytotic vesicles, and nuclear material have all been suggested as possible precursors of the mitochondria. The unit membrane theory was one of the criteria for assuming a biogenetic relationship among the membraned structures of the cell.

Much experimental evidence indicates that in some cells the mitochondria are formed from preexisting mitochondria; that is, they grow and divide. Such a mechanism infers biosynthetic pathways in the mitochondria which differ from those found in the rest of the cell. Membrane transport problems would be too great to overcome if formed protein had to be moved into the mitochondrion. All evidence suggests a high protein synthesis ability in this organelle which is not mediated by ribosomal particles. There is DNA and RNA in the mitochondrion, but formed aggregates have not been found. Portions of phospholipid synthetic pathways have been demonstrated to be present also in these organelles. It seems plausible, then, to suggest that the mitochondria has the capacity to synthesize some of its components and thus has a biochemical independence from the other cell structures.

The possibility of separate control of division of the mitochondria from that of the cell is an extraordinary property of intracellular organelles and leads to a host of theories about their evolutionary origin. The other properties of the mitochondria may have application to processes found in other parts of the cell. As an organelle, the dynamics of its function charge it with an important role in the cell.

THE CHLOROPLAST

Chloroplasts share many similar properties with mitochondria. These can be enumerated as follows.

1. Both have electron transport systems.

2. Both produce ATP—the mitochondria through oxidative phosphorylation and the chloroplast through photophosphorylation.
3. Both contain cytochromes, although not the same ones.
4. Both contain a quinone—plastoquinone in the chloroplast and ubiquinone in the mitochondrion.
5. Both are sites of oxidative and synthetic activities.
6. Both have a double-membrane structure.
7. Both have developed inner membrane systems, the cristae in mitochondria and the lamellae in chloroplasts.
8. Both have particles containing aggregates of active compounds—the elementary particle, and perhaps the outer particles, of mitochondria and the quantasomes of chloroplasts.

Chloroplasts are organelles of plant cells which have a basic internal organization although there are many variables so far as size, shape, and number are concerned.

The internal structure consists of a series of lamellae, or layers, comprised of membranes which are stacked together in the chloroplast. The membranes of chloroplasts are high in neutral lipids such as the galactolipids and are relatively low in phospholipids. Although their basic structures are similar, the lipid content of chloroplasts and mitochondria differs. Associated with the lamellae are discrete structures called grana, which are high in chlorophyll content. The grana are believed to be thickenings or bifurcations of the lamellar membranes. This offers more concentrated areas for the chlorophyll to trap the photon energy.

In the grana, as subunits, are the basic particles which can undergo the light reaction of photosynthesis. These quantasomes consist of chlorophyll, cytochromes, and those compounds necessary to carry out the light reaction and photophosphorylation. The dark reaction, or carbon cycle, is attributed to the nonmembrane structure of the chloroplast, although the initial steps may be in the lamellar membranes.

The precision of fine structure and its correlation to function are not as well-known as those of the mitochondrion. It is known that the quantasomes are particles which are analogous to the electron transport particles in both content and function. Furthermore, there must be a series of membrane phenomena to allow transport of various metabolites into and out from the chloroplast.

The biogenesis of chloroplasts is much different from that of mitochondria. It is believed that chloroplasts originate from very small ameboid bodies called proplastids. They increase in size, later developing lamellae from initial invaginations from the inner membrane.

THE GOLGI COMPLEX

The history of the Golgi complex, body, or apparatus has been fraught with uncertainties. The presence of this complex was established early in the microscopic studies of the cell. Later, its existence was doubted, but now it again seems to clearly be a cell entity. (Plate 12, p. 314).

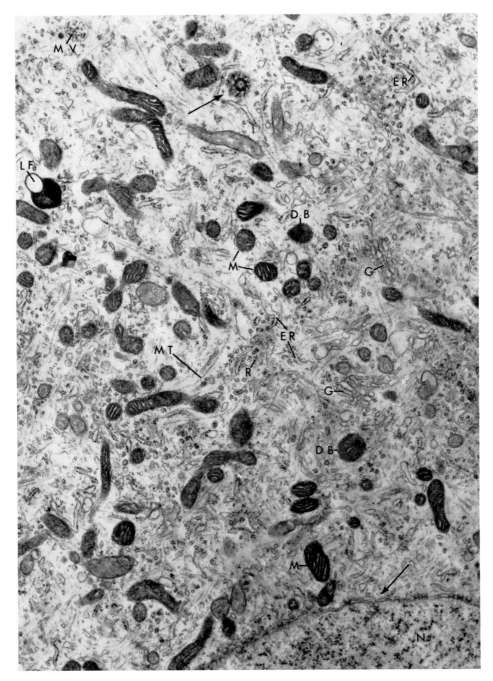

Plate 1. Electron micrograph of a neuron in cat spinal cord, showing major cell organelles. *N*, Nucleus. *Lower arrow*, Nuclear membrane. *M*, Mitochondrion. *DB*, Dense body (presumably a lysosome). *G*, Golgi complex (smooth membranes). *ER*, Endoplasmic reticulum (rough surfaced). *R*, Rosette ribosomes. *MT*, Microtubules. *Upper arrow*, Centriole with transitional fibers. *LF*, Lipofuscin body. *MV*, Multivesicular bodies. (Glutaraldehyde and osmic acid fixation; x18,000.)

303

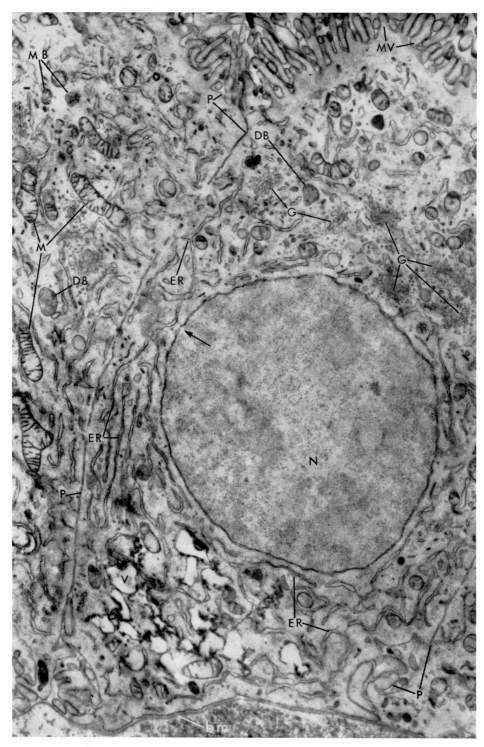

Plate 2. Electron micrograph of epithelial cell of chick choroid plexus, showing general cell organization. *bm*, Basement membrane. *V*, Vacuole. *ER*, Endoplasmic reticulum. *P*, Plasmalemma. *N*, Nucleus. *Arrow*, Nuclear pore. *G*, Golgi complex. *M*, Mitochondria. *DB*, Dense body (presumably a lysosome). *MV*, Microvilli. *MB*, Multivesicular bodies. (Potassium permanganate fixation; x12,000.)

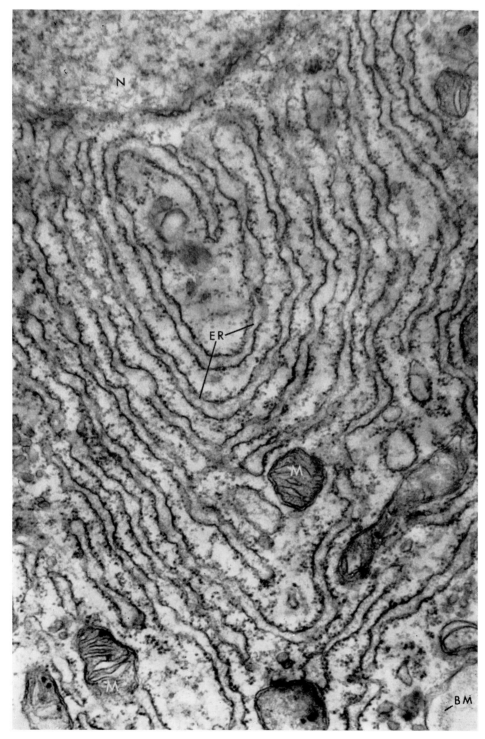

Plate 3. Electron micrograph of epithelial cell of chick choroid plexus, showing the elaborate internal membrane system in this cell. *N,* Nucleus. *ER,* Endoplasmic reticulum. *M,* Mitochondrion. BM, Basement membrane. (Osmic acid fixation; x47,800.)

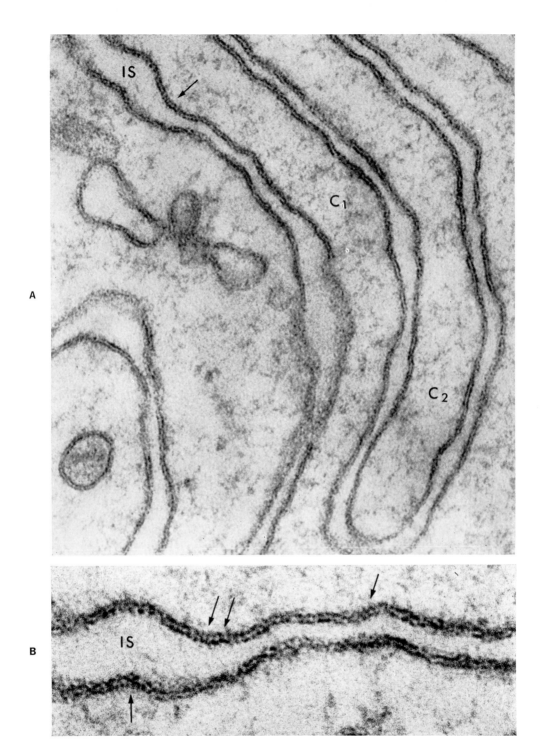

Plate 4. A, Electron micrograph of interdigitating plasma membranes of two epithelial cells (C_1 and C_2) of chick choroid plexus, showing the "unit membrane." *IS,* Intercellular space. (Osmic acid fixation; x176,000.) **B,** Region opposite arrow in **A** enlarged to show fine bridges across the unit membrane. *IS,* Intercellular space. (x324,500.)

306

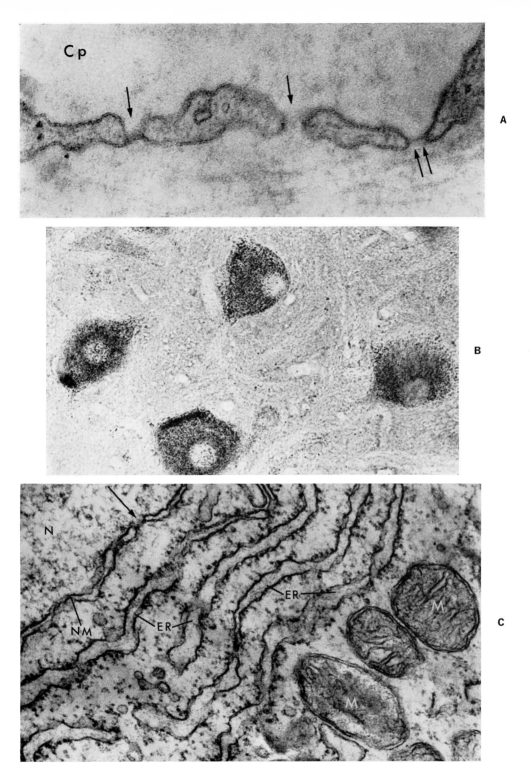

Plate 5. A, Electron micrograph showing fenestrations in capillary endothelium of chick choroid plexus. Note the thin bridge marked by double arrows. *Cp,* Capillary lumen. (Glutaraldehyde and osmic acid fixation; x99,000). **B,** Oil-immersion photomicrograph of motor neurons of cat packed with lysosomes (black dots). **C,** Electron micrograph showing nuclear pores and close association of endoplasmic reticulum with the nuclear membrane. *N,* Nucleus. *NM,* Nuclear membrane. *Arrow,* Nuclear pore. *ER,* Rough-surfaced endoplasmic reticulum. *M,* Mitochondria. (Osmic acid fixation; x60,500.)

307

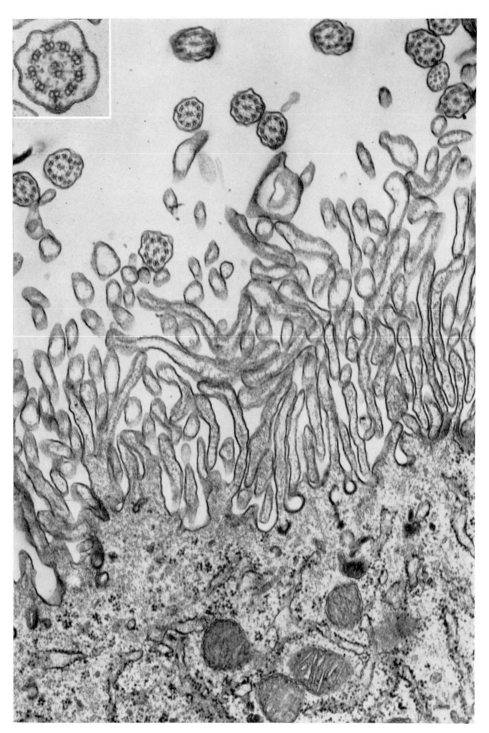

Plate 6. Electron micrograph of the complex apical border of an epithelial cell of chick choroid plexus. Note the many microvilli and cilia. (Glutaraldehyde and osmic acid fixation; x39,844.) Inset, A cilium shows the classical pattern of nine double fibers at periphery and two single fibers at center. Note secondary filaments in the matrix between peripheral and central fibers. (x72,250.)

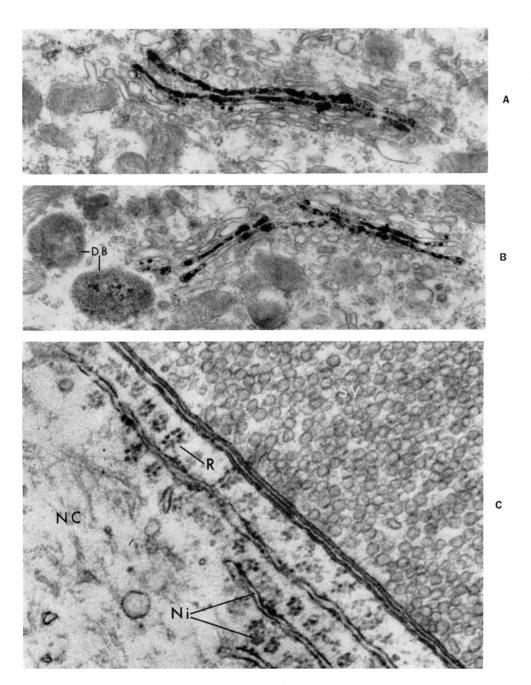

Plate 7. **A** and **B,** Electron micrographs of neuron of central nervous system of cat, showing nucleoside diphosphatase activity (substrate thiamine pyrophosphate) in the Golgi complex and lysosome *(DB).* (Fixation in formaldehyde, followed by incubation and then osmic acid fixation; x48,000.) **C,** Electron micrograph of cat spinal cord, showing nerve terminal (bouton) containing numerous synaptic vesicles *(SV).* The boutons are in contact with the adjacent motor neuron. *NC,* Neuronal cytoplasm. *R,* Free rosette ribosomes unattached to endoplasmic reticular membranes. *Ni,* Nissl substance (basophilic substance represented by ribosomal masses interspersed with endoplasmic reticular profiles). (Glutaraldehyde and osmic acid fixation; x106,250.)

309

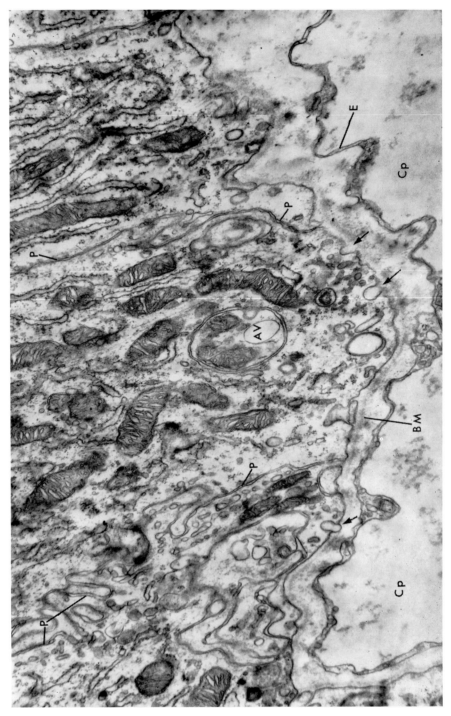

Plate 8. Electron micrograph of chick choroid plexus epithelium showing presumptive pino-cytotic vesicles (*arrows*). *Cp,* Capillary lumen. *BM,* Basement membrane. *P,* Plasma membrane. *AV,* Presumptive autophagic vacuole. (Osmic acid fixation; x44,000.)

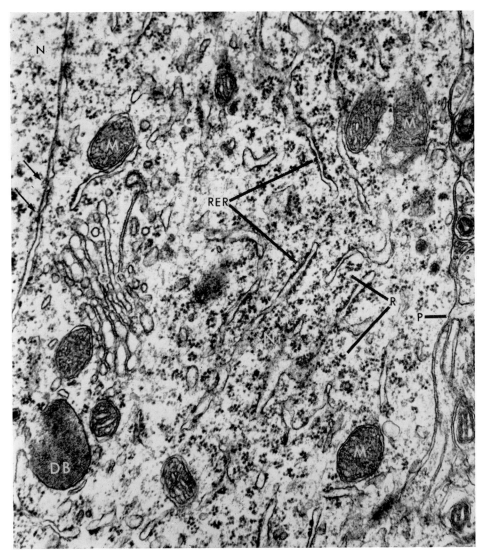

Plate 9. Electron micrograph of a nerve cell of central nervous system of cat, showing major organelles. *N*, Nucleus. *Arrows*, Nuclear pores. *M*, Mitochondrion. *GC*, Golgi complex. *RER*, Rough-surfaced endoplasmic reticulum. *R*, Ribosomes not attached to endoplasmic reticulum. *DB*, Lysosome. *P*, Plasmalemma. *Ni*, Nissl substance. (Formaldehyde and osmic acid fixation; x42,750.)

311

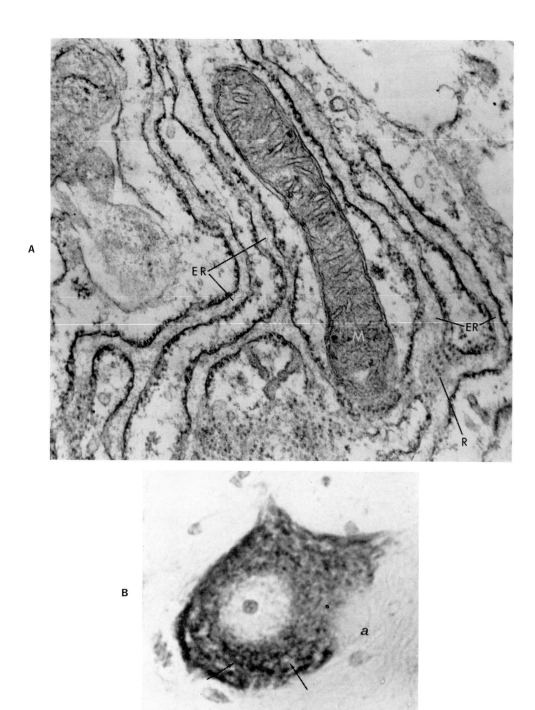

Plate 10. A, Electron micrograph showing close association of a mitochondrion (*M*) with the endoplasmic reticulum (*ER*). *R,* Ribosomes. (Osmic acid fixation; x59,500.) **B,** Photomicrograph of a frozen-sectioned neuron showing Nissl substance. Arrows point to reticulum of the Nissl network. Note absence of Nissl material from axon hillock, **a.** (Formalin-calcium fixation; x500.)

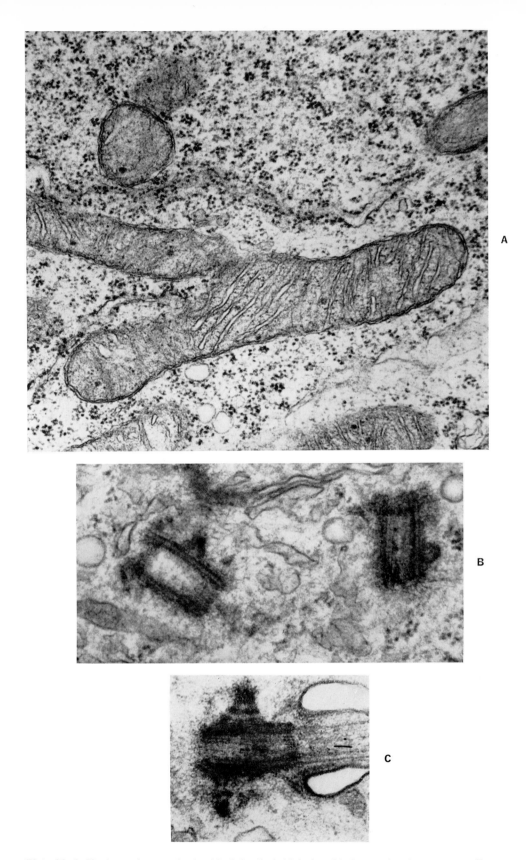

Plate 11. A, Electron micrograph of epithelial cell of chick choroid plexus, showing many rosette ribosomes unattached to membranes. (Glutaraldehyde and osmic acid fixation; x48,000.) **B,** Electron micrograph of epithelium of chick choroid plexus, showing a pair of centrioles. **C,** Electron micrograph of epithelium of chick choroid plexus, showing basal body of a cilium. Note similarities between centrioles (**B**) and basal body (**C**). (**B** and **C,** Glutaraldehyde and osmic acid fixation; x71 and 180.)

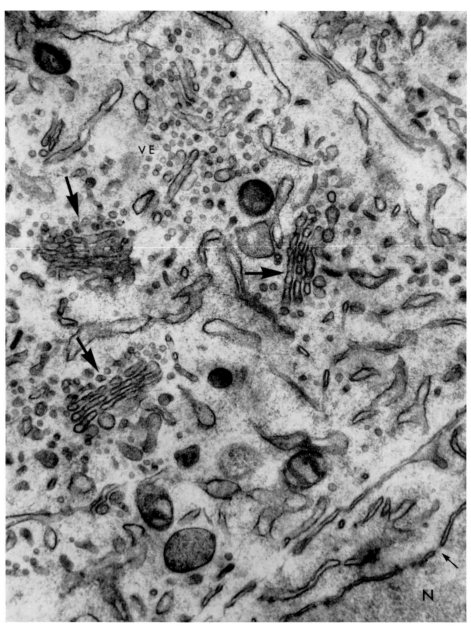

Plate 12. Electron micrograph clearly showing the Golgi complex (large arrows) in the choroid plexus epithelium of chick embryo. *VE*, Golgi vesicles. *N*, Nucleus. *Small arrow* (right-hand corner), nuclear pore. (Potassium permanganate fixation; x36,000.)

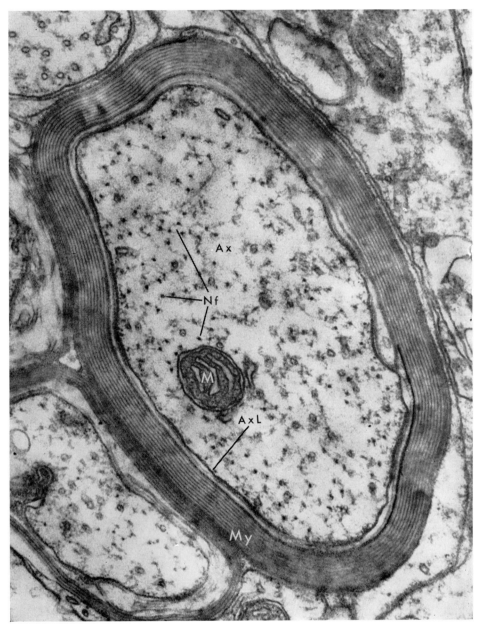

Plate 13. Electron micrograph of myelinated axon in feline central nervous system. *My,* Myelin. *Ax,* Axolemma or nerve cell membrane. *M,* Mitochondrion. *Nf,* Neurofilaments. *Ax,* Axoplasm. (Glutaraldehyde and osmic acid fixation; x63,750.)

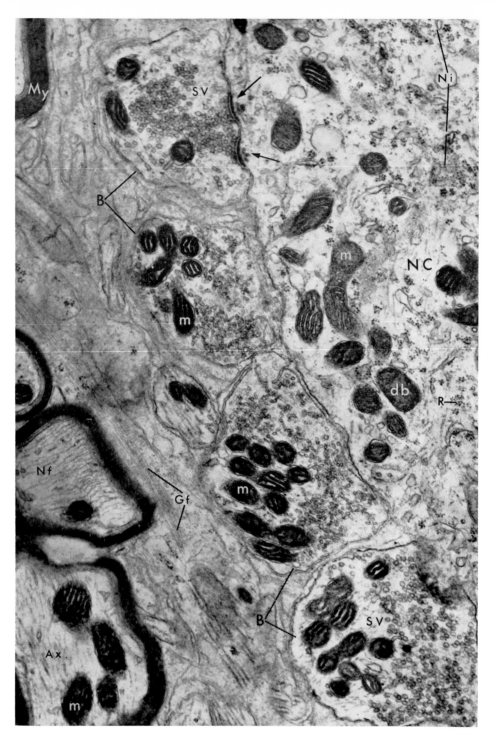

Plate 14. Electron micrograph of cat spinal cord showing myelinated axons (*My*) and boutons or nerve terminals (*B*), containing synaptic vesicles (*SV*). *Nf*, Neurofilaments. *M*, Mitochondria. *N*, Nissl substance. *Ax*, Axoplasm. *NC*, Cytoplasm of motor neuron. *Gf*, Neuroglial cell filaments. *db*, Lysosome. *R*, Ribosomes. Arrows point to synaptic region (functional contact between neuronal elements). Neurons and boutons are separated by a space of approximately 80 Å. Note postsynaptic thickening. (Glutaraldehyde and osmic acid fixation; x68,000.)

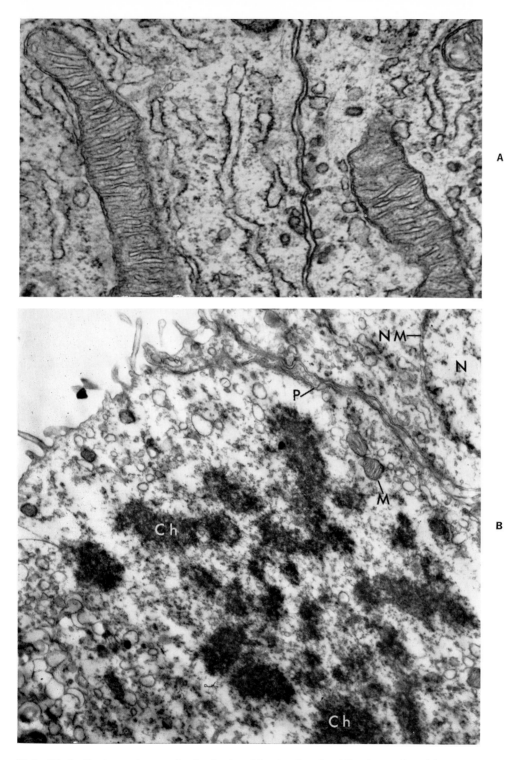

Plate 15. A, Electron micrograph of mitochondria showing the trilaminar external layer and trilaminar cristae. The membranes have particles on or in them which house the respiratory chain and the Krebs cycle enzymes. (See text.) **B,** Electron micrograph of epithelial cell of chick choroid plexus, undergoing mitosis. *Ch*, Chromosomes. *P*, Plasma membrane. *NM*, Nuclear membrane. *N*, Interphase nucleus. *M*, Mitochondira. (Osmic acid fixation; x15,900.)

317

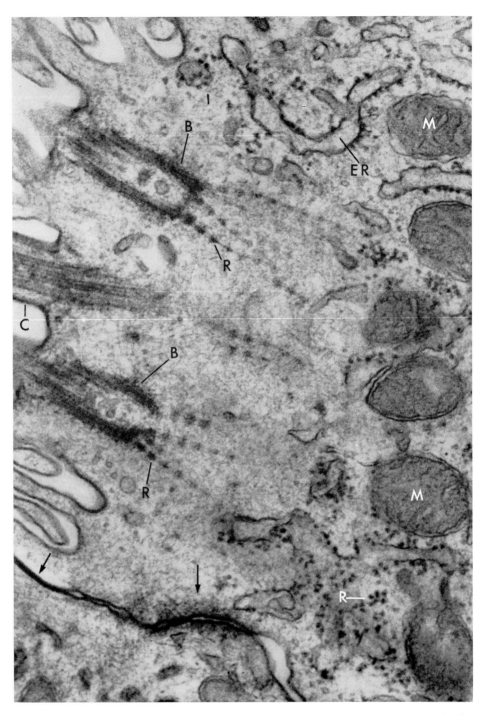

Plate 16. Electron micrograph of a longitudinal section through cilia (C) and their basal bodies (B) of epithelium of chick choroid plexus. Note cross-striated rootlets (R) attached to basal bodies. *ER*, Endoplasmic reticulum. *M*, Mitochondria. *White R*, Rosette ribosomes. Arrows point to terminal bar region where adjacent cells are tightly apposed at their apical junction. (Glutaraldehyde and osmic acid fixation; x89,250.)

318

The function of this complex is still not completely resolved. Its structure, with its parallel rows of membranes, resembles organized endoplasmic reticular membranes in which there are no ribosomes. There are cisternae which are similar to those in the reticulum, but the staining properties and the enzyme content of the membranes are different. In fact, very few enzymes are found in the Golgi complex, and in particular, those enzymes involved in synthetic processes are conspicuously absent. This fact dissuades the suggestion that the Golgi complex is the secretory organelle of the cell, as was originally thought.

It is now believed that the Golgi body is a complex possibly derived from endoplasmic reticular membranes through cytodifferentiation, and that its function is to store and channel secretory products which are produced in other portions of the cell and transported to the Golgi body. (Plate 7, A and B, p. 309.) The evidence as to any active participation of the Golgi apparatus in the actual secretion of materials from the cell is meager.

The appearance of the Golgi complex in cells follows the same pattern as the other organelles. That is, there is a great variety of organization, but the organization in any one cell type is constant. As a rule, the Golgi complex is organized in plants and some invertebrates into special bodies called dictyosomes.

LYSOSOMES

The isolation by de Duve of particles which were intermediate in size between ribosomes and mitochondria introduced another cell organelle. This organelle, called the lysosome, is a membrane-bound cytoplasmic structure replete with hydrolytic enzymes, and therein probably lies its function. The limiting membrane is single, in contrast to many other organelles which have a double-lined structure.

Lysosomes bear some relationship to the endoplasmic reticulum and the Golgi body, but the exact alliance is uncertain. It has been suggested by a number of workers, including Novikoff and associates,[5] that the enzyme content of lysosomes is manufactured in the ribosomes, as must be other proteins, and then these enzymes are moved to the Golgi apparatus. At this point some uncertainties arise. According to certain ideas, the vesicles of the Golgi body collect the enzymes and then become lysosomes, but this is an hypothesis only.

The classification of lysosomes is not much clearer. There are two general classes, primary and secondary lysosomes. The primary lysosome is the particle containing the lytic enzymes which have not as yet become functional. Secondary lysosomes are those which have undergone or are undergoing enzymatic activity.

Many enzymes have been reported as being present in the lysosomes. Among these are both ribonuclease and deoxyribonuclease, acid phosphatase, cathepsin, and glucosidase. These enzymes are representative of those which digest or break down nucleic acids, proteins, and carbohydrate materials. These enzymes, in many cases, are latent and may require some disruption of the particle before maximum activity can occur. (Plate 5, B, p. 307.)

The functions, then, seem fairly apparent. Lysosomes are digestive and phagocytic bodies which are involved in the breakdown of materials which originate both extracellularly and intracellularly. Whether these particles are actually involved in excretion of the digested residue from the cell is one of the uncertainties. Specific activities in which lysosomes participate are metamorphosis, embryological development, and phagocytosis. These activities are in addition to the normal dynamics of the cell. Disease, physiological shock, and the process of cell death all trigger high lysosome activity, and release of the enzymes is influenced by such substances as vitamins, hormones, and various toxins.

THE NUCLEUS

The nucleus has two primary functions in the cell:
1. To transmit genetic information from one generation to the next
2. To transmit and receive information from the cytoplasm and thereby control the functions of the other organelles of the cell

These major topics will be discussed in Chapters 26, 29, and 31. Therefore, discussion of the nucleus as a cell organelle here will be limited to its gross structure and some functions separate from the two mentioned previously.

The nucleus is present in all living cells, and because of its great importance in control of cellular activity, cell dynamics depends upon its functioning correctly. The nucleus is bounded by a membrane, the nuclear envelope or membrane, which has the unit membrane appearance of the typical lipoprotein arrangement. The pores in this membrane are generally larger than those found in the cell membrane, but this is probably due to the large molecules which must pass out through the membrane.

With the exception of some protozoan cells and a few other isolated examples, the internal structure of the nucleus is simple from a microscopic view. In fact, with the exception of some granulation in the nuclear sap, the main structure which can be seen is the nucleolus. Contained within the nucleus is the DNA, which is usually in a diffuse, hydrate form except during cell division. The DNA is localized in the chromosomes and is present in a constant amount in any one type of cell. The molecular structure of the DNA in the chromosome will not be considered here, but it should be pointed out that this nucleic acid is in a complex with a protein matrix in the chromosome. The exact arrangement of the complex is somewhat in doubt.

The nucleolus is a spheroidal body located in the nucleus which contains some RNA, possibly some enzymes, and a few coenzymes. The enzymes present may be those involved in RNA and NAD syntheses. They both require purines or pyrimidines and are found also in the nucleolus. The nucleolus does not appear to have an outer limiting membrane, but it still remains distinct until nuclear division occurs.

The function of the nucleus involved with cytoplasmic control may correlate with the inner membrane arrangement where the endoplasmic reticulum comes in contact with both the nuclear and plasma membrane. There is some evidence that the nucleus incorporates amino acids and synthesizes its own protein, although some protein migrates in from the cytoplasm where it has been formed by the ribosomal apparatus.

The nucleus represents the controlling mechanism of the cell, and as such its importance is not to be overlooked. The additional aspects of its control and function are considered in Chapter 26.

SUMMARY

The cell, like any whole, is only as good as its parts. The various subcellular structures are what give the cell its identity and characteristics, both structural and functional. These organelles have their discrete functions, but they do not operate as a separate entity. That is, in any dynamic system such as the cell, there is coordination of function among its various components. The individual functions are discussed; the relationships should become implicit.

The endoplasmic reticulum is the internal membrane network of the cell, serving as a possible circulatory system for the various compounds which must be transported intracellularly. Specific enzyme functions are also assigned to these membranes—for example, neutral fat synthesis and electron transport. The fluid surrounding these membranes, the hyaloplasm, contains the enzymes for the Embden-Meyerhof pathway. The fluid within the membranes which form sacs, or cisternae, may contain synthesized material.

Associated with the endoplasmic reticulum are the ribosomes, distinct particles composed of RNA and protein, which function in protein synthesis. Ribosomes may appear separately, or in a polysome arrangement which is physiologically active.

One of the most important cell organelles is the mitochondrion which houses the enzymes for ATP production by oxidative phosphorylation, the electron transport system, and the Krebs cycle and fatty acid pathway. This organelle is interesting because of its elaborate structure and independence. The basic structure consists of a double sac in which the inner one has projections, called cristae, arising from it. These villi-like structures contain specific particles, the electron transport particles, which are believed to house the components of the respiratory chain. The outer membrane may also have particulate arrangements of the Krebs and fatty acid enzymes. Some unique features of the mitochondria are the presence of a contractile protein which allows movement of the organelle, structural changes during various physiological conditions, the ability to accumulate ions, and an independent biogenesis process.

Chloroplasts are the photosynthetic organelles of the plant cell. These structures, which are a double-sac with lamellae of layers of protein and lipoids, also have an elaborate organization. Discrete particles, called quantasomes, contain all the necessary components for the light reaction of photosynthesis. There are many biochemical similarities between the chloroplasts and the mitochondria.

The Golgi complex is a network of membranes which may have been derived from the endoplasmic reticulum. Their function is believed to be that of storing products formed in other organelles. Associated with the Golgi, and perhaps derived from it, are small bodies called lysosomes which contain large amounts of hydrolytic enzymes. They function in intracellular digestion and phagocytosis.

Finally, the nucleus is the control center of the cell, being involved in many nucleocytoplasmic relationships which are important for maintenance of cell dynamics. Chapter 26 takes up the role of the nucleus in these relationships.

Literature cited

1. Revel, J. P., D. W. Fawcett, and C. W. Philpott. 1963. Observations on mitochondrial structures. Angular configuration of the cristae. J. Cell Biol. 16:187.
2. Sjöstrand, F. S., and L. Elfin. 1964. The granular structure of mitochondrial membranes and of cytomembranes as demonstrated in frozen-dried tissue. J. Utrastruct. Res. 10:263.
3. Blair, P. V., T. Oda, D. E. Green, and H. Fernández-Morán. 1963. Studies on the electron transport system. LIV. Isolation of the unit of electron transfer. Biochemistry 2:756.
4. Green, D. E. 1964. The mitochondrion. Sci. Am. (Jan.), p. 63.
5. Novikoff, A. B., E. Essner, and N. Quintana. 1964. Golgi apparatus and lysosomes. Fed. Proc. 23:1010.

General references

Chance, B. (editor). 1963. Energy-linked functions of mitochondria. Academic Press, Inc., New York.
Chance, B., and D. F. Parsons. 1964. Cytochrome function in relation to inner membrane structure of mitochondria. Science 142:1176.
Davson, H. 1959. A textbook of general physiology. 2nd ed. Little, Brown & Co., Boston.
DeRobertis, E. L. P., W. W. Nowinski, and F. A. Saez. 1965. Cell biology. 4th ed. W. B. Saunders Co., Philadelphia.
Fernández-Morán, H., et al. 1964. A macromolecular repeating unit of mitochondrial structure and function. J. Cell Biol. 22:7.
Granick, S. 1959. Chloroplasts, vol. 2, p. 489. In Brachet, J., and A. E. Mirsky (editors): The cell. Academic Press, Inc., New York.
Grell, K. 1964. The protozoan nucleus, vol. 6, p. 1. In Brachet, J., and A. E. Mirsky (editors): The cell. Academic Press Inc., New York.
Lehninger, A. L. 1964. The mitochondrion. W. A. Benjamin, Inc., New York.
Locke, M. (editor). 1964. Cellular membranes in development. Academic Press, Inc., New York.
Mirsky, A. E., and S. Osawa. 1961. The interphase nucleus, vol. 2, p. 677. In Brachet, J., and A. E. Mirsky (editors): The cell. Academic Press, Inc., New York.
Palade, G. 1959. Functional changes in the structure of cell components, p. 64. In T. Hayashi (editor): Subcellular particles. Ronald Press Co., New York.
Porter, K. 1961. The ground substance; Observations from electron microscopy, vol. 2, p. 621. In Brachet, J., and A. E. Mirsky (editors): The cell. Academic Press, Inc., New York.
Waddington, C. H. 1959. Biological organisation. Pergamon Press, Inc., New York.
Wolken, J. J. 1961. The chloroplast, p. 85. In M. V. Edds, Jr. (editor): Macromolecular complexes. Ronald Press Co., New York.
Wolstenholme, G. E. W., and C. M. O'Conror (editors). 1961. Quinones in electron transport. Little, Brown & Co., Boston.

26

DNA and RNA—macromolecules with a purpose

T **INTRODUCTION**
wo basic properties of living material are the ability to reproduce and the ability to metabolize. The two macromolecules, DNA and RNA, are involved in both of these functions. The genetic information resides on the DNA molecule, and thus the DNA must precisely replicate to ensure the passage of correct genetic information to the next generation. DNA and RNA together form a working partnership to produce the enzymes of the cell. These two tasks—replication of the genetic material and use of this same information to control protein synthesis will be considered.

MOLECULAR STRUCTURE OF DNA

The basic structure of deoxyribonucleic acid was considered previously; however, it should be reviewed at this time. The primary structure of DNA is that of a single, long, unbranched chain of nucleotides which occurs in tandem with another similar chain coiled in an α-helix. These chains are arranged in such a manner that there is a sugar-phosphate skeleton from which project the various purines and pyrimidines. These latter, the bases, are paired and are joined by hydrogen bonding. The entire complex is described as being analogous to an uneven spiral staircase where the bases are the steps and the phosphate and sugar are the framework.

The base pairing is not haphazard, for there are only certain combinations which normally appear in the molecule. These are cytosine:guanine and adenine:thymine. Thus, running up and down the strands are these series of bases, always arranged to each other in complementary pairs.

The primary structure does not dictate the order in which the bases are to be arranged along the chains. The only stated fact is that regardless of the order, guanine can only pair with cytosine and adenine with thymine. Both theory and experimentation bear out the fact that the sequence of bases run in opposite directions on the two chains; that is, each strand of the double helix runs in an opposite direction to its complement. Thus, if one strand has a sequence of —GACTTACGT— reading from left to right, its complement would have a sequence —CTGAATGCA— reading from right to left.

$$- G - A - C - T - T - A - C - G - T -$$
$$| \quad | \quad | \quad | \quad | \quad | \quad | \quad | \quad |$$
$$- C - T - G - A - A - T - G - C - A -$$

DNA REPLICATION

A fascinating aspect of deoxyribonucleic acid is that it contains the template for its own production. Since the bases on each strand can only fit with the complement bases, each strand carries the template to form its mate. Thus, the right-hand strand dictates formation of the left-hand strand, and, conversely, the original left-hand strand dictates the formation of a new right-hand strand.

To have a replication occur, then, requires that the hydrogen bonds be broken, that the strands be separated, and that the new strands be formed. One difficulty with this simple explanation is that the two strands of the DNA are coiled in a plectonemic fashion, that is, like two pieces of rope. This means that the only way in which separation can occur is for the ends of the strand to revolve in a direction opposite from the coil. This coiling is in contrast to paranemic coiling which allows the strands to be separated without revolving the ends, that is, like two springs pushed together and pulled apart.

Nevertheless, all evidence points to the fact that each DNA strand does, in fact, serve as a template for the formation of its complement mate.

Lining up of the complementary bases is determined by the bases in the formed strand. The biochemical mechanism which attaches these together involves an enzyme, the bases as their triphosphate nucleotides, and Mg^{++}. Some primer DNA is also required. The process can be depicted as follows

$$n_1 \begin{cases} TTP \\ dATP \end{cases} + n_2 \begin{cases} dCTP \\ dGTP \end{cases} + DNA \xrightleftharpoons[Mg^{++}]{DNA\ polymerase} DNA \begin{bmatrix} TMP \\ dAMP \\ dCMP \\ dGMP \end{bmatrix}_{2(n_2+n_1)} + 2(n_2+n_1)\ PP_i$$

The nucleotides are present as the deoxynucleotides, as would be expected since the deoxyribose is a characteristic of DNA. This mechanism was worked out on DNA obtained from *Escherichia coli*. To what extent this parallels DNA synthesis in vivo is uncertain. The enzyme, DNA polymerase, must be specific for the triphosphate nucleotides, and as such, it must attach in specific loci in the chromosome, if not on the strands themselves.

Regardless of the problems of coiling and enzyme biosynthesis, there seems no doubt that the bases of the DNA strands dictate the order of the bases in the newly formed strands and, as such, act as a template for the replication.

THE GENETIC CODE

The problem

Each cell type has its own peculiar set of enzymes, and as a result of this the cell is distinct morphologically and physiologically from other kinds of cells. The genetic information which must be passed on from generation to generation is the set of enzymes which the cell is to make. Since it has been established that the DNA also controls protein synthesis in the cell, the information on the DNA molecule must be serving a dual function. The same set of information is used for control at the local level as well as for information for newly formed cells. This duality can only imply one thing: not all of the information on the DNA molecule is used at any one time. This sets up the problem of the control of what information is to be used as well as what the information will be.

Establishing the code

Since any genetic information which is used intracellularly is directly involved with the production of protein, the clue to the genetic code must reside in the protein synthesis mechanism. How, then, does DNA participate in protein synthesis? The DNA does not leave the nucleus, and yet it exerts its control in the cytoplasm. Early experimenters suggested that RNA might be involved when it was demonstrated that the total RNA content of the cell increased when the cell was actively synthesizing protein. The concept of RNA involvement was strengthened with establishing of ribosomes as the sites of protein synthesis. Finally, the finding that there were three distinct types of RNA, each with a particular function was clinching evidence that the RNA must somehow translate any information which resides in the DNA and convert this information into a set of directions for protein synthesis.

The facts from which a genetic code is proposed are the following:
1. DNA has a characteristic molecular structure.
2. RNA is involved in protein synthesis as a component of the ribosome.
3. Three distinct classes of RNA are present.
4. There are only four different bases on both the DNA and the RNA.
5. There are at least 20 amino acids to code for.
6. Most evidence bears out the one gene—one enzyme theory.

From this, one could postulate that the groups of the bases arranged in a particular order could code for an amino acid. Two bases would give only 16 possible combinations; three bases, on the other hand, offer 64 different combinations to code for the 20 amino acids. The idea of a triplet code is very prevalent and seems to explain most of the data. The synthesis of artificial nucleotide polymers has helped to break the code. Although the number of synthetic messenger RNA's which can be made is small, the ones successfully synthesized have been demonstrated to code for a particular amino acid. Polyuridine, or Poly-U, was found to cause the synthesis of a polyphenylalanine chain. Thus, UUU is apparently one of the codes for phenylalanine.

Assuming that a grouping of three nucleotides (called a codon) codes for an amino acid, the question has to be answered as to how the codes for each amino acid are assembled together to code for an entire protein. In a protein containing 100 amino acids, the minimum number of nucleotides required would be 300, assuming that there is no overlap of the "letters" in the protein "word." This sequence would have to be read correctly in order for the protein to be "spelled" correctly. Apparently, the codons are read in order, starting at one end of the chain. This nucleotide sequence would constitute a gene if it codes for one protein enzyme.

Two further questions arise concerning the coding. The first query would be whether all combinations of three nucleotides code for amino acids or do some have no coding value and are thus nonsense syllables. It turns out that most of the triplet arrangements do code for amino acids, but there are some which are nonsense and do not code. The code words for some amino acids have been established (Table 26-1). There is good evidence that the code may be a universal one. The 64 combinations offer the possibility of overlap where the same amino acid may be coded for by different triplet arrangements. The triplet arrangement for any one amino acid in one organism would not be used to code for any other amino acid in other forms if the code is, in fact, universal.

The second question is what separates the codes for the different enzymes. In other words, each DNA molecule contains the codes for many proteins, and it must delineate where one protein ends and another begins. Two possibilities have been proposed. The first, and on the surface more obvious, solution would be that each genetic word is separated from the next by a nonsense syllable. The second proposal is that the DNA is not a continuous molecule, but that there are breaks in it. Each break would then separate the codes for two protein

Table 26-1. Codon nucleotide sequences or RNA codewords for some amino acids*

Amino acid	Nucleotide sequence of codon
Alanine	CCG
Arginine	CGC; AGA
Asparagine; glutamine	ACA; AUA†; AGA‡
Aspartic acid	GUA
Cysteine	UUG
Glutamic acid	GAA
Glycine	UGG; AGG
Histidine	ACC
Isoleucine	UAU; UAA
Leucine	UU (G, C, A, or U)
Lysine	AA (A, G, or U)
Methionine	UGA
Phenylalanine	UUU
Proline	CC (C, U, A, or G)
Serine	UC (U, C, or G)
Threonine	CAC; CAA
Tryptophan	GGU
Tyrosine	AUU
Valine	UGU

*Codon sequences from Nirenberg, M. 1963. The genetic code. II. Sci. Am. (Mar.), p. 80.
†Asparagine only.
‡Glutamine only.

enzymes. The magnitude of the number of different codes which the DNA of each chromosome must carry would seem to necessitate a precise separation device between codes. However, this has not as yet been resolved.

PROTEIN SYNTHESIS

The ultimate role in the cell of the two macromolecules, DNA and RNA, is the task of precise protein synthesis. The mechanism is a fascinating one, and even though the story is not complete, it demonstrates the interrelationships between the nuclear control and the functional cytoplasm.

The RNA's

The DNA molecule contains specific sequences of nucleotides which code for the manufacture of a protein in the ribosomes of the cytoplasm. Two problems are immediately evident. The first is the transcription mechanism. If the DNA is a template containing a coded message, there must be some device for transcribing this message on to some molecule which will carry it to the ribosome. The second interrelated problem is how this message is translated into a specific amino acid sequence in the ribosomes. The answers were partially supplied by discovery and characterizing of the three kinds of RNA.

Messenger RNA

The presence of amounts of RNA in the nucleus has been reported for some time, but its function was merely speculation until isotope studies revealed that the nuclear RNA was formed as a complement strand to portions of the DNA molecule. The template sequence of bases in the DNA strand which codes for a protein induces formation of a single strand of RNA, which is called the messenger RNA (mRNA). The mechanism for the transcription is not totally clear. Uracil substitutes for the thymine and ribose for the deoxyribose when the mRNA is formed. The reaction of zipping up the nucleotides is catalyzed by RNA polymerase, but what other factors are involved is uncertain. It is also unclear as to what causes the mRNA, once formed on the DNA template, to separate off and migrate to the cytoplasm. Another related and vexing problem is to explain how the mRNA reads the code from the DNA while the deoxyribonucleic acid is in the double α-helix. Some studies indicate that the hydrogen bonds between the bases in the two strands might be broken where the mRNA is being formed. This would imply that there are a limited number of locations on the DNA which can be active at the same time in order to maintain the integrity of the total DNA molecule.

The mRNA, once formed on the DNA template, must leave the nucleus in order to exert its action in the cytoplasm. One speculation of how this occurs is that the mRNA is extruded out through the nucleus in blebs of the nuclear membrane which pinch off and enter the cytoplasm.[1] This theory also suggests an intimate relationship between the nuclear membrane and the membranes of the endoplasmic reticulum. (Plate 5, *C*, p. 307.) Nevertheless, the mRNA does leave the nucleus and migrates to the ribosomes where it attaches. The sequence of bases in the mRNA are specific for determining the sequence of amino acids to be synthesized into a protein.

Transfer, soluble, or adaptor RNA

Nature cannot trust randomness as a means of getting amino acids to the ribosomes. These acids are escorted to the ribosome site by specific, small molecules of RNA. The RNA with this role is called transfer, soluble, or adaptor RNA, abbreviated, sRNA.

The sRNA is probably formed in the nucleus and then migrates to the cytoplasm where it performs its role of picking up amino acids and taking them to the ribosome site. Different from the other RNA molecules, the sRNA is a helix. It is not a helix of the same kind as the DNA, however, in that the sRNA is a single-stranded structure which twists back upon itself very much like a twisted hairpin (Fig. 26-1).

Three types of RNA are involved in protein synthesis: ribosomal, messenger, and transfer RNA, and their characteristics are ideally suited for their individual roles (Table 26-2). How they function together is a precise and amazing story.

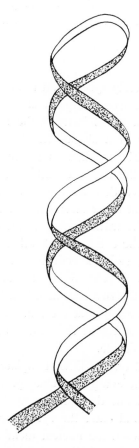

Fig. 26-1. Diagrammatic representation of transfer RNA showing single strand folding back upon itself to form a double helix.

Table 26-2. Characteristics of the classes of RNA

RNA	Characteristics
Messenger RNA (mRNA)	Single-stranded chain; complement of portion of DNA chain; transcribes peptide synthesis sequence from DNA
Transfer or soluble RNA (sRNA)	Single-stranded chain folded back on itself to form double-spiral structure; specifically binds amino acids
Ribosomal RNA (RNP, when associated with protein)	Macromolecular particle; attaches to messenger RNA and sets up chain for synthesis
Polysomal RNA	Functional unit in protein synthesis; translates code on messenger RNA into peptide sequence

The synthesis

The first step in protein synthesis is attachment of the amino acid to the transfer RNA. This process depends on the amino acid's being activated by ATP and an amino acid activation enzyme.[2]

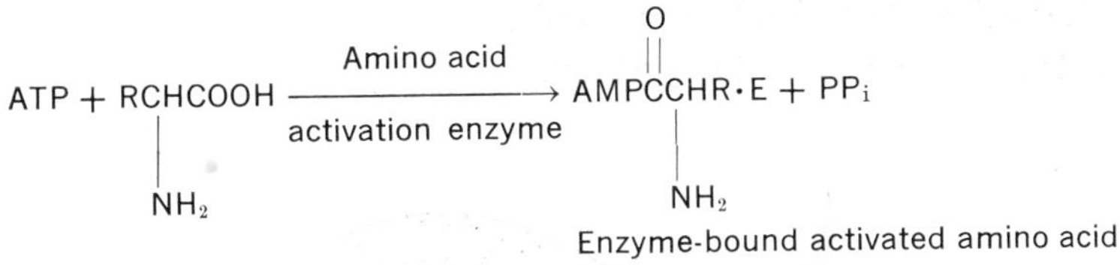

$$\text{ATP} + \underset{\underset{NH_2}{\mid}}{\text{RCHCOOH}} \xrightarrow[\text{activation enzyme}]{\text{Amino acid}} \underset{\underset{NH_2}{\mid}}{\text{AMPC}\overset{\overset{O}{\|}}{}\text{CHR·E}} + \text{PP}_i$$

Enzyme-bound activated amino acid

This high-energy complex then attaches to the sRNA in the region of the three unpaired nucleotides at the terminal end, or tail, of the helix (Fig. 26-1).

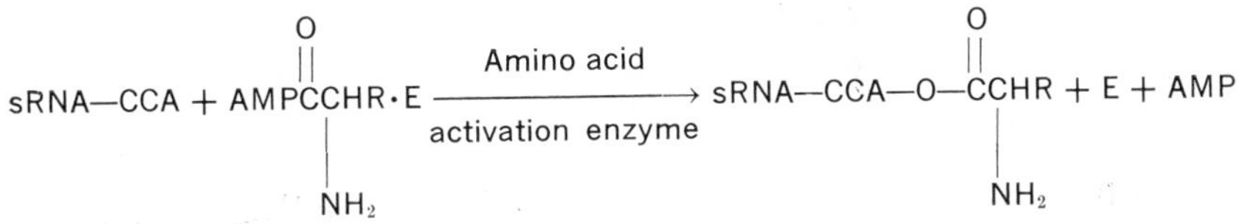

$$\text{sRNA—CCA} + \underset{\underset{NH_2}{\mid}}{\text{AMPC}\overset{\overset{O}{\|}}{}\text{CHR·E}} \xrightarrow[\text{activation enzyme}]{\text{Amino acid}} \underset{\underset{NH_2}{\mid}}{\text{sRNA—CCA—O—C}\overset{\overset{O}{\|}}{}\text{CHR}} + \text{E} + \text{AMP}$$

The transfer RNA now is free to carry its amino acid load to the ribosome. The triplet at the tail of the helix is specific for each amino acid, but the code probably bears no relation to the code on the messenger RNA. In fact, the code on the mRNA is for the triplet code on the head of the transfer RNA and not for the amino acid. This was proved by changing the nucleotide sequence on the tail and discovering that the sRNA-amino acid acted as if no change had occurred; that is, the nucleotide code on the head end, and not what amino acid is present, is the determining factor as to how the sRNA will react.

Earlier it was mentioned that ribosomal particles occurred in different sizes, and that the large-sized particles were the active ones so far as protein synthesis is concerned. The particle size is characterized by the sedimentation rate and given a Svedberg number. For example, a particle of 30s size is smaller than one of 50s or 70s, and so on. The numbers are not additive in that the 70s particle, which seems to be the active ribosome, is composed of two portions, one of which is the 30s subunit and one the 50s subunit.

Basically, the protein synthesis mechanism can be outlined as follows:

1. The messenger RNA transcribes the nucleotide sequence from the DNA; that is, it is a complementary strand to a genetic unit of the DNA.
2. The mRNA migrates to the cytoplasm, either passively through the pores or by an active process such as blebbing.
3. The mRNA attaches to the ribosomal site.
4. The active ribosomes, each composed of two portions (the 30s and 50s subunits), aggregate as a polysomic complex.
5. The messenger RNA is stretched between the active ribosome particles.
6. The transfer RNA binds to the ribosome and then attaches to the messenger RNA in a complementary base pairing, matching the triplet code.
7. The ribosomal particle "reads" the mRNA either by moving along the sequence of nucleotides or by the mRNA moving through the ribosome.
8. As each mRNA triplet-sRNA-amino acid complex is reached, the amino acid is incorporated into the growing peptide chain, releasing the sRNA.
9. A series of ribosomes in the polysome complex move across the mRNA, each synthesizing a protein molecule.

These events are summarized in Fig. 26-2.

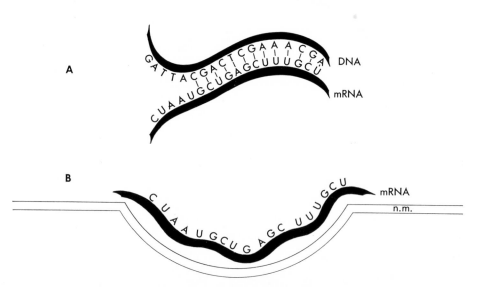

Fig. 26-2. Schematic summary of events in protein synthesis. **A,** Messenger RNA (mRNA) transcribes the nucleotide sequence from the DNA. **B,** Messenger RNA (mRNA) leaves nucleus through nuclear membrane (*n.m.*). **C,** The messenger RNA (mRNA) is attached to a polysome complex composed of an aggregate of ribosomes (*rib.*). The transfer RNA (sRNA) with its specific amino acid (*a.a.*) then attaches to the messenger RNA by complementary base pairing. The amino acids polymerize to form the start of a polypeptide chain. **D,** The messenger RNA (mRNA) moves across the ribosomes (*rib.*), forming a polypeptide sequence at each site. Sequence (1) has five amino acids in the chain since five sets of triplet codons have passed across the first ribosome. Sequence (2) has only two amino acids in the chain, with the third one about to be attached.

There are still many unanswered questions concerning this synthesis sequence. Enumerated, they are the following.

1. What separates the sRNA from the amino acids and from its complement-base attachment to the messenger RNA, and is the energy from the cleavage of the ester bond utilizable for bringing about formation of the peptide linkage?

2. What degrades the messenger RNA? Accumulated evidence indicates that one mRNA molecule may be used for a template only ten or twenty times. Theories suggesting RNase and nucleotide phosphorylase are still in the speculative stage.

3. What confers the secondary and tertiary structures to the formed protein? The possibility that the ribosomes are specific for making a particular

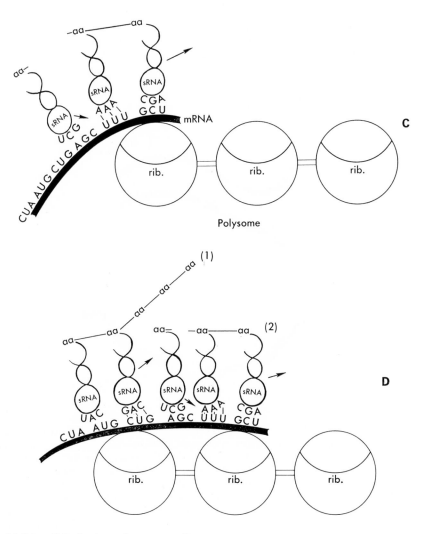

Fig. 26-2 (cont'd). For legend see opposite page.

protein and thus offer a three-dimensional mold through which to pull the mRNA has been suggested. Another possibility is that the secondary and tertiary structures are inherent in the arrangement of the amino acids, but neither suggestion has much conclusive evidence to bear it out.

4. How does a globulin which has several polypeptide chains get together? The secondary and tertiary structures of a single-stranded protein are difficult to envision; the problem of multistrands merely complexes the situation.

The sequence for protein synthesis is apparently an orderly transfer of information from the DNA to the ribosomes mediated by messenger RNA. The ribosomes read the message on the mRNA and then incorporate the amino acids brought to the ribosomes by the sRNA into a peptide chain.

The polynucleotides redefined

The RNA's

On the basis of the protein synthesis scheme, the classes of RNA could be redefined. Messenger RNA contains a sequence of polypeptides which can be translated into peptide sequences by the ribosomal system. This mRNA, however, is not the only RNA which can bring about this event. It has been mentioned that artificially synthesized polynucleotide chains can be used to force synthesis of a particular peptide chain. Viral RNA can also bring out this result. The major effect of a virus on the cell is that the virus RNA forces the ribosomal system to make protein of the virus instead of normal cellular enzymes. The virus RNA also must contain a base sequence which can be read by the ribosomes. These three groups of RNA—messenger, synthetic, and viral—all show the same property of being able to be translated into peptide sequences by the ribosomal system. The class of RNA containing these three is called translatable RNA.

The ribosome RNA does not function in coding or decoding as such. It apparently only forms the surface upon which the messenger RNA attaches, although if it imparts some of the configurational properties of the protein, the attachment may be very specific. Ribosomal RNA is termed nontranslatable because of its inability to code or decode.

Finally, translational RNA is the classification given to the transfer or sRNA.

DNA segments

The mRNA transcribes the base sequence from a particular section of the DNA, and this base sequence codes for the synthesis of a polypeptide chain. The segment of the DNA providing the original code for this chain is called a cistron. It may not be identical with a gene since a gene, by definition, controls the synthesis of one whole enzyme.

A muton is the smallest segment of the DNA chain which can be altered and still bring about a mutation. These terms will be useful in the discussion of the control of the protein synthesis.

Control of protein synthesis

The cell would end up in chaos if all the enzymatic syntheses which it potentially can initiate were occurring at once. It seems obvious that only certain genes are being translated by mRNA at any one time. This implies a precise mechanism for guaranteeing that certain genes are turned off and others turned on. The concepts necessary to explain this control are found in Section VIII.

SUMMARY

The macromolecules, DNA and RNA, are designed to carry out two functions in the cell. The genetic information which passes from generation to generation is primarily in the DNA molecule, although RNA carries the same type of information in some instances. DNA and RNA, working together, utilize this genetic information intracellularly to produce the characteristic proteins of the cell.

The DNA molecule, with its paired bases and complementary strands, has a built-in mechanism for self-replication. Each strand of the double-stranded structure induces the formation of its partner, forming new DNA with exactly the same nucleotide pattern as the old. The sequence of nucleotides on the DNA strands code for the amino acid sequence which is interpreted in the ribosome and translated into the forming of a specific protein. The sequence for one amino acid is believed to be three nucleotides. This triplet arrangement may be both specific and universal.

The sequence for polypeptide synthesis is given. In a similar manner to self-replication, a portion of the DNA strand (cistron) which codes for a single polypeptide induces formation of a messenger RNA molecule which is complementary to the nucleotide sequence of the DNA (uracil substituting for thymine). This messenger RNA leaves the nucleus (by blebs?) and goes to the ribosomal system. Here, amino acids carried on sRNA are present and attach specifically to the coded areas of the messenger RNA. The ribosomes read the message and synthesize the peptide chain together in the order dictated by the messenger RNA.

There are many unanswered questions concerning the synthesis of proteins, particularly in the area of conferring the specific secondary and tertiary structures on the newly formed peptide chain.

Literature cited

1. Gay, H. 1960. Nuclear control of the cell. Sci. Am. (Jan.), p. 126.
2. Stulberg, M. P., and G. David Novelli. 1962. Amino acid activation, vol. 6, p. 401. In Boyer, P. D., H. Lardy, and K. Myrbäck (editors): The enzymes. Academic Press, Inc., New York.

General references

Barry, J. M. 1964. Molecular biology: Genes and the chemical control of living cells. Prentice-Hall, Inc., Englewood Cliffs, N. J.
Crick, F. H. C. 1962. The genetic code. Sci. Am. (Oct.), p. 66.
Davidson, J. N., and W. E. Cohn (editors). 1963. Progress in nucleic acid research. Academic Press, Inc., New York. Vol. 1 and 2.

Gellhorn, A., and E. Hirschberg (editors). 1962. Basic problems in neoplastic disease. Columbia University Press, N. Y.

Grunberg-Manago, M. 1963. Enzymatic synthesis of nucleic acids. Prog. Biophys. 13:175.

Herskowitz, I. H. 1965. Genetics. 2nd ed. Little, Brown & Co., Boston.

Hinegardner, R. T., and J. Engelberg. 1963. Rationale for a universal genetic code. Science 142:1083.

Hultin, T. 1964. Ribosomal functions related to protein synthesis. Internat. Rev. Cytol. 16:1.

Jacob, F., and J. Monod. 1961. Genetic regulatory mechanisms in the synthesis of proteins. J. Molec. Biol. 3:318.

Kornberg, A. 1960. Biologic synthesis of deoxyribonucleic acid. Science 131:1503.

Nirenberg, M., and P. Leder. 1964. RNA codewords and protein synthesis. Science 145:1399.

Nirenberg, M. 1963. The genetic code: II. Sci. Am. (Mar.), p. 80.

Rich, A. 1963. Polyribosomes. Sci. Am. (Dec.), p. 44.

Roberts, R. B. (editor). 1958. Microsomal particles and protein synthesis. Pergamon Press, Inc., New York.

Setlow, R. B., and E. C. Pollard. 1962. Molecular biophysics. Addison-Wesley Publishing Company, Inc., Reading, Mass.

Srinivasan, P. R., and Borek, E. 1964. Enzymatic alteration of nucleic acid structure. Science 145:548.

Synthesis and structure of macromolecules. 1963. Cold Spring Harbor Symposium on Quantitative Bioliolgy. Vol. 28.

The living cell is a fundamental unit which is capable of exhibiting a series of processes which enables it to maintain itself in its local environment, respond to changes in this environment, and perpetuate itself through the time span. The cell must be aware of external and internal stimuli and must adjust to them accordingly. The survival of the cell depends on awareness, just as survival of the cell species depends on the basic function of reproduction.

The basic physiological properties of irritability, conductivity, and contractility can be demonstrated in almost all cells. Irritability, the response to a stimulus, and conductivity, the movement of an impulse elicited by a stimulus, are exploited in the nerve cell. The specializations of structure and biochemical function illustrate how a differentiated cell is designed to perform a particular function (Chapter 27). In Chapter 28, the striated muscle cell and its adaptation for contraction are described. There is a unified theme running through all types of movement, and this is brought out in the chapter.

Finally, Chapter 29 explains the steps of a complete cell cycle, starting with division, progressing through growth, and ending at cell death. The principles underlying these processes are cloaked in uncertainty and speculation.

27

Irritability and conductivity

INTRODUCTION

The cell must be able to respond to any environment or change, whether this change be ion strength, temperature, pressure, or any of the series of conditions which can potentially elicit a response. The ability to respond to the environmental change, or stimulus, is called irritability. Living systems must be aware of their external environment, and irritability is the physiological property which allows the response to the conditions of the environment to occur. All cells exhibit the property of irritability, but some are more specialized for this task; that is, some cells have a low threshold of excitation for certain stimuli.

The ability to conduct an electrochemical impulse elicited by a stimulus is called conductivity. Again, all cells exhibit this property to some degree, but the nerve cells, epithelial gland cells, and muscle cells are especially adapted to carry out this physiological function. Adaptation for conductivity concomitantly implies adaptation for receiving stimuli, and this property is, in fact, inherent in these cells. Of all of the classes of cells which exhibit the properties of conductivity and irritability, only the nerve cell specializes in these two properties.

THE NEURON

The nerve cell, or neuron, is one of the most differentiated cells that exists. It has lost many of its basic properties in order to concentrate on its prime function, that of conduction. Nerve cells cannot undergo division, differentiation, or dedifferentiation once they have attained their "adult" form. For a permanent communication system, the neuron is the ideal cell, since it focuses its energy toward one goal.

The generalized cell

There are many variations of nerve cells, particularly among those found in receptor organs. However, one can still generalize on the structure of the typical neuron (Fig. 27-1). The primary adaptation of the nerve cell is the

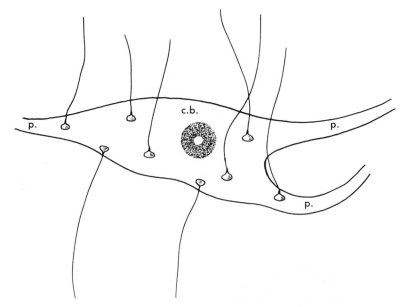

Fig. 27-1. Diagrammatic representation of a typical neuron, showing presynaptic boutons on surface of the cell body (*c.b.*) and the processes (*p.*).

extension from its cell body, the cyton or perikaryon, of a series of protoplasmic processes which increase the potential area of contact with other cells. The two basic types of processes are the dendrites which carry impulses toward the cyton and the axons which carry impulses away from the center of the cell. These processes are often asymmetrically arranged, and in many cases, there may be only one axon and many dendrites, or vice versa. By mass, these processes far exceed the weight of the cell body; some axons are 1 meter or more in length.

Some of the cell organelles, in particular the nucleolus, ribosomes, endoplasmic reticulum, and the Golgi apparatus, are well developed. The darkstaining Nissl substance represents the ribosomal and endoplasmic reticular material (Plate 10, *B*, p. 312). The development of these organelles implies a high synthetic ability. The maintenance of the cytoplasm in normal, dynamic turnover in all of the processes requires a large amount of energy directed toward synthesis. The RNA content of the neurons may be involved in information storage, and if this is true, the nucleolar development and the great number of ribosomes are corroborating evidence. There is conclusive evidence that materials move down the processes from the cyton. The endoplasmic reticulum may be involved in conducting the materials to the axons and dendrites.

The cell processes are generally swaddled with a multilayered envelope, the myelin sheath (Plate 13, p. 315). This sheath is composed of a lipoprotein complex and acts as an insulator between the cytoplasm of the processes and the outer membrane encasing the sheath where the impulse is carried. This insulation expedites the movement of the impulse during conduction. Not all

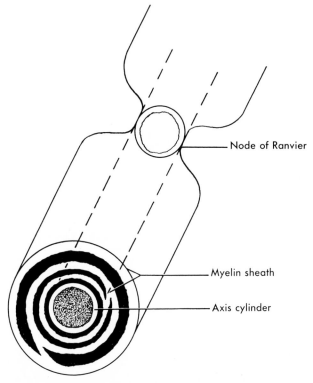

Fig. 27-2. Diagrammatic representation of a cross section of a nerve fiber showing axis cylinder with the myelin sheath wrapped around it at all points except the node of Ranvier.

processes are believed to have a myelin sheath, although a majority do. The formation of the myelin sheath around the naked process occurs during development when a cell, the Schwann cell, envelops the process in a series of spirals, extruding its cytoplasm and compacting the remaining membranes (Fig. 27-2). This figure also shows that the process (axis cylinder) is exposed between the sections of myelin sheath formed by individual Schwann cells in gaps called the nodes of Ranvier.

Running through both the cytoplasm of the processes and the cell body are thin fibers, the neurofibrils, which are made up of a tubular element, the neurotubule, and small neurofilaments. Their exact function has not been ascertained, but evidence suggests that they may be involved in conduction of an impulse in the cytoplasm itself. Another possibility is that they form a conveyance system for carrying essential materials from the cell body through the processes.

On the surface of the cell body and the processes are a series of special structures which are in reality extensions of processes from other cells. The nerve cells must intercommunicate in order to more efficiently carry out their function. One means employed is the interconnections among the nerve cells. The cytoplasmic processes branch into many strands which can then attach to many other neurons. The specialized swollen ends of these extensions are called the presynaptic knobs or *boutons*. They are scattered over the surface of the entire neuron. Their detailed structure has been revealed in electron photomicrographs (Plate 14, p. 316).

The special cells

Some cells lend themselves to experimentation. In the study of neurons, mammalian preparations are very hard to obtain, prepare, and maintain. Thus, much of the enlightenment about the characteristics of neurons and their ability to conduct has been brought forth by work done on various invertebrate nerves. The giant axon of the squid, a fortuitous discovery, is large enough to allow micropipets and microelectrodes to impale the membrane and enter the cytoplasm without too much damage. Neuron preparations from crustaceans and insects have also been used.

The large pyramidal cells in the central nervous system are often used if mammalian tissue is needed. These cells, which are motor neurons, have probably the largest of nerve cell bodies in mammals.

THE MEMBRANE POTENTIAL

The fact that a potential can exist across a membrane has already been considered. A review, with some extension, however, seems in order since the basis of the nerve impulse is this potential. In review, the two primary conditions which are necessary for the membrane potential to develop are the following:

1. The membrane must be selectively permeable, allowing ions of one charge to permeate more easily than ions of the opposite charge.
2. The concentration of the diffusible ions must be greater on one side of the membrane than on the other, and the concentration gradient must be maintained.

The Nernst equation

$$E_{ion} = \frac{RT}{FZ} \, ln \, \frac{C_2}{C_1}$$

allows calculation of any potential created across the membrane due to the ion concentration difference. The surface membrane of the neuron separates aqueous media which have different ionic concentrations. If the three major ion species, Na^+, K^+, and Cl^- are taken, the values outside and inside the membrane surface are quite different. The potassium ion is almost thirty times as concentrated on the inside of the membrane as it is on the outside. This large difference is compensated for to some degree by the sodium and chloride ions which are more concentrated on the outside; sodium has a tenfold difference, and chloride has approximately a fourteenfold disparity.

The ionic imbalance is due in part to physical characteristics and in part to an energy-requiring mechanism. The inside of the membrane is normally negative to the outside, and this makes it more difficult for the chloride ion to penetrate,

Table 27-1. Relationship between ion differences across neuron membrane and equilibrium potential of -70 mv

Ion	Concentration outside (C_2)	Concentration inside (C_1)	Concentration differential	Voltage drop outside-inside	Effective voltage differential
Na$^+$	150 mmoles	15 mmoles	10 X	$+60$	-130
K$^+$	5.5 mmoles	150 mmoles	27 X	-90	$+20$
Cl$^-$	125 mmoles	9 mmoles	14 X	-70	0

even if the membrane were totally permeable to the ion. The inside negativity of -70 mv is enough to explain the imbalance between the chloride concentration inside and outside the cell. The membrane is much more permeable to potassium than to sodium, but both of these ions are not at equilibrium with the -70 mv potential imposed on the system. The potassium has only a 20 mv discrepancy to make up by active processes, but the sodium has a discrepancy of 130 mv to overcome (Table 27-1). This represents an energy input requirement of

$$\Delta F = -nF\Delta E$$
$$= -1 \cdot 23{,}060 \cdot 0.13$$
$$= 3000 \text{ calories}$$

which must be derived from some energy source. The pump-leak Na$^+$ influx and active sodium expulsion mechanism are believed to be involved in this potential, and it must be coupled with some energy-producing mechanism, in this case probably an ATPase system.

The positive ions, Na$^+$ and K$^+$, are believed to be primarily responsible for the resting steady state potential, although there is some evidence that other ion species may also affect this potential more than just secondarily. Nonetheless, most of the theories for explaining the resting potential have been predicated on the idea that sodium and potassium exert the most significant effect on the creation of the potential. The ratio of the permeability constants for Na$^+$ and K$^+$ are a prime factor in determining the steady state potential. In maintenance of the steady state resting potential, there should be a one-for-one exchange of sodium with potassium. This would be necessary to keep the exact imbalance of ions. The permeability, though, is critical, because just as the voltage is determined by the permeability, the permeability is in turn affected by the voltage. This fact is one of the underlying premises in the action potential.

THE ACTION POTENTIAL

It has been established that the neuron membrane is essentially polarized. This polarization occurs with the ratio of sodium$_{outside}$ to sodium$_{inside}$ being 10:1, the potassium$_{outside}$ to potassium$_{inside}$ being a reverse ratio of 1:30 and the inside of the membrane being electronegative to the outside. When a stimulus is applied to the membrane with this steady state resting potential, severe changes in the properties of the membrane occur. These alterations are expressed by changes in both the electrical properties and the permeability of the membrane (Fig. 27-3).

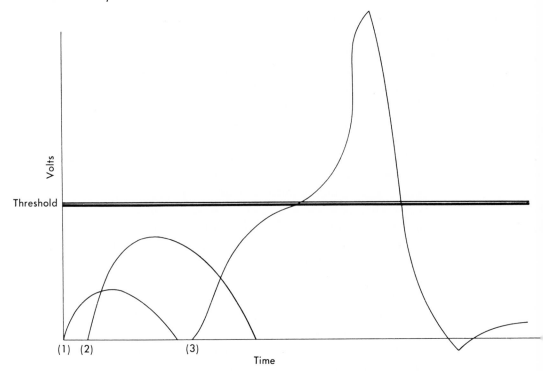

Fig. 27-3. Diagram showing necessity of reaching threshold disturbance before the permeability shift triggers the action potential in nerve cells. In (1) and (2), the disturbance was subthreshold, and no action potential was elicited. In (3), however, the threshold was reached, and the full action potential reaction occurred.

by changes in both the electrical properties and the permeability of the membrane (Fig. 27-3).

The basis of the potential

The first, overt change which occurs is the immediate shift in the polarity of the membrane. Whereas the resting potential finds the inside of the neuron with a voltage of −70 to −90 mv, immediately after stimulation the voltage quickly jumps to a positive value, demonstrated to be as high as +50 mv. The measured potential when a stimulus is applied to the membrane is called the action potential. This fact seemed to preclude the possibility of the change being merely a breakdown of the membrane, since this would result in a steady state potential of 0, or a difference of 70 mv from the resting potential. The breakdown would give free movement of the ions, and an equilibrium approaching 1:1 inside to outside should occur. Work by Hodgkin,[1] Katz,[2] Huxley,[3] and many others substantiated the proposal that this discrepancy must be explained by increasing the permeability of the sodium ion during the stimulation which, in turn, allows the inside of the membrane to become positive to the outside. This infers that the creation of the action potential depends on the level of sodium in the surrounding medium. Experiments have borne this out, although there is some evidence that other ions may substitute for the sodium during the shift. It does not apply, however, to the resting potential where the imbalance of the potassium is probably more effective in creating the potential.

The steps leading to attainment of the action potential and the subsequent return to the resting state could be enumerated as follows:

1. The resting potential is established with the inside of the cell electronegative to the outside with a concentration of sodium on the outside and a high level of potassium on the inside.
2. The stimulus causes a modification of the permeability of the membrane to sodium, increasing the passage of the ion through the membrane. The permeability to potassium essentially remains the same.
3. There is a sudden influx of sodium to the inside of the cell.
4. This influx sets up a situation where the inside of the membrane now is electropositive to the outside at the point where the stimulus is applied; that is, the membrane is depolarized.
5. The membrane again lowers its permeability to sodium. At this point the maximum action potential is attained.
6. The potassium now flows out from the cell, reestablishing the original polarity; that is, repolarization occurs.
7. The sodium is actively pumped out from the cell, and potassium is brought back inside during the recovery phase.
8. The resting potential and original ion imbalance are again at the initial steady state level.

This is an oversimplification, certainly, but it does express the type of ion shifts necessary to bring about an action potential of the magnitude recorded on nerve fibers.

Characteristics associated with the action potential

One unique characteristic of the action impulse is the all-or-none phenomenon. Each nerve fiber has a distinct threshold of activation which, when reached, always produces the same action potential. Stating this premise another way, the membrane requires application of a certain level of stimulus before the change in permeability is triggered. Once the mechanism begins, it is self-reinforcing until the shift in ions is such as to attain the level of the action potential. The all-or-none law defines those phenomena in which, under any given set of conditions, there is only one level of physiological activity.

The mode by which the action potential is produced is that this potential changes the electrochemical properties of the fiber, and as a result, the irritability is changed. Immediately after triggering of the mechanism which sets up the action potential, the nerve will not react to any stimulation, regardless of the level. This absolute refractory period corresponds to the time period when the sodium influx is occurring. Following this period of inactivity, the nerve will react to stimuli again, but during the time when the nerve is repolarizing, the threshold is higher, and thus it requires a greater than normal stimulus to trigger the mechanism. This is called the relative refractory period.

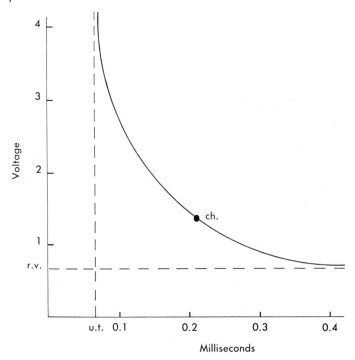

Fig. 27-4. Voltage-duration of stimulus curve. Rheobase voltage (*r.v.*), utilization time (*u.t.*), and chronaxie (*ch.*) are indicated. Notice that the chronaxie is that time necessary for a stimulus to elicit a response when the voltage is twice that of the rheobase.

Although the final potential reached is the same once the mechanism for creating the action potential is triggered, there is a strength of stimulus–time duration relationship which does exist. A low voltage applied to a nerve fiber will take longer to stimulate than a higher voltage which can initiate the process with only a short burst of electricity. The least possible time for stimulation to occur is called the utilization time. The lowest voltage at which a response can be elicited is called the rheobase voltage. These minimal values are difficult to use quantitatively. The chronaxie, which is the time required to elicit the response at a voltage twice that of rheobase, is often used as a term of reference (Fig. 27-4).

THE TRANSMISSION OF THE IMPULSE—THE CONDUCTION PROCESS

The point has been made that an action potential can be established across the membrane of a neuron at the locus of stimulus application. Irritability, however, is only one of two major properties of nerve cells. The other, conductivity, deals with the movement of this impulse through each cell and from one neuron to the next. Conduction is primarily a membrane phenomenon, and it must be treated as such. The concepts developed in the discussion on the cell membrane apply to the conduction process. Propagation of the nerve impulse requires physical, chemical, and biological devices and mechanisms to carry out this function.

The propagation of the impulse along a single fiber

There are several theories concerning the passage of the impulse along a single nerve fiber. Depending on the physiological and structural conditions any, or all, of these may be correct. Their concepts are nevertheless important for characterizing the nature of the nerve impulse. Large nerve fibers can be impaled with electrodes along their length. This allows transmission of an impulse to be recorded as it passes along the nerve fibers. Early experimentation indicated that if a stimulus is applied near one electrode the recorded action potential is the same as the recorded potential at some other point along the length of the fiber. This means that the impulse is carried along the fiber without decrement; that is, the level of excitation is the same on any portion of the fiber as the wave of impulses pass. The theories for propagation of the nerve impulse have to account for this fact.

Core conduction, or cable properties, of the neuron

The membrane of the neuron is a lipoprotein structure which may or may not be in association with the lipoid myelin sheath. The conductivity of the material is extremely low, particularly in comparison to the ionic medium which surrounds the membrane on both sides. Thus, one would expect some conduction of any impulse to be carried down the center of the axoplasm (or cytoplasm of any process). However, the membrane leaks too much current to the outside of the cell, and as a result, core conductance does not play an important role in transmitting the impulse any great distance without the current being reinforced by an active process. The fact that the current can move short distances in the central core of the neuronal process is one of the important considerations for formulating other theories on transmission of the nerve impulse.

Local circuit theory

When a membrane is stimulated to the level of excitation, the sodium shift mechanism is triggered. The sudden presence of large numbers of positively charged sodium ions may cause a chain reaction in which the depolarized area causes ions in adjacent areas to be attracted into the field. In other words, the excitation area is negative on the outside and positive on the inside of the membrane, the exact opposite from the remainder of the nerve fiber. This could set up a traveling circuit, with a wave of depolarization being moved along the fiber.

Saltatory conduction

The local circuit theory seems inapplicable to those nerve fibers having heavy myelin sheaths. The sheath would impede the facile movement of ions across it causing the impulse to travel very slowly if propagation were by the local circuit mechanism. Measurements on myelinated and nonmyelinated fibers demonstrate that the impulse travels faster on neurons with myelin than on the nonmyelinated fibers; in fact, the heavier the myelination, the faster the impulse will travel.

At the nodes of Ranvier there is little or no myelination, and the membrane is exposed to both external and internal media. The sodium influx mechanism could occur at these nodes, and the impulse could effectively jump from node to node. This process, saltatory conduction, incorporates the local circuit theory in that this must occur at each node; the core properties, which could explain how the impulse would be carried from node to node, must also be part of the process. Use of the cable properties would also explain why the impulse travels faster in a heavily myelinated sheath than in a lightly myelinated one. The heavier coating more effectively blocks leakage of current, causing more to be directed through the core of the neuronal process to the next node of Ranvier

This theory is the most attractive one for the peripheral nerves of the vertebrates. However, the inability to demonstrate nodes in some neurons of the central nervous system suggests that this may not have general applicability.

Synaptic transmission

The integrational function of a nervous system depends on the ability of the individual neurons to communicate with each other. The propagation of the nerve impulse in a single nerve fiber does not offer an explanation of the transmission between cells. Since the axon is the process carrying impulses away from the cell body, the function of providing a link falls to this neuronal extension. At the distal end of each axon, the axoplasm undergoes separation into a series of subfibers. Branching of the main trunk into the many small units has led to the expression *terminal arborization* for this complex. Each of these smaller fibers, in turn, attaches to another neuron, or a muscle cell.

The junction between the axon terminal and the other cell is called the synapse. The synapse has had a very uncertain history, particularly as to whether or not there is a physical gap between the axon end (the presynaptic knob) of one neuron and the second nerve cell. Recent evidence from electron photomicrographs indicates clearly that a physical gap does, in fact, exist[4] (Plate 7, *C*, p. 309).

Early experimentation indicated that the synapse was the link in the transmission chain which was subject to fatigue and high sensitivity to drugs and other substances known to interfere with transmission of the impulse. This suggested that there was some mechanism at the synapse which required more input of energy to maintain and was probably different from the propagation of the nerve impulse in the single fiber.

The theory that a chemical transmitter was involved in carrying the impulse from one part of the synapse to the other gained rapid acceptance. Further work has demonstrated a series of compounds which can elicit an impulse when released from the presynaptic knob of one neuron to the membrane of the second cell. Among these compounds are epinephrine, acetylcholine γ-amino butyric acid, and serotonin. Epinephrine was the first to be recorded, but it soon became Among these compounds are epinephrine, acetylcholine, γ-amino butyric acid and serotonin are found in the central nervous system as transmitter substances.

The excitatory synapse

The anatomy of the presynaptic bulb and the dendrites which pick up the impulses gives some clue to the mechanism of excitation. The knobs are membrane-covered bulbs which are in juxtaposition to the membrane covering the processes of the dendrite. The bulbs are filled with synaptic vesicles which contain the transmitter substance (Plate 7, *C*, p. 309).

In order for an impulse to be carried across a synapse, there must be a potential created in the next neuron which is high enough to trigger the sodium influx mechanism. This, then, allows the impulse to travel along the next fiber. The excitation potential created at the synapse is called the excitatory post-synaptic potential (EPSP). It is postsynaptic since it occurs at the nerve fiber to be fired and not at the nerve fiber which is setting up the potential. Evidence supports the hypothesis that the EPSP is again set up by the shift of positive ions. The mechanism for creating this shift by the release of a chemical transmitter has been the subject of much experimentation and debate. The confluence of cytological studies and physiological data has led to an hypothesis which satisfies most of the evidence. The sequence of events is outlined below.

1. An impulse traveling along the presynaptic knob or *bouton* causes some

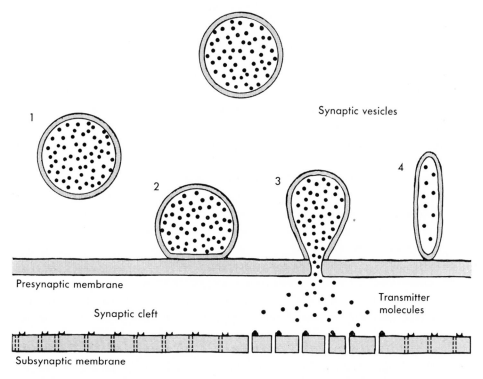

Fig. 27-5. Synaptic vesicles containing a chemical transmitter are distributed throughout the synaptic knob. They are arranged here in a probable sequence, showing how they move up to the synaptic cleft, discharge their contents, and return to the interior for recharging. (From Eccles, John C. 1965. The synapse. Sci. Am. Jan., p. 62.)

of the vesicles containing acetylcholine to move up to the membrane of the knob and release their contents into the synaptic cleft.

2. The acetylcholine diffuses across the synaptic cleft; this cleft is a space several hundred angstroms wide between the membrane of the presynaptic knob and the membrane of the dendrite or cell body of the neuron.

3. The acetylcholine attaches to specific sites on the membrane of the dendrite (the subsynaptic membrane), causing a permeability change.

4. The permeability change may be due to opening of pores for the passage of sodium ions which are normally closed.

5. This creates an EPSP.

6. If the EPSP is high enough, the second nerve fiber is fired, and the impulse is propagated across it.

7. The acetylcholine is destroyed by acetylcholinesterase, allowing the membrane to repolarize and the process to be repeated (Fig. 27-5).

There are many uncertainties about this scheme. The mechanism of release from the synaptic vesicles is unknown. The receptor site for attachment of the transmitter substance is undescribed, and the mode by which the permeability change occurs is conjecture. It may turn out that a simple premise may be correct. For example, the acetylcholinesterase could be a structural protein overlying the pores which is forced into another configuration when the acetylcholine attaches to form an enzyme substrate complex. During the formation of this complex, the pore may be momentarily opened, allowing the influx of sodium. These areas still require investigation.

The inhibitory synapse

Recent work[5] has shown that some synapses may be inhibitory instead of excitatory. The anatomy of the synaptic structure appears similar to that of the excitatory synapse, and both share the property of having cumulative effects. Whereas the release of a transmitter substance from an excitatory synapse causes the internal core of the fiber to become positively charged, the inhibitory synapse gives rise to increased negativity on the inside. This effectively blocks transmission of the impulse since the positive-charged interior is a necessary step to trigger propagation. In other words, when inhibitory synapses are functioning, it requires many more excitatory synapses to be utilized before the EPSP can be high enough to trigger propagation.

The inhibitory postsynaptic potential (IPSP) is probably due to the movement of potassium out from the cell or the movement of chloride in. Both of these movements would create greater negativity; however, the exact mechanism for generating the IPSP is uncertain. Eccles[6] has suggested a scheme for the generation of both the EPSP and IPSP which is illustrated in Figs. 27-6 to 27-8.

Importance of the synapse

The synapse allows precise integration of function of the neuron complexes which comprise the nervous system. From control and feedback points of view,

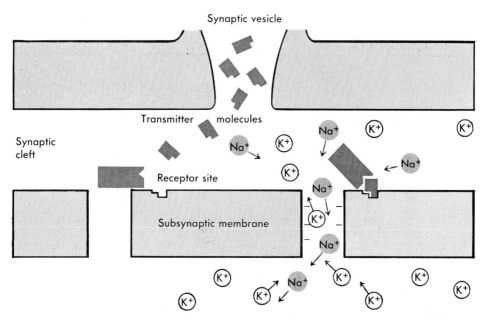

Fig. 27-6. Excitatory synapse may employ transmitter molecules that open large channels in the nerve-cell membrane. This would permit sodium ions, which are plentiful outside the cell, to pour through the membrane freely. The outward flow of potassium ions, driven by a smaller potential gradient, would be at a much slower rate. Chloride ions (not shown) may be prevented from flowing by negative charges on the channel walls. (From Eccles, John C. 1965. The synapse. Sci. Am. Jan., p. 66.)

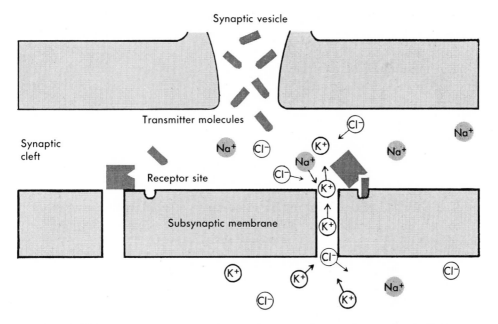

Fig. 27-7. Inhibitory synapse may employ another type of transmitter molecule that opens channels too small to pass sodium ions. The net outflow of potassium ions and inflow of chloride ions would account for the hyperpolarization that is observed as an inhibitory postsynaptic potential (IPSP). (From Eccles, John C. 1965. The synapse. Sci. Am. Jan., p. 66.)

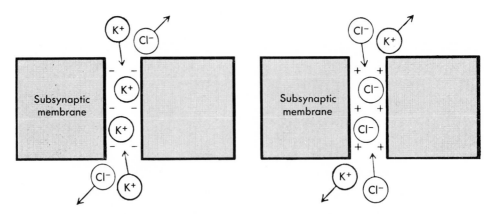

Fig. 27-8. Modifications of inhibitory synapse may involve channels that carry either negative or positive charges on their walls. Negative charges (*left*) would permit only potassium ions to pass. Positive charges (*right*) would permit only chloride ions to pass. (From Eccles, John C. 1965. The synapse. Sci. Am. Jan., p. 66.)

this interrelationship is a prerequisite to coordination of function as exhibited in the higher animals. At the neuronal level, the synapse permits flexibility of pathways and gradation of impulse transmission. Some simple examples are shown in Fig. 27-9.

SUMMARY

Irritability and conductivity are basic properties of all cells, but the cells of the nervous system seem adapted best to exhibit these properties. The highly differentiated nerve cell poignantly demonstrates the structure-function tenet of biology.

The membranes of cells have a resting potential across them due to an imposed imbalance of ions which has the outside electropositive and the inside electronegative. The conditions leading to the distinct concentrations on the two sides of the membrane are a differential permeability to the various ions and an energy-requiring mechanism for pumping ions in one direction or the other. The primary ions which seem to exert the most influence on creating the resting membrane potential are the cations sodium and potassium. The latter, however, has the greater effect.

The polarized state of the resting membrane potential, with a concentration of sodium on the outside and a concentration of potassium on the inside, can be altered when a stimulus is applied to the membrane. The potential created when the original polarity is disturbed is called the action potential. Attainment of the potential is an all-or-none phenomenon; that is, under a given set of conditions once the mechanism for its creation is triggered, the same level of potential is always reached. The mechanism involves an influx of sodium ions from the outside of the membrane, causing the membrane to become electropositive on the inside. This abnormal distribution of ions creates a potential electrical circuit which then is propagated through the nerve fiber. In heavily

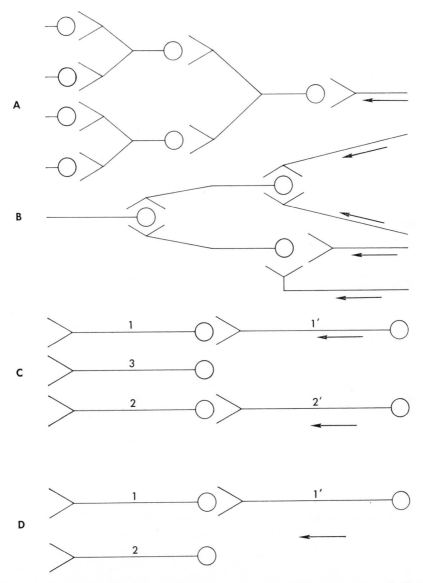

Fig. 27-9. Some simple neuronal pathways in which gradation of impulse occurs. **A,** Divergent pathway. Impulse from one nerve fiber irradiates to spread the impulse out to many other fibers. **B,** Convergent pathway. Impulses from many nerve fibers converge to form a final common pathway. **C,** Spatial summation. When impulse travels along *1'*, fiber 1 will fire. When impulse travels along *2'*, fiber 2 will fire. If impulse travels along both *1'* and *2'*, fibers 1, 2, and 3 all fire. **D,** Temporal summation. When the impulse travels along *1'*, fiber 1 will always fire. At a high volley rate (impulses/sec.) fiber 2 will also fire.

myelinated fibers, the transmission of the impulse may occur by a saltatory jump of the charge from one node of Ranvier to the next. The core of conductance of voltaic current probably accounts for the actual movement of the impulse from node to node. The membrane events at the node boost the current so that effectively there is transmission without decrement.

Transmission of the impulse from one neuron to another must pass across a synapse. The synapse is composed of the presynaptic knob from an axon fiber, a synaptic cleft which is a physical space, and the membrane of the second neuron. Transmitter chemicals are released at the presynaptic knob which diffuse across the cleft to the subsynaptic membrane. This creates an excitatory postsynaptic potential (EPSP) which, if high enough, will trigger firing of the second fiber. Some synapses are inhibitory and can set up an inhibitory postsynaptic potential (IPSP).

There are many unanswered problems concerning the nature of the nerve impulse. The revealing works of many investigators have given much insight into the processes involved.

Literature cited

1. Hodgkin, A. L. 1964. The ionic basis of nervous conduction. Science 145:1148.
2. Katz, B. 1959. Nature of the nerve impulse. Rev. Modern Physics 31:466.
3. Huxley, A. F. 1964. Excitation and conduction in nerve: Quantitative analysis. Science 145:1154.
4. Brock, L. G., J. S. Coombs, and J. C. Eccles. 1952. The recording of potentials from motoneurons with an intracellular electrode. J. Physiol. 117:431.
5. Eccles, J. C. 1964. Ionic mechanism of postsynaptic inhibition. Science 145:1140.
6. Eccles, J. C. 1965. The synapse. Sci. Am. (Jan.), p. 56.

General references

Casey, E. J. 1962. Biophysics. Concepts and mechanisms. Reinhold Publishing Corp., New York.

Davson, H. 1959. A textbook of general physiology. 2nd ed. Little, Brown & Co., Boston.

DeRobertis, E. L. P., W. W. Nowinski, and F. A. Saez. 1965. Cell biology. 4th ed. W. B. Saunders Co., Philadelphia.

Eccles, J. C. 1957. The physiology of nerve cells. Johns Hopkins University Press, Baltimore.

Gerebtzoff, M., and E. Schoffeniels. 1960. Nerve conduction and electrical discharge, vol. 2, p. 519. In Florkin, M., and H. S. Mason (editors): Comparative biochemistry. Academic Press, Inc., New York.

Giese, A. C. 1962. Cell physiology. 2nd ed. W. B. Saunders Co., Philadelphia.

Hydén, H. 1960. The neuron, vol. 4, p. 215. In Brachet, J., and A. E. Mirsky (editors): The cell. Academic Press, Inc., New York.

Katz, B. 1961. How cells communicate. Sci. Am. (Sept.), p. 209.

Kuyper, Ch. M. A. 1962. The organization of cellular activity. Elsevier Publishing Co., Inc., New York.

Locke, M. (editor): 1964. Cellular membranes in development. Academic Press, Inc., New York.

Miller, W. H., F. Ratcliff, and H. K. Hartline. 1961. How cells receive stimuli. Sci. Am. (Sept.), p. 222.

Ruch, T. C., and J. F. Fulton. 1960. Medical physiology and biophysics. W. B. Saunders Co., Philadelphia.

Setlow, R. B., and E. C. Pollard. 1962. Molecular biophysics. Addison-Wesley Publishing Co., Inc., Reading, Mass.

Strumwasser, F. 1965. Nervous function at the cellular level. Ann. Rev. Physiol. 27:451.

28

Contractility and cell movement

C INTRODUCTION

Contractility is one of the basic properties of living material and as such has been demonstrated in most cell types. The movement of protoplasmic structures is an expression of the mechanical activity to which some of the energy of the cell can be directed. The overt indication of mechanical movement may be as obvious as that which occurs in muscular movement, or it may be as subtle as protoplasmic streaming which occurs without deformation of the cell involved. All levels of contractility occur between these extremes.

Contractility often leads to specific cell movement; among the movements are ameboid, ciliary, and flagellar and muscular motion. The highest development of contractility is attained in skeletal muscular movement where the cells are highly differentiated for performing this function. In fact, they are so adapted to yield mechanical work that some are capable of contracting as fast as once every 10 milliseconds, and others can move objects many hundred times their weight. The mechanism of action and the structural characteristics of the muscle cell have been worked out to a higher degree than other cells exhibiting movement. It seems logical, then, to develop the picture of muscle movement and extrapolate backward to the other forms of motion, comparing similarities and differences.

MUSCULAR CONTRACTION

The skeletal muscle cell is another example of a structural differentiation for a physiological function. Most muscle cells are extremely long and spindle-shaped. They have a highly differentiated interior with the following features:
1. Large numbers of mitochondria
2. Special fibers, called myofibrils, running lengthwise in the cell
3. An outer membrane, the sarcolemma, which is in contact with the sarcoplasmic reticulum

4. Sarcoplasmic reticulum, whose functions parallel the endoplasmic reticulum with several notable exceptions

The contraction process itself makes full use of these distinct morphological features. The logical place to start a discussion of contraction is with the myofibril, which is the contractile element of the muscle cell.

The myofibrillar structure and function

The fine structure of the myofibril is quite revealing and has led to a number of theories of muscular contraction as its own structure became more and more concretely established. The myofibril is the functional unit of the contraction process of a single fiber (fiber is a name given to a single muscle "cell" in the same way the term is used for a single neuron). Each muscle fiber is composed of many of these fibrils. One can expect the following questions that must be asked about such a unit:

1. What is its macromolecular organization?
2. What physical changes does it undergo during the contraction process? That is, how is the shortening of the muscle fiber caused by the fibril complex?
3. What means of communications exist for coordinating the myofibrils of any one fiber?
4. What are the chemical dynamics by which energy of the cell is converted to mechanical activity?

These topics will be reviewed one at a time, each subsequent discussion building on the knowledge gained from the previous ones.

Macromolecular organization

The myofibrils are long, rodlike structures approximately 1 μ in diameter and up to several hundred microns in length. They are subdivided along the length into fundamental subunits called the sarcomeres, which are separated by a dark band of material, as seen in the electron microscope. This band, the Z band, is a point of reference in discussing the macromolecular makeup of the fibril. Between every two Z bands is the following sequence of bands. Next to each of the Z bands is a light band, called the I band (isotropic). Sandwiched between the two I bands is a large, dark band, the A (anisotropic) band. Finally, running through the center of the A band is a small band of lighter density called the H band. The sequence of bands in a sarcomere (Fig. 28-1) is as follows:

$$\left| \; Z - I - A - H - A - I - Z \; \right|$$

The bands are not artifacts of staining or of casual orientation of material in them. The submicroscopic structure of the myofibril is so precise that these bands are a consistent characteristic of skeletal muscle. Thus the name striated is applied.

I   Z   I   A   H   A   I   Z   I

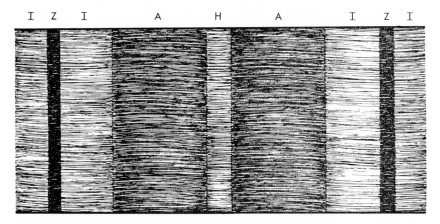

Fig. 28-1. Diagrammatic representation of the bands of a muscle cell.

Z   I   A   H   A   I   Z

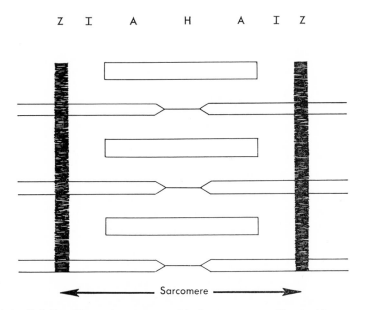

Sarcomere

Fig. 28-2. Interdigitating filament arrangement in the sarcomere. (See text.)

The myofibrils are further subdivided into two types of smaller filaments. One filament type is approximately 100 Å thick and 1.5 μ long, whereas the other type is thinner (50 Å) and longer (2 μ). In the relaxed state, these myofibrillar subunits are arranged in an interdigitating filament arrangement[1] in such a way that the I bands contain only the thin filaments, the A bands contain both types, and the H band contains essentially only the thick filaments. The arrangement according to Huxley[1] is seen in Fig. 28-2.

Chemical analysis of the myofibrils shows the presence of two primary substances, actin and myosin, although a low molecular weight compound, tropomyosin, is also present which may be associated with the Z band. The actin can exist in either a globular (G-actin) or a fibrillar (F-actin) form. The conversion of the G-actin to the F-actin is a polymerization which can be demonstrated in vitro when KCl and ATP are added. These actin filaments are believed to contain two chains, each composed of a series of globular G-actin; the two chains are then twisted around each other in a helix.[2]

Myosin is a protein with relatively high molecular weight, and under the electron microscope it appears similar in characteristics to the thick filaments of the myofibril. The myosin, which is present in a magnesium salt, has ATPase activity and as a result binds most of this high-energy compound which is found associated with the myofibril. Two fractions of the myosin have been isolated: a high molecular weight molecule, the H-meromyosin; and a light-weight component, the L-meromyosin.

Most evidence suggests the following arrangement of actin and myosin:

1. The myosin, that is, both the H-meromyosins and the L-meromyosins, are located in the thicker filaments in the A band.
2. The actin is located in the thinner filaments in the I and A bands.
3. Both the actin and myosin are necessary in order to obtain any contraction; they apparently form an actomyosin complex.

Theories of muscular contraction—changes in the macromolecular structure

The theories of muscular contraction have depended to a great degree on the extent of the knowledge about the macromolecular structure of the contractile unit. Each new segment of information opens a new facet of knowledge, and a new hypothesis arises.

There are two basic categories of mechanisms which have been proposed—the folding filament and the sliding filament theories.

The basis of the folding mechanisms is simple. The myofibril, which has the longitudinally oriented filaments, is held rigid by similar charges along these filaments. The release of ATP and the subsequent hydrolysis to ADP and phosphate is proposed to either neutralize the positive charges or form covalent bonds involving the phosphate to bring about the shortening. Once popular, these theories do not have many proponents left. Recent enlightenment on the substructure has forced these theories into the background.

The sliding mechanisms which have been proposed are based on the interdigitating filament structure aforementioned. All of the variations of the theory propose that the actin filaments slide together further into the A band, and that on maximum contraction, the I band completely disappears; that is, the Z bands are moved up to the border of the A band. Perry[3] has summarized the proposed mechanisms for the sliding movement:

1. The actin filament condenses or moves in order to increase binding sites with the myosin.
2. There is electrostatic interaction between a negatively charged actin and a positively charged myosin. The negative charge is attributed to ATP hydrolysis.
3. The actin undergoes a series of small, sequential shortenings. On each

shortening, the actin inches along the myosin, being held from slipping by bonding; this theory attempts to take into account the polymerization of G-actin to F-actin.

4. The myosin contains contractile elements in the projections which link to the actin. These contract and pass the actin down the myosin filament in a manner similar to pulling in a rope hand over hand.

Other theories have also been proposed. The evidence that the sulfhydryl bonds can cause localized shortening by forming disulfide bridges is attractive for application to a theory of contraction. It offers the possibility that either the actin filament may undergo folding, using the myosin as a support to move against, or that disulfide bridges are formed between the actin and the myosin, thus compacting the actin filament.

Any theory for muscle contraction has to include a mechanism for relaxation. In order for fibers to contract as rapidly as has been recorded, the relaxation, or the moving apart of the filaments, cannot be a passive process. The polymerization of the actin may be involved in the elongation of the fiber after the contraction.

No one theory has full acceptance at this time, and perhaps full concurrence is not in the near future. The level of sophistication of how filaments contract and relax is so high that modern science has not yet risen to that level.

The sarcoplasmic reticulum

Regardless of the molecular mechanism for contraction, the response which originally elicits the contractility has to start from an impulse tripping a change in membrane potential. This, in turn, results in a series of biochemical shifts which lead, finally, to the contraction process. The membrane system of the muscle fiber has the role of conducting the impulse which triggers the contractile process; the bulk of the membrane system is comprised of the sarcoplasmic reticulum.

The problem in transmission of the impulse is that many myofibrils are buried deep in the fiber. In order to contract nearly simultaneously, the action potential of the fiber cannot be restricted to the outer membrane, the sarcolemma. The rediscovery of the sarcoplasmic reticulum and its fine structure offered a strong hypothesis.[4]

Structure

The main components of the sarcoplasmic reticulum lie parallel to the individual fibrils. Each fibril is engirdled with channels of membranes, and each series of myofibrils is enclosed in a sheath of the sarcoplasmic reticular channels. The second component are transverse tubes which run from the sarcolemma inward. These are called the T system. At the union of the T system running across the fibers and the reticulum running parallel to the fiber is a swollen portion of the parallel channel, called the cisternae. The three portions, the T channel and the two swollen channels from the parallel membranes, form the triad (Fig. 28-3). The T tubes penetrate the muscle fiber

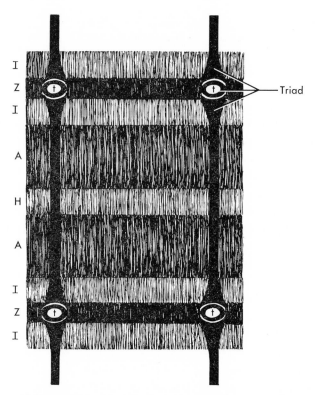

Fig. 28-3. Diagram of the sarcoplasmic reticulum components as seen from a face-on view of a longitudinal section of the striated muscle. Some tubes (*t*) of the T system run perpendicular to the orientation of the filaments. (See text.)

at the Z band, which is the border of the sarcomeres. The cisternae are found in the adjacent A band.

Function

The relationship to the endoplasmic reticulum of other cells suggests that the sarcoplasmic reticulum has similar functions. The channels of the system offer a network for distributing the necessary energy-rich compounds which are required for the contraction process. The system may also serve as a reservoir of the ions necessary for contraction. Finally, the sarcoplasmic reticulum, due to its membrane nature, may conduct the excitatory impulse to the interior myofibrils.

Comparison of the structure of the sarcoplasmic reticulum in three types of muscle of different characteristics gave still another clue to the function of this network. Physiologically, three types of striated muscle are as follows:

1. Those muscles which contract constantly, but not in a rapid manner (for example, heart)
2. Typical skeletal muscle which reacts rapidly and occasionally
3. An intermediate type which alternately works constantly for periods of time and then ceases for other periods

Type one requires a continual supply of energy; type two requires quick, available energy, with a continual supply being created to be prepared for the rapid degrading of the high-energy compounds. The third system must utilize both methods for obtaining energy. The distribution of both the sarcoplasmic reticulum and the mitochondria correlates perfectly with the suggestion that the sarcoplasmic reticulum is the source of immediate energy and, as such, must be able to produce ATP quite rapidly. Type one muscle has many large mitochondria, but a poorly developed sarcoplasmic reticulum; type two has a well-developed reticulum and a normal number of mitochondria. Type three has essentially a balanced distribution of both.[5,6,7]

Therefore, closely associated with the channels of the sarcoplasmic reticulum in typical skeletal muscle are the mitochondria of the muscle fiber. This affiliation turns out to be more than accidental. This is where the integration between structure and function begins.

The dynamics of the excitation-contraction sequence

The following scheme fits most of the evidence which has accumulated for explaining the sequence of excitation and contraction. The impulse for muscular contraction normally originates from the nervous system. The action potential travels down an axon and is transferred to the sarcolemma at the neuromuscular junction. The excitatory impulse is transmitted along the sarcolemma, diving into the interior of the fiber at the pits in the membrane, the T system. As the potential passes across the T system and the sarcoplasmic reticulum, calcium ions are released from a bound state in the membranes into the myofibril area. The release of calcium causes the ATP which is bound by the myosin to be released, and as it is, the ATPase of the myosin hydrolyzes the ATP, yielding ADP plus the available energy which is used to bring about the contraction. The relationship between the calcium and ATP may parallel the events in the mitochondria; in addition, the mitochondria may accumulate calcium which could be used to replenish the supply of the sarcoplasmic reticulum. Immediately after the contraction, the calcium is reabsorbed by the sarcoplasmic reticulum and relaxation occurs. At the same time, the ADP is converted back to ATP by the creatine phosphate which is present in the sarcoplasm. The ΔF of creatine phosphate is more negative than that of ATP; therefore the reaction allows for rapid regeneration of the ATP.

The creatine phosphate and some ATP are regenerated during the recovery time from glycogen via the Embden-Meyerhof pathway. The accumulated pyruvic acid is converted to acetyl-CoA and is passed to the nearby mitochondria for further production of ATP. The lactic acid excess could be transported to the surface of the fiber by the sarcoplasmic reticulum to be carried away by the blood supply.

This scheme is, of course, theoretical, but it is not farfetched. It is based on sound judgment and knowledge of the biochemical machinery which, in this case, is tightly linked to the mechanical machinery of muscle contraction.

OTHER TYPES OF CONTRACTION AND MOVEMENT

The contraction of skeletal muscle is obviously limited to those organisms which have distinct muscle tissue or muscular elements in their structure. The ability to move, however, is not restricted to organisms having a definite musculature. Many single-celled organisms—in fact, most single-celled organisms —have an ability to move. Many individual cells of higher organisms are capable of movement. Gametes, phagocytes, and ciliated epithelial cells are just a few examples. The question arises as to what the similarities might be between these forms of movement and muscle contraction as just described.

Visceral muscle contraction

The lack of striations in visceral muscle cells is the first clue that there are some basic differences between this and skeletal muscle so far as means of contraction and basic characteristics are concerned. There are myofibrils in smooth muscle cells, but they are not packed as tightly as in skeletal muscle cells. They are, doubtless, the actual contractile element.

One property which is unique for these cells is that they are capable of generating contraction without an action potential from a nerve. That is, the excitation-contraction sequence is not dependent on nervous stimulation. This myogenic tendency to contract allows coordination which neural stimulation apparently only modifies and regulates.

The exact mechanism for contraction has not been ascertained. The percent of contractility is so high, to a few percentage of the maximal length, that the theories proposed for skeletal muscle contraction could not apply without great modifications being made in them.

Protoplasmic streaming* and cyclosis

The movement of material within the interior of a cell without deformation of the outer limiting membrane is called protoplasmic streaming, or cyclosis. This type of motion occurs frequently in plant cells and rigid-walled protozoans. The process is not simply a physical movement. It is a biological process, and the Q_{10} values bear this out (see Chapter 11). In addition to temperature, various chemicals, light, and ion concentration affect the rate of the streaming. The mechanism of this movement, however, is undetermined.

Ameboid movement

Ameboid movement is characterized by plastic deformation of the cell as it undergoes motion. Cytoplasmic projections, the pseudopodia, are extended from the cell and aid in the movement. The cytoplasm flows into this projection, bringing about a shift of the orientation of the cell and, thus, movement.

---

* The term *protoplasmic streaming* is used by some authors to indicate any overt shift of cytoplasmic contents during movement. The dividing line used here is whether or not the external membrane is moved. Streaming does occur in other forms of motion, but the term *protoplasmic streaming* is reserved as a synonym for cyclosis.

Many cells are capable of ameboid movement. The amebae, from which the name is derived, demonstrate this movement. Other protozoans, some sperm cells, undifferentiated embryological cells, and phagocytes all exhibit ameboid movement. Generally, a substrate is necessary for attachment during the actual movement.

The theories of how ameboid movement is generated have been many and, for the most part, unsatisfactory. Those based on surface tension changes or sol-gel transformation alone are incorrect or at least inadequate. The outer layer of the ameba is more gellike than the fluid interior, but this fact alone does not explain all the evidence. The proteins in the gel layer are linked together in a fibrous network. Contraction of some of these fibers would leave an area which is essentially a sol, and protoplasm could flow in this direction. Unfolding of the proteins and the formation of more polymerized fibers would again establish a gel layer on the outside. There is some evidence bearing out this hypothesis. Contractile protein has been found in some forms exhibiting ameboid motion. The injection of ATP into the cortical gel has caused liquifying to occur.

In addition to the theory of gelation of the outer cortex, with the resultant shear of the endoplasm (sol-gel transformation), two alternate theories for ameboid movement have been proposed. The first of these, the front gel contraction hypothesis, suggests that contractile proteins in the forward end contract, pulling the cortex up toward the head end. By contrast, the third theory postulates that the contraction occurs at the caudal end and squeezes liquified endoplasm forward in the direction of the movement. However, there are still some doubts as to the mechanism, and general agreement has not been gained.

Ciliary and flagellar movement

Many cells employ either cilia or flagella as a means of movement, and of all of the types of motion which are not "muscular movement," more cells are motile due to these structures than to any other process.

The cross section of either a cilium or a flagellum under the electron microscope shows surprising uniformity of structure regardless of the source of the material. The ultrastructure consists of an outer limiting membrane surrounding a series of fibrils arranged in a circle, with the exception of two which are centrally located. The number in the outer ring is always nine single fibrils or nine couplets, giving the characteristic 9 + 2 arrangement (Plate 6, p. 308). These fibrils apparently can contract, and if the contraction occurs alternately from one side to the other, the structure will wave back and forth— a typical ciliary motion. The movement may be controlled by the basal bodies of the cilia (Plate 16, p. 318). This movement could also apply to certain flagellar movements. Contraction of the fibrils individually in sequence around the structure would result in a whipping action, as is seen in some bacteria and other forms. The ciliary and flagellar movements are both stimulated by the addition of ATP. In some forms, ATP addition causes the structures to contract rhythmically for hours.

Movement of subcellular particles

Time-lapse photography of a living cell dramatically shows that the subcellular structures do not remain in a fixed position. Membranes are seen to undulate, particles to move, chromosomes to migrate, and mitochondria to contract and change shape (Chapter 25). Many workers[8,9,10] have shown that the contractile units of the mitochondria have many of the same characteristics as the myofibrils; that is, they may both be actomyosin and behave in the same fashion. Both systems react upon addition of ATP and have an ATPase activity which is located in a membrane. The two systems also share similar sensitivities to inhibitors, and they both exhibit the same biochemical reactions.

● ● ●

The relationship between these other forms of movement and muscular contraction is evidence of the stimulation of both of these by addition of ATP. The fact that contractile protein has been isolated from many forms, and that it resembles actomyosin, suggests some unification at the molecular level. Beyond this, the analogy may stop, in that muscular contraction is probably a highly modified form of the basic process.

SUMMARY

Contractility is the ability of the cell to change its shape by an active energy-requiring process. The result of this contractility is often cell movement. The striated muscle cell has attained the highest degree of specialization and differentiation, and most of the experimental work has been carried out on these cells. The structure of the cell is ideally adapted to its function. The myofibril, which is the contractile unit, has a unique macromolecular organization composed of two types of subunits, or filaments, which interdigitate in parallel fashion along the length of the muscle fiber. The two major components of the cell are located in these two filament types; the actin is present in thin filaments, and the myosin, and its subunits, H-meromyosin and L-meromyosin, are located in thicker filaments. The actin and the myosin interact in such a way as to bring about shortening of the cell.

Two schools of theory have arisen concerning the changes which occur in the macromolecular structure during the contraction process—folding filaments and sliding filaments. The latter seems to fit more of the data.

A singular feature of the striated muscle fiber is the interlacing network of the sarcoplasmic reticulum. This membrane system is instrumental in the excitation-contraction sequence in that it conducts the action potential to the individual myofibrils and also releases and absorbs the calcium ion which is necessary for the contraction to occur. The release of the calcium triggers the ATPase mechanism inherent in the myosin, thus giving the energy for the mechanical activity.

Other types of contraction and movement which are energy-requiring are visceral muscle contraction, protoplasmic streaming or cyclosis, ameboid movement, ciliary or flagellar movement, and movement of subcellular structures.

All of these require or are enhanced by addition of ATP to their medium, and actomyosin or an actomyosin-like protein has been isolated from forms exhibiting these movements.

Literature cited

1. Huxley, H. E. 1961. Muscle cells, vol. 4, p. 365. In Brachet, J., and A. E. Mirsky (editors): The cell. Academic Press, Inc., New York.
2. Hanson, J., and J. Lowy. 1963. The structure of actin and of actin filaments isolated from muscle. J. Molec. Biol. 6:46.
3. Perry, S. V. 1960. Muscular contraction, vol. 2, p. 245. In Florkin, M., and H. S. Mason (editors): Comparative biochemistry. Academic Press, Inc., New York.
4. Bennett, H. S., and K. R. Porter. 1953. An electron microscope study of sectioned breast muscle of domestic fowl. Am. J. Anat. 93:61.
5. Fawcett, D. W., and P. Revel. 1961. The sarcoplasmic reticulum of a fast-acting fish muscle. J. Biophys. Biochem. Cytol. 10: (supp.), p. 89.
6. Revel, J. P. 1962. The sarcoplasmic reticulum of the bat cricothyroid muscle. J. Cell Biol. 12:561.
7. Porter, K. R., and C. Franzini-Armstrong. 1965. The sarcoplasmic reticulum. Sci. Am. (Mar.), p. 72.
8. Neubert, D., A. B. Wojtczak, and A. L. Lehninger. 1962. Purification and identification of mitochondrial factors. I and II. Proc. Nat. Acad. Sc. 48:1651.
9. Neifakh, S. A., and T. B. Kazakova. 1963. Actomyosin-like protein in mitochondria of mouse liver. Nature 197:1106.
10. Vignais, P. V., P. M. Vignais, C. S. Rossi, and A. L. Lehninger. 1963. Restoration of ATP-induced contraction of pretreated mitochondria by contractile protein. Biochem. Biophys. Res. Commun. 11:307.

General references

Allen, R. D. 1961. Ameboid movement, vol. 2, p. 135. In Brachet, J., and A. E. Mirsky (editors): The cell. Academic Press, Inc., New York.

Bayliss, L. E. 1960. Principles of general physiology. 5th ed. John Wiley & Sons, Inc., New York. Vol. 2.

Casey, E. J. 1962. Biophysics. Concepts and mechanisms. Reinhold Publishing Corp., New York.

Davies, R. E. 1963. A molecular theory of muscle contraction: Calcium-dependent contractions with hydrogen bond formation plus ATP-dependent extensions of part of the myosin-actin cross bridges. Nature 199:1068.

Davson, H. 1959. A textbook of general physiology. 2nd ed. Little, Brown & Company, Boston.

DeRobertis, E. L. P., W. W. Nowinski, and F. A. Saez. 1965. Cell biology. 4th ed. W. B. Saunders Co., Philadelphia.

Epstein, H. T. 1963. Elementary biophysics. Addison-Wesley Publishing Co., Inc., Palo Alto, Calif.

Giese, A. C. 1962. Cell physiology. 2nd ed. W. B. Saunders Co., Philadelphia.

Hasselbach, W. 1964. Relaxing factor and the relaxation of muscle. Prog. Biophys. 14:169.

Hayashi, T. 1961. How cells move. Sci. Am. (Sept.), p. 184.

Hill, A. V. 1960. Production and absorption of work by muscle. Science 131:897.

Hoffman-Berling, H. 1960. Other mechanisms producing movements, vol. 2, p. 341. In Florkin, M., and H. S. Mason (editors): Comparative biochemistry. Academic Press, Inc., New York.

Huxley, A. F. 1957. Molecular structure and theories of contraction. Prog. Biophys. 7:89.

Huxley, H. E. 1957. The double array of filaments in cross-striated muscle. J. Biophys. Biochem. Cyt. 3:631.

Huxley, H. E. 1960. Muscle cells, vol. 4, pp. 365-481. In Brachet, J., and A. E. Mirsky (editors): The cell, Academic Press, Inc., New York.

Huxley, H. E. 1963. Electron microscopic studies on the structure of natural and synthetic protein filaments from striated muscle. J. Molec. Biol. 7:281.

Perry, S. V. 1965. Relation between chemical and contractile function and structure of skeletal muscle cell. Physiol. Rev. 36:1.

Szent-Györgyi, A. G. 1960. Proteins of the myofibril, vol. 2, pp. 1-54. In G. H. Bourne (editor): Structure and function of muscle. Academic Press, Inc., New York.

The sarcoplasmic reticulum. 1961. J. Biophys. Biochem. Cytol. (supp.), vol. 10.

29

The cell cycle—division, growth, differentiation, and death

INTRODUCTION

The cell cycle incorporates all of the biochemical and physiological principles into a sequence which interrelates them into an organized pattern. The cell, during its life-span, can perform any or all of the basic operations of division, growth, differentiation, and death. The groundwork has already been laid for discussing these processes.

The concepts of biochemical thermodynamics, metabolism, the functional portions of the cell, the omnipotence of DNA, and the basis of the various fundamental physiological properties come to play in the cell cycle. The skillful way in which these are integrated by the cell toward a directed goal is truly amazing.

The basic features of mitosis and meiosis will be assumed to be second nature, as will, by now, such mechanisms as DNA replication and ribosomal protein synthesis. Since background knowledge is assumed, the discussion can proceed without being redundant and repetitious.

CELL DIVISION

Cell division in its broad definition implies division of both the cytoplasmic and nuclear components of the cell. The implication, however, goes deeper. Cell division, or better yet, cell reproduction, provides the mechanism for the continuity of life. It confers upon living material the opportunity to persist long after any one cell or organism can survive. At the molecular and supramolecular levels, cell reproduction means that precise biochemical and physiological processes must be used to ensure a rigidly exact division. These processes are the basis for our discussion on division.

Fundamentals of the process

The most basic process in cell division is the replication of the DNA. The necessity for precise duplication of the genetic material of the cell has already been pointed out, and the biosynthesis of DNA has been discussed. It may not have been apparent, however, that replication of the DNA actually occurs in the cell long before any division processes take place. In fact, doubling of almost all of the cellular components occurs before the actual division. It should be kept in mind that very few molecules or organelles are capable of self-reproduction. As a result, the energy load falls to the DNA and the protein synthesis mechanism, the synthetic pathways of metabolism, and the organelles which produce, store, or modify these products.

The division process—mitosis and cytokinesis

The quiescent appearance of the interphase cell is totally misleading. As was just indicated, the synthetic processes of the cell are working at a feverish pitch to prepare for cell division. Although passing along of the genetic information is the prime purpose of the division process, duplication of the other functional parts of the cell is not without importance.

The chromosomes, with the DNA having been replicated, begin to compact into distinct bodies. This is the first clue that division will occur (Plate 15, *B*, p. 317). These chromosomes then proceed through a series of regulated steps in which they line up, pair, and move to opposite ends of the cell, after which division normally occurs. The arbitrary classification of the stages into prophase, metaphase, anaphase, and telophase should be fingertip knowledge. The morphological aspects of the division process pose some distinct physiological problems:

1. What triggers the division process?
2. What are the macromolecular aspects of the migration of the chromosomes to the poles of the cell?
3. What mechanisms ensure duplication of the cellular components?
4. What is the source of energy for the division?
5. What is the effect of artificially imposed conditions on the process?

The basis behind the actual triggering of cell division is not clear. At one time it was thought that there was a point of cell mass and/or volume above which the cell was triggered into dividing. This so-called critical mass hypothesis does not hold up in the face of modern evidence. There are some events, such as self-duplication of the centrioles, which are correlated with the beginning of division, but no causal relationship has been established. The possibility exists of a genetic control which is held in check until the process is induced.

The mechanisms behind the movement of chromosomes to the poles has always perplexed cytologists. The orderly manner in which this occurs would seem to infer that there might be a regulated mechanical force involved. In animal cells, the bodies which are always present at the poles during the migration of the chromosomes are the centrioles (Plate 11, *B* and *C*, p. 313). These particles, which, strangely enough, are related structurally to the basal bodies of cilia, are cylindrical bodies which occur in sets. There are normally two sets in the dividing cell. The two individual components of each set are oriented perpendicular to each other.

Evidence indicates that the centrioles are duplicated before the actual division process. They then migrate to what will be the poles of the dividing cell. Between these two poles are stretched a series of fibers, called the spindle, which is a macromolecular aggregate assembled for the purpose of guiding the chromosomes to the poles. Confirming evidence shows the presence of actual fibrils in this apparatus under the electron microscope, but attempts to isolate it in vitro did not meet with much success until Mazia[1] and co-workers found that the stability of the spindle fibers was enhanced by the presence of an added disulfide compound. The integrity of the natural disulfides must be maintained, apparently, if the macromolecular aggregate is to remain as a functional fiber.

The mitotic apparatus—the spindle and the poles—has high amounts of a special protein which has been demonstrated to have ATPase activity. In addition, RNA and lipids are sometimes found in association with the apparatus. The function of the RNA is unknown, although several hypotheses have been presented. One of them suggests that the RNA may help assemble the fibers by adding the building block of these fibers to the aggregate.

The occurrence of a macromolecular aggregate in an oriented state is not peculiar to the spindle. Chloroplasts, mitochondria, and plasma and nuclear membranes have similar aggregates.

What the centrioles do during the chromosome movement is not clear. They must act as an anchor or attachment for the fibers, but whether they participate actively in the synthesis, aggregation, or disassembling of the spindle is uncertain.

Indirect evidence concerning the mechanism is accumulating, but the facts have not been pieced together. Studies on cell cultures which divide synchronously have yielded some valuable information. There appears to be no synchrony with respect to DNA production in *Tetrahymena*, even though the cells are dividing synchronously.[2] Furthermore, there may exist a regulatory mechanism for the control of protein release from the ribosomes which will occur in phase with the synchronized cell divisions, although no causal relationship has been definitely established.[3]

One of the more perplexing problems in cell division is the actual splitting in two of the cell. It seems fairly clear that the mitotic apparatus has some role in the inducing of a membrane to form. Turning of the spindle in the cell causes the new cell membrane to orient itself across the mitotic apparatus as if it had not been turned. The removal of the apparatus has been demonstrated to stop cell division if the removal occurs before the chromosomes start to move to the poles.

Many factors have been attributed to be critical for cytokinesis to occur. Ameboid movement, infolding of the cell membrane due to rapid proliferation of the lipoprotein stroma, and active contraction by an ATP-induced contractile protein have been reported to play a role in this process in animal cells. Plant cells, which do not often deform during division, have another set of factors which may be involved. Orientation of the endoplasmic reticulum and dictyosomes and fusion of some vesicular material are related to the formation of the new plasma membrane and cell wall.

Intracellular control of the division process is also an area where much more information is necessary. The fact that a large variety of metabolic inhibitors, such as azaguanine, chloramphenicol, ethionine, and 5-methyl tryptophan, as well as special inhibitors such as colchicine, all interfere with triggering of the process indicates that the mechanism has many facets. Radiation is also known to exert a blocking effect on cell division. Cells have been found to be the most sensitive to X rays at the time just preceding the mitotic process; ultraviolation can also bring about the division block (Chapter 12).

Mitosis is one of the basic processes of the cell; from a survival standpoint, it is *the* basic process. The physiology and the biochemistry of its intricacies, however, have eluded detection to a satisfactory degree.

Meiosis

Whereas mitosis is the means of survival of a cell culture, meiosis is the guarantee of the production of the selfsame in multicellular forms. This topic is dealt with at length in cytology and cytogenetics texts, but a few factors should be stated here:

1. The end result of the meiosis process (two divisions) is a cell with one half of the DNA quantity of the original cell.
2. The physical arrangement of the chromosomes during the process allows some exchange of DNA material between strands. The mechanism for this is uncertain.
3. The divisions are often unequal, with one formed cell being much larger than its sister cell.
4. The intracellular behavior of the chromosomes is more involved than in mitosis.
5. The physiological and biochemical processes which occur must be more complex than in mitosis, particularly in steps 2 and 3.

Whatever triggers the meiotic process ceases when the germ cells formed by the process unite to again form the diploid cell. At this point, mitosis occurs. The regulatory mechanism which turns one process on and the other off is far from being elucidated.

GROWTH

The subject of growth encompasses many different aspects of the cell. The increase in size of the individual cell is one phase of this process; the increase in number of cells in a cell culture or in a multicellular form is another. All growth is bound together by one simple principle—the overall entropy of the system is decreasing at the expense of metabolic energy.

The growth curve

The common procedure for cell division is for one cell to split into two.

This leads to an increase of cells in a culture by a geometric progression of

$$N = 2^n \tag{1}$$

where N is the number of cells and n the number of generations. This formulation, however, is impractical for laboratory situations since a culture does not start with a one-cell inoculation.

Letting N_o equal the initial population and N, the number of cells at any given time, then

$$N = N_o \times 2^n \tag{2}$$

Taking a log function of this

$$\log N = \log N_o \times n \log 2 \tag{3}$$

the generation time can then be solved for.

Since

$$n = \frac{\log N - \log N_o}{\log 2} \tag{3a}$$

and

$$1/\log 2 = 3.3$$

then, substituting in (3a)

$$n = 3.3 \log (N/N_o) \tag{4}$$

From this, the number of generations which have elapsed over a time period, t, can be calculated. The generation time, then, is equal to the time elapsed divided by the number of generations

$$G = \frac{t}{3.3 \log (N/N_o)} \tag{5}$$

These equations are quite useful for expressing the growth of a cell population, particularly for comparing rates between cell populations which may be under different experimental conditions. The generation time for any one

Table 29-1. Generation time of several species of bacteria grown in broth at 37° C.*

Organism	Generation time (min.)
Aerobacter aerogenes	16-18
Bacillus cereus	18.8
Bacillus megatherium	31
Bacillus thermophilus	18.3
Clostridium botulinum	35
Diplococcus pneumoniae I	24.5
Diplococcus pneumoniae II	33
Escherichia coli	17
Mycobacterium tuberculosis (in synthetic)	792-932
Proteus vulgaris	21.5
Pseudomonas fluorescens	40
Staphylococcus albus	24-25
Staphylococcus aureus	27-30
Treponema pallidum (in living material)	1980
Vibrio costatus	42

*Data from Spector; W. S. (editor). 1956. Handbook of biological data. W. B. Saunders Co., Philadelphia.

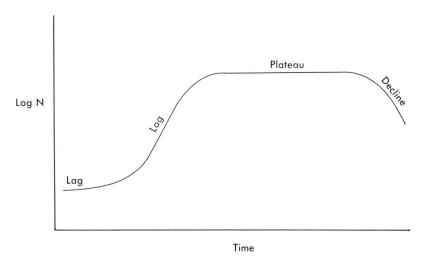

Fig. 29-1. Hypothetical growth curve.

cell type is relatively constant under a given set of conditions. Some examples are given in Table 29-1.

Depicting of the growth curve of a cell population is almost always done by using a logarithmic plot. The advantages of this have been previously expressed. In the growth curve, the specific importance of the log plot is that the exponential growth (2^n) of the cells is a straight line relationship.

The total growth curve is characterized by several phases which again are distinct for the organism involved. A hypothetical growth curve of a cell population is shown in Fig. 29-1. The phases, and their characteristics, are as follows:

1. *The lag phase.* After being introduced to a new medium, the cell rarely divides immediately. Although biosynthesis occurs, the adjustment of the membrane enzymes and the triggering mechanism for division apparently repress the division process. Turbidity measurements may not show this plateau because of the synthesis of protoplasm in preparation for division.

2. *The accelerated growth phase.* In this phase, the triggering mechanism of some of the cells causes them to divide. All of the cells have not yet started the division, and thus the slope is not as it would be for exponential growth.

3. *The log phase, or exponential phase.* This phase is typified by a straight line whose slope approaches 1. All of the cells in the population are actively dividing on a time schedule dictated by the generation time. Biosynthesis is occurring at a maximum rate, and the entropy of the system is decreasing.

4. *The stationary phase or steady state plateau.* This phase shows a steady state level, in that the number of new cells being produced equals the number of cells dying. The entropy of the system is stationary. The limiting factors here are the numbers of cells per unit area and the available nutrients. Often, this stationary phase is typified by no division

at all, but the balance between division and death is probably more common.

5. *The death phase, or phase of decline.* The biosynthetic processes begin to fail because of nutrient deficiency or from some other cause. The system begins to act as an inanimate one, in that there is an approach toward maximum entropy. However, this is not irreversible since inoculation of these cells into a new medium will result in the propagation of a new growth. The phase from which the inoculation is made determines the lag phase of the next cycle. In many cases, there may be no lag phase, particularly if the inoculation is made from the log phase.

Biosynthesis

The growth process at once implies that the cell has given up one steady state level for a new one. The new one is lower in entropy and causally higher in free energy. What mechanism in the cell generates the impetus for attaining the new level is one of the problems facing cell physiologists. Experimentally, growth and biosynthesis can be enhanced, modified, and inhibited, but the cell still retains the final control as to when biosynthesis will overcompensate for biodegradation.

The specific biosynthetic pathways of the cell have been dealt with in the section on metabolism. They will not be discussed in detail here. The criteria for successful biosynthesis leading to growth, however, might be outlined.

1. Biosynthesis requires a large amount of available energy.
2. The entropy must decrease in a system in which growth is the end result of biosynthesis.
3. The cell must have flexibility of metabolism; that is, there must be adequate interconversions among the major pathways.
4. Specific enzymes and mechanisms must guide the energy from metabolism into certain activities (for example, DNA replication and ribosomal protein synthesis).
5. Other major physiological functions, such as division, are generally repressed during active growth.
6. Available external energy sources and specific requirements must be present.
7. External factors can modify the rate of biosynthesis (for example, cell synchrony).
8. Control mechanisms are implied.

Measurement of growth

Growth, and thus biosynthesis, can be measured in several ways, both directly and indirectly. The quantitative estimation of growth, however, may be hampered by other factors. The basic modes of a quantitative measurement are the following:

1. *Increase in cell number.* This technique is best applied to cell cultures where the counts can be made with a fair degree of ease.
2. *Cell mass.* This can be determined by a variety of techniques. Among

them are direct weighing, use of interference microscopy, turbidometry, and determination of nitrogen as an index of weight.

3. *Biochemical activity.* Certain enzymes which are exclusively used in biosynthetic pathways can be specifically tested for, or the average activity per population size can be determined.

The detection of the biosynthesis leading to growth is, therefore, not a problem. Beyond this, however, the ground is unsteady.

Growth at the subcellular level

The internal components of the cell increase before cell division and during differentiation. The specific mechanisms which are known will be discussed.

The membranes of the cell are believed by some to be interrelated in function as well as in origin. Robertson, with his unit membrane (Chapter 24), is a proponent of the idea that a basic membrane structure is synthesized and then used to make the various cell organelles. Whaley and co-workers[4] have outlined some of the hypotheses which are prevalent in the field.

1. The labile endoplasmic reticulum is formed from the cytoplasm ground substance. The network changes character as the physiology of the cell changes.

2. The Golgi body is derived from the membranes of the endoplasmic reticulum either directly or as an outcrop of the same process which forms the endoplasmic reticulum.

3. Some Golgi material has been seen to pass out through the membrane of some plant cells.

4. Vacuoles formed are related to the Golgi body and possibly the plasma membrane.

5. The endoplasmic reticulum, plasma membrane, Golgi apparatus, and vacuolar membranes may be interrelated, but the mitochondria seem to operate independently.

These facts suggest that growth and development of many of the organelles may be mediated through a common process, even though the "adult" membranes may differ. This final difference is due to any differentiation which might occur after original growth and development occur.

The mitochondrion serves as a good example of growth and biosynthesis at the subcellular level. It must be remembered, however, that this organelle is somewhat atypical since it is probably more independent than other structures.

The majority of evidence indicates that the mitochondria grow and divide as a means of maintenance instead of being formed *de nova* or from preexisting membranes. This infers a high biosynthetic rate in these organelles. The metabolic turnover rate—the number of times each molecule in the structure is replaced—has been calculated to be around three for the liver cell.[5] However, this number would vary considerably for different cell types. Isolated mitochondria are capable of carrying on the following biosynthetic activities:

1. Production of some phospholipid
2. Nonribosomal production of proteins

3. Fatty acid synthesis

In addition, both RNA and DNA have been located in the mitochondria; they may represent some regulatory control. From the synthetic activities of the mitochondria, it would appear that membrane material could be formed, although in vivo the endoplasmic reticulum is necessary for complete synthesis of some of the phosphatides.

The problems of growth and organization at the subcellular and molecular levels are extreme. Synthesis of the material at the expense of cellular energy is only one facet. Organization of the material into three-dimensional structures poses quite a task. The series of bonds, all with different calories per mole formation requirements, must be created in order to have a three-dimensional structure. For example, covalent bonds with 60,000 calories per mole and ionic bonds with up to 20,000 calories per mole necessitate the input of fantastic amounts of energy. The weaker bonds, such as the hydrogen (1000 to 3000 calories per mole) and van der Waals (1000 to 2000 calories per mole), do not require as much energy to create, but the precise patterns in which they must exist pose a logistics problem. Growth at the biological level, then, is not merely biosynthesis of material.

CELL DIFFERENTIATION

After a cell divides, the choice must be made as to whether it will divide again or differentiate into a specialized form of cell. The decision is not irreversible in many cases. The many familiar forms of specialized cells—nerve, muscle, tracheids, and the like—had their origin from less specialized cells. The process of developing morphologically distinct characteristics and physiologically defined functions is the process of differentiation. Whereas growth is increase in size, differentiation is usually the increase in complexity and organization. These two processes are not separate, in that the latter is almost totally dependent on the former.

Cell differentiation exhibits two fundamental characteristics. It is, first, a universal process, occurring at all phylogenetic levels. Second, the specialization which the cell undergoes is progressive, transforming a more general cell into a specialized unit. The net result of cell specialization is the creation of a diversity upon which many biological axioms are based. The specialization allows, at the organism level, penetration of many ecological niches. At the multicellular level, the specialization of cells within the organism creates a diversity of function among the cells where the interdependence permits individual cells to become extremely differentiated to the point at which they have lost their ability to maintain themselves separately.

Spratt[6] has categorized the different types of developmental patterns to show the diversity of function and cell type. The major patterns, he feels, are the following:

1. Continuous addition to the adult multicelled organism (for example, cambium, stratum germinativum of skin, teeth, and plant buds)
2. Regeneration of lost parts

3. Reorganization at both the cellular and cell population levels

4. Origin of a new individual

The basic differences between specialized and nonspecialized cells are many. Diversities of general function and structure are obvious. In addition, these cells also differ in their metabolism. A specialized cell will expand certain metabolic pathways at the expense of others. A photosynthetic plant cell has a much higher activity of pentose shunt enzymes than some nonphotosynthesizing plant cells. The protein synthetic capacity of an animal secretory cell is much higher than that of a nonsecretory one. Specialization of metabolism in the muscle cell was previously described. Mitotic activity is significantly lower in cells which have specialized. The nerve cell, as an example of a highly specialized structure, does not undergo mitosis at all.

Differentiation at the cell level can be either intercellular or intracellular (No. 3, above). Both of these categories of differentiation are dependent on two major factors—cell heredity and microenvironment. The genetic information of a cell dictates the kinds of differentiation which may occur. What actually occurs may be dependent on the microenvironment in which the cell is differentiating. A balance must be struck between the two in order to develop the characteristic traits of a particular cell type.

At the intracellular level of development, several examples of events which are resultant within the cell are given. Moulé[7] points out that the development of the endoplasmic reticulum often parallels the level of cell differentiation. This would not be unexpected since protein synthetic enzymes are located near these membranes. The specialized pathways occur within the endoplasmic reticulum or in the ground substance since the enzyme complement of the mitochondria varies very little. In a related fashion, the Golgi apparatus differentiates rapidly and, to a large degree, particularly in cells destined to become secretory. The development of myofibrils, neurofibrils, and pigment areas are just other examples of intracellular variations.

At the intercellular and extracellular levels, various factors have been shown to influence the development within the cell. The general factors of the environment, as discussed in Section III, have been shown to influence cell differentiation. Contact with other cell types can modify the cell structure. At a more specific level, distinct extracellular factors have been demonstrated to exert an influence. For example, Levi-Montalcini[8] claims that growth, differentiation, and maintenance of nerve cells are dependent on a specific protein factor, and that its antiserum suppresses all three of these activities.

Dedifferentiation can also occur in some cells, although there seems to be a point of no return in many cases. But the fact remains that once a cell begins to differentiate this does not always preclude its developing into another cell type. This ability of potency is not present, however, in all cells.

CELL DEATH

The sequence of events which lead to senescence and cell death are no more understood than the ones leading to cell division. A number of observations have been made as to *what* happens. Little is known as to *why*.

In certain cells, there is an accumulation of a pigmentlike substance which occurs before the cell senesces and dies. The pigment is lipoid in nature, and a breakdown of excretory mechanisms may lead to the abnormal retention of the products making up the material. Other morphological changes have been observed in a variety of forms. The nucleus often shrinks and the membrane system may undergo dissolution. Some cells lose their motility, and others round up before death.

Biochemical changes are also occurring during this phase of the life cycle. General dehydration (syneresis?) is prevalent, leading to increased numbers of cross-linkages among the proteins. Respiration and enzyme rates are severely depressed. Calcium is known to accumulate in the outer cortex of plant cells and in some invertebrates. Permeability becomes aberrant, and, finally, in the last stages, the content of hydrolytic enzymes of the lysosomes increases. In general, there is return to the closed system state where entropy seeks a maximum and finally attains it.

SUMMARY

The cell can undergo any or all of the steps in the sequence of the cell cycle. These steps—division, growth, differentiation, and death—are the possible fates of any cell, whether it occurs as a unicellular form or in a multicellular organism. All of these processes infer a change in the metabolic balance or a shift in entropy, and the interrelationships among them are apparent.

The process of cell division is poorly understood. There are many observations and much evidence but few good theories as to what triggers the reaction at both the molecular and cellular levels. For example, movement of the condensed chromosomes to the poles during mitosis can be observed by beginning biology students. What causes the formation of the fibers the chromosomes move on and what actually causes them to move perplex the advanced scientist. There are many gaps of information concerning the cell division process.

Meiosis is more poorly understood. The problems are compounded by the occurrence of two divisions. The related problems are what determine when a cell will undergo meiosis and when will it continue dividing by mitosis.

The subject of growth includes both the increase in number of cells in a population or organism and the increase in size and amount of internal material of a single cell. Both imply decrease of entropy at the expense of cellular energy. The growth curve of any organism growing in culture can be characterized under any given set of conditions.

Biosynthesis occurs at all times during the life of the cell. If it is balanced with the degradation processes, a steady state system persists, and *dynamic turnover* is the term applied to this condition. During growth, biosynthesis must occur at a faster rate than degradation, leading to a decrease of entropy and an increase of the free energy of the system. The cell is attaining a new steady state, but only if external and internal conditions are correct. Growth can be measured quantitatively by biological and biochemical techniques.

At the subcellular level, growth involves an increase of the internal organelles, principally the membranes. The endoplasmic reticulum may form a basis for the membranes of other organelles. Mitochondria, however, are more independent and have biosynthetic mechanisms of their own.

Not all cells continue to divide at regular intervals. Some direct the energy of the cell toward cell differentiation. This process entails conversion of a cell from a general, homogeneous system to one which is specialized and heterogeneous. Differentiation is both universal and proceeds through a regulated progression of steps.

Cell death occurs when a sequence of events no more understood than the other processes occurs. A general increase of entropy and decrease of free energy bring about a series of morphological and biochemical changes which characterize senescence and cell death.

Literature cited

1. Mazia, D. 1961. Mitosis and the physiology of cell division, vol. 3, p. 77. In Brachet, J., and A. E. Mirsky (editors): The cell. Academic Press, Inc., New York.
2. Zeuthen, E. 1963. Independent cycles of cell division and of DNA synthesis in *Tetrahymena*, p. 1. In Harris, R. J. C. (editor): Cell growth and division. Academic Press, Inc., New York.
3. Plesner, P. 1963. Nucleotide metabolism and ribosomal activity during synchronized cell division, p. 77. In Harris, R. J. C. (editor): Cell growth and division. Academic Press, Inc., New York.
4. Whaley, W. G., J. E. Kephart, and H. H. Mollenhauer. 1964. The dynamics of cytoplasmic membranes during development, p. 135. In Locke, M. (editor): Cellular membranes in development. Academic Press, Inc., New York.
5. Fletcher, M. J., and D. R. Sanadi. 1961. Turnover of rat liver mitochondria. Biochim. Biophys. Acta 51:356.
6. Spratt, N. T. 1964. Introduction to cell differentiation. Reinhold Publishing Corp., New York, P. 3.
7. Moulé, Y. 1964. Endoplasmic reticulum and microsomes in rat liver, p. 97. In Locke, M. (editor): Cellular membranes in development. Academic Press, Inc., New York.
8. Levi-Montalcini, R. 1964. Growth control of nerve cells by a protein factor and its anti-serum. Science 143:105.

General references

Bertalanffy, F. D., and C. Lau. 1962. Cell renewal. Internat. Rev. Cytol. 13:359.
Davson, H. 1959. A textbook of general physiology. 2nd ed. Little, Brown & Co., Boston.
DeRobertis, E. L. P., W. W. Nowinski, and F. A. Saez. 1965. Cell biology. 4th ed. W. B. Saunders Co., Philadelphia.
Harris, R. J. C. (editor). 1963. Cell growth and cell division. Academic Press, Inc., New York.
Mazia, D. 1961. How cells divide. Sci. Am. (Sept.), p. 100.
Stern, H., and Y. Hotta. 1963. Facets of intracellular regulation of meiosis and mitosis, p. 57. In Harris, R. J. C. (editor): Cell growth and division. Academic Press, Inc., New York.
Steward, F. C. 1963. The control of growth in plant cells. Sci. Am. (Oct.), p. 104.
Tamiya, H. 1963. Control of cell division in microalgae.. J. Cell Comp. Physiol. 62: (supp. 1).

Section **VIII**

Control mechanisms

The dynamic cell can only function insofar as the aspects of its catabolic and anabolic processes are regulated. An increase of the degradation over the biosynthetic processes has been shown to be a causal factor in cell death. Conversely, a cell cannot synthesize at the expense of all other cellular processes without suffering some damage. In spite of the variables, both physiochemical and metabolic, the cell is capable of maintaining itself without suffering any great loss of function. The cell adjusts to variables, and this adjustment is part of the living dynamics. This adaptation is not a haphazard, random handling of microenvironmental factors. Implied in this adjustment is a series of precise and finely graded control mechanisms which must be operative in cells surviving in the open system of biology.

The open system, although invaluable to biological systems, places an added burden on regulatory mechanisms which might exist in the system. The constant influx of metabolites and required materials, coupled with the efflux of waste products and other substances, places stress on the cell to maintain this exquisite balance. The importance of regulating the entropy level of the cell has already been mentioned.

Thus, the control mechanisms of the cell are what allow the cell to have both the flexibility of function and the ability to maintain itself in its environment. It is difficult to conceive of any physiological function that is occurring in the cell taking place without control. Also, for precise regulation, the other parts of the cell must be apprised of what actions are occurring elsewhere. There are, then, two aspects of control—the mechanisms themselves and the feedback of information to the other parts of the cell. These two are so closely related in one functional entity that it is difficult to separate them.

Perhaps the best way to handle the discussion is to outline the basic concepts involved in feedback control (Chapter 30) and then apply these concepts to specific cellular situations (Chapter 31). Since little occurs in the cell without control, it would be impossible to enumerate all of the mechanisms involved. However, representative models can serve as examples of the exacting ways by which a cell behaves as a self-regulating system.

30

The feedback concept and
control theory

INTRODUCTION

The concepts of feedback and the control theory have existed for some time, but it was not until recently that they were applied to biological systems. The realization that control mechanisms must exist in cells was apparent to earlier workers, but until accumulated data from more refined techniques indicated that a quantitative analysis could be made, biological systems were considered to have too many uncertainties and variables for this type of treatment. Thus, cybernetics, the study of feedback mechanisms at the mathematical level, is a new dimension of biology. The principles of feedback and control are borrowed from the physical systems, but as is often the case, allowance has to be made for the living state. Nevertheless, the concepts of feedback and the control theory can be applied to biological phenomena, and it is from this basis that many theoretical control mechanisms have arisen.

This chapter is designed to introduce the subject of feedback and control theories in general terms as a means of developing the vocabulary necessary to discuss some specific control mechanisms of the cell. Biological systems do not lend themselves to as stringent and rigorous quantitative analysis as physical systems, but the terminology is essentially the same. Biological systems, however, have developed some mechanisms of their own which are not often seen in the physical systems.

TERMINOLOGY

Control theories involve an input of information and a corresponding output of reaction or further information. Often in this relay, information about the output is referred back to the point of input. This information return is called feedback, and it forms the basis for most servomechanisms (automatic control) of the cell.

The components of a control system are quite simple. There is an input of information, the system proper with its limiting properties, and the output:

Input → |System proper| → Output

On the surface, the system appears to react as a black box. Information is fed into it, something occurs, and an output is sent out. In a biological system, the "black box" may be as simple as a single biochemical pathway or as complex as the whole mechanism for protein synthesis.

For a system to qualify as a control system, there must be some provision for an error-sensing device. That is, there must be a mechanism whereby the output which is actually produced is compared with the output which in theory should be produced. Inherent in error-sensing, therefore, is the ability to control the output. The information concerning output is returned to the input by feedback mechanisms.

A simple servomechanism is illustrated below:

Furnace → Heated room → Heat detector
⌐ Feedback of information ⌐

The heat produced by the furnace causes a rise in temperature. The increase in temperature is relayed back to the furnace, and depending on the increase, the furnace will either continue to heat or will shut off.

In theory, the feedback may be one of two types. If a biochemical sequence is used in illustration, the types are as follows:

1. Negative feedback

$$A \rightarrow B \rightarrow C \rightarrow D$$

In this negative feedback example, as the level of D increases, the information is fed back to inhibit the A → B reaction.

2. Positive feedback

$$A \rightarrow B \rightarrow C \rightarrow D$$

or

$$A \rightarrow B \rightarrow C \rightarrow D$$

In positive feedback, the substance, A, can enhance its own metabolism (autocatalysis, for example), or the products can cycle back to cause the A → B reaction to increase.

In a biological system, these feedback mechanisms have thermodynamic overtones. Since entropy is the increase in disorder in a system, negative entropy would be the decrease in disorder. In biosynthesis or in negative feedback where an increase in entropy is prevented, there is conservation of negative entropy. Negative entropy is called information and is designated H.

In synthetic pathways where energy is used to create a more ordered molecule, the information of the system is increased. Conversely, degradation pathways, which are associated with a positive feedback, show a decline in information and an increase in entropy. These pathways are, of course, a necessary part of the biological steady state system since energy must be derived from some compounds in order to be used for the syntheses of others.

It is obvious that a protein contains more information than the individual amino acids. What might not be as obvious, however, is that the synthetic process for forming the protein, although a requirement for cell survival, must be controlled and prevented from draining too much of the energy from the cell. This is where the feedback enters the picture. Negative feedback is used to regulate synthesis of a particular substance. When the synthesized compound reaches a certain level, the information is fed back to the center of synthesis, apprising it of the situation, and the biosynthetic plant is shut down. By the same token, negative feedback also prevents excess degradation of a compound, thus conserving information and preventing a rise in entropy.

Positive feedback mechanisms are important for those pathways which are used primarily as an energy source. Under the appropriate stimulus, the cell must quickly activate these pathways which yield the high-energy bonds. Often, the catabolic processes take precedence over the anabolic synthesis, with the resultant increase in entropy level. This is generally a temporary situation which is compensated for by a subsequent decrease in entropy.

CLOSED-LOOP SYSTEM VERSUS OPEN-LOOP SYSTEM

The servomechanism control with a feedback component is not the only type of control system. This feedback control is called a closed-loop system in which some element in the system feeds information back to earlier elements. It may be a positive or negative feedback, and it may be direct or indirect. The fact remains, however, that there is this loop of information flowing back to the system.

1. Closed-loop system

$$\rightarrow A \rightarrow B \rightarrow C \rightarrow D$$

Regardless of how much A is present, the level of D controls the conversion of A to B.

In contrast, some control mechanisms can be a one-way sequence without information feedback. This type of system is known as the open-loop system in that the early components of the system have no information about subsequent reactions.

2. Open-loop system

$$A \rightarrow B \rightarrow C \rightarrow D \rightarrow$$

The level of D is automatically dictated by the level of A in the system.

Both types of control have their advantages. The open-loop system offers a quicker acting mechanism if the individual components are simple. The closed-loop system, however, is more accurate and precise for controlling output release, but at the expense of being more complex. The closed-loop system is used more

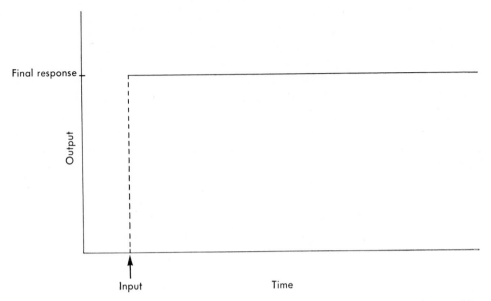

Fig. 30-1. Zero-order control system. Final response is attained immediately after input, without any lag.

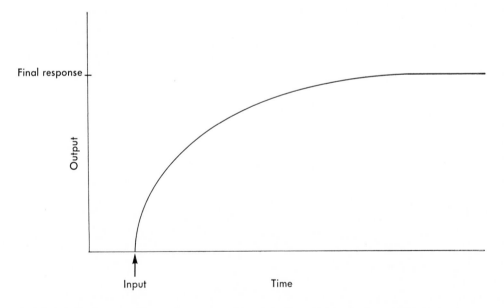

Fig. 30-2. First-order control system. Final response is approached slowly after the input value is put into system.

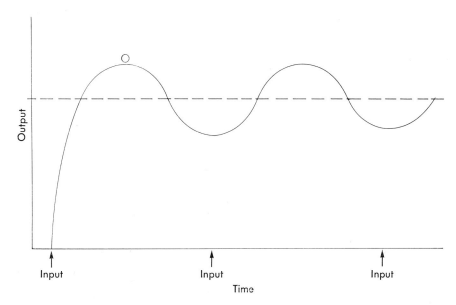

Fig. 30-3. Higher-order control system with overshoot and oscillation. Output values oscillate around the final response value (*broken line*). Input is triggered as output reaches a certain minimum, causing the output value to reach the overshoot level. *O*, Overshoot.

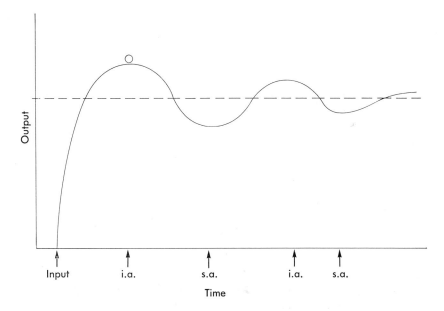

Fig. 30-4. Higher-order control system with overshoot, oscillation, and damping. The damping effect is a means of approaching the final response value (*broken line*). A series of inhibitory and stimulatory adjustments are made to lower the oscillation around the final response values. In higher organisms, these adjustments may be due to stimulatory and inhibitory hormones whose levels are balanced in order to maintain a certain homeostatic condition (steady state, or final response). *O*, Overshoot; *i.a.*, inhibitory adjustment; *s.a.*, stimulatory adjustment.

often in the cellular mechanisms, but there are instances in which the control is through the open-loop system.

BASIC CONTROL SYSTEMS

Control systems and cybernetics imply a quantitatively predictable set of results for any given set of input. However, the means by which the output is attained may differ. Grodins[1] has divided the response to input into four basic categories: zero-order, first-order, second-order, and higher-order systems.

In the zero-order system, there is an exact value of output for every input value, and the output value is attained at once without delay (Fig. 30-1). This is essentially an open-loop system.

In the first-order system, there is a definite lag before the output value reaches a finite point as dictated by the input. The curve for the output value as it approaches its final steady state is exponential, showing no fluctuation or overshoot (Fig. 30-2). Reactions in a biochemical sequence often show this type of behavior. The feedback is generally from one reactant in the chain, and the effect is channeled back to the enzyme regulating a previous step in the sequence.

As the complexity of the control system increases, the feedback mechanism of the closed-loop gives a characteristic curve to the control. The oscillation around the final value of the output as the system seeks the steady state level is typical of many biological systems. The second-order and higher-order control systems all show this behavior. The basis of the fluctuation is that the feedback can only relay certain bits of information back to the input which will either increase or decrease the value, or turn off or on the input. In other words, there is more than one input for the final output. Because of the delay in the system, the output does not go immediately to its steady state value, but instead, oscillates above and below it until the value is reached, if ever. This fluctuation is known as the seeking of the steady state level. Several different control systems demonstrating this oscillation are seen in Figs. 30-3 and 30-4.

The damping effect seen in Fig. 30-4 is an important characteristic of the higher systems, particularly the endocrine system.

SUMMARY

Rashevsky[2] has stated that a living system must have at least one cyclic process, and that the existence of this process implies control. Any control theory utilizes an input of information which can be recovered as some output value. In an open-loop system, the input has no awareness of the output.

In closed-loop systems, however, there is a feedback of information from the output to previous components of the control system. If the feedback causes a diminishing of input, usually the feedback is negative; conversely, if the output causes an increase in input utilization, the feedback is positive.

Applied to a biological system, the feedback mechanism is a precise means by which biosynthesis and degradation can be controlled. Biosynthetic pathways are associated with a negative feedback. In these sequences, the entropy is decreased; negative entropy is called information. In degradative pathways, positive feedback is often involved. These sequences bring about a loss of information, a gain of entropy, and a possible gain of some high-energy compounds. The application of positive and negative controls is not limited to just the biosynthetic and biodegradative pathways of the cell. All physiological phenomena are subject to this control.

There are four basic control systems:

1. Zero-order, in which output is attained immediately after input value is placed into the system
2. First-order, in which there is a lag before output reaches its final value, but no overshoot or oscillation
3. Second-order or higher-order, in which there is overshoot and oscillation of the output value around the steady state value
4. Second-order or higher-order, in which there is overshoot, oscillation, and a damping effect so that fluctuation of the output value around the steady state diminishes and the value is finally reached

Literature cited

1. Grodins, F. S. 1963. Control theory and biological systems. Columbia University Press, New York. p. 5.
2. Rashevsky, N. 1948. Mathematical biophysics. University of Chicago Press, Chicago.

General references

Bellman, R. 1964. Control theory. Sci. Am. (Sept.), p. 186.
Brown, G. S., and D. P. Campbell. 1948. Principles of servomechanisms. John Wiley & Sons, Inc.
Fischberg, M., and A. W. Blackler. 1961. How cells specialize. Sci. Am. (Sept.), p. 124.
Grodins, F. S. 1963. Control theory and biological systems. Columbia University Press, New York.
Porter, A. 1952. An introduction to servo-mechanisms. 2nd ed. Metheun & Co. Ltd., London.
Ritow, I. 1956. A servomechanism primer. Doubleday & Company, Inc., Garden City, N. Y.

31

Control mechanisms in cell processes

INTRODUCTION

One of the major differences between living and nonliving systems is the maintenance of low entropy and the orderliness of the activities of the former. A consequence of the open system steady state which occurs in living systems is the need for control and highly efficient regulatory mechanisms. All facets of biological systems effect some control, and as a result, there are no levels in the cell in which control is not exerted.

Many of the mechanisms of control have been implicitly or explicitly outlined in the discussions of the various physiological processes of the cell. There are many areas of cellular regulation which have not been brought forth. The concepts of feedback and control systems introduced a whole spectrum of possibilities for regulatory mechanisms, and many of these will be specifically dealt with.

Basically, three types of controls are exerted in the cell. First, and foremost, is the genetic control. The deoxyribonucleic acids code for the particular proteins which will be produced on the ribosomes. In addition to actual production of the enzymes, genetic control dictates how much of and when the enzyme will be synthesized. The story of the gene takes on new flavor with the advent of modern theories on gene control.

The second area of control is biochemical. Traditional controls such as mass action and physiochemical factors are inadequate in a cellular environment. Innovations such as feedback inhibition (or end product inhibition), alternate pathways, interdependence of reaction components from different sets of reactions (alternate paths), and controlled microenvironment all add to the possible variation in control mechanisms.

The final area of control is imposed upon the physiology of the cellular system by the very structural framework in which the reactions are occurring. The internal milieu of the cell is not a potpourri of compounds and structures;

it is a very orderly and precise arrangement of organelles, membranes, and fluid matrix designed to give not only maximum efficiency but also exacting control of cell processes.

There are special problems of cell control which are important also. One of these, cell differentiation, depends on a shift of control levels in order to direct cellular energy toward a particular goal. On the other hand, aberrancies in cell control mechanisms are what allow viruses and neoplasias to have an overt effect. The inability to maintain certain control mechanisms is what leads eventually to cell death.

The control mechanisms in cell processes can be achieved by a variety of means, and rarely are they independent of each other. The precision and exactness which they approach permits the living cell to exist in its environment. Since control implies adaptation, the presence of flexible control systems also gives the cell the ability to adjust to changes in environment, the limits of the change being dictated by the control systems.

GENETIC CONTROL

The primary regulatory mechanism in the cell is the deoxyribonucleic acid, for on this molecule lies all the accumulated information from past generations. The sequences of bases on the DNA provide information to the cell, and the synthesis of the enzymes depends on these triplet-coded letters to spell out the nucleotide words that are transcribed and translated into peptide molecules. Without the correct enzymes, control mechanisms have little meaning. The DNA, then, must be considered the first level of cellular control.

The one gene–one enzyme hypothesis has become firmly established as a basic tenet of biochemical genetics. Evidence in support of this theorem is overwhelming. Mutant studies on microorganisms combined with the data of natural mutations in higher organisms indicate that each enzyme of a biochemical pathway is controlled by a mendelian unit. There are too many examples to ignore as happenstance.

The pathways of metabolism of the amino acids phenylalanine and tyrosine substantiate the one gene–one enzyme idea quite well (Fig. 31-1). Each of the indicated conditions behaves in a genetically predictable manner; that is, offspring phenotypes can be predicted from parental phenotypes. Thus, the factors involved mimic the mendelian unit, and all evidence points to the fact that synthesis of the enzymes involved in each condition must be under the influence of one genetic factor. The fact that the other enzymes of the pathway have not been demonstrated to be controlled by a single genetic unit does not preclude the general application of the one gene–one enzyme theory. There are several possible explanations for this. The most obvious is that the lack of these other enzymes either produces such a minor effect that it cannot be spotted or the missing enzyme may cause a lethal effect, preventing adequate study.

Assuming the one gene–one enzyme theory to be correct, one can see the obvious control exerted by the DNA. The individual codons code for a single amino acid in a peptide sequence in the enzyme. If one pyrimidine or purine is

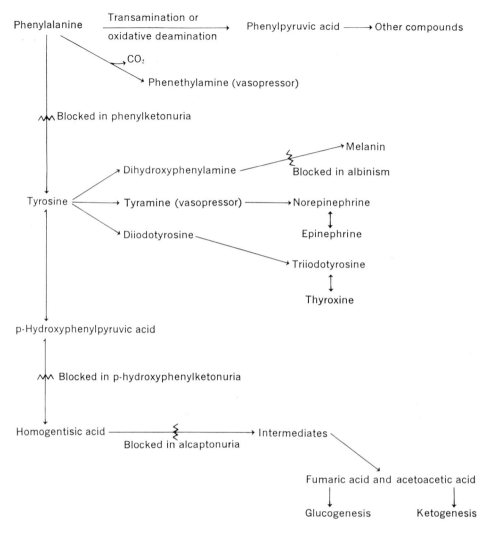

Fig. 31-1. Metabolic pathway of phenylalanine and tyrosine, indicating enzymatic steps which can be deleted by genetic mutation. Substantiates one gene—one enzyme theory.

altered, the resulting nonsense or mis-sense letter may result in formation of an enzyme whose activity is different from the normally occurring protein. This control is subtle in design but not necessarily in expression. It is a precise cell regulatory mechanism whose importance overshadows many other controls. To restate this importance, the control of *what* enzymes are present has to be established before the control of the activity of the enzymes can even be considered.

Control of nucleic acid synthesis

Replication of the double-stranded DNA by the complement base pairing is nature's way of ensuring exact duplication of the DNA from generation to generation. With the advantage of hindsight, it is hard to envision a more precise means of copying this controller macromolecule.

Various conditions have been demonstrated to affect DNA synthesis in vitro, and others have been shown to occur during the cell cycle. The synthesis of DNA is an enzyme-controlled mechanism and is therefore subject to the same kinds of biological variables as any other biochemical process. In review, DNA synthesis requires the presence of the nucleotides of adenine, guanine, cytosine, and thymine, a primer DNA as a template, Mg^{++}, and the enzyme DNA polymerase. When all of these are present in a compatible physiochemical environment, the DNA is capable of undergoing synthesis. However, if one of the nucleotides is removed from the medium, either the synthesis will slow or an atypical sequence of bases will be formed. Both of these situations could drastically affect the cell, either by not providing the code for the necessary enzymes or by coding for a nonfunctional protein.

These drastic, in vitro circumstances would probably not occur within the cell, but evidence does indicate that regulatory mechanisms for DNA synthesis are present in vivo. For example, production of the deoxyribonucleic acid apparently is stopped during nuclear division. Some control mechanism has inhibited synthesis during this phase of the cell cycle. Furthermore, it seems that not all portions of the chromosomes duplicate at the same time, which again implies a regulation of some kind.

Finally, other complications which might complex the picture are the possibilities either that variant purine or pyrimidine bases might become incorporated into the DNA or that the normally occurring bases might substitute for one another (for example, adenine for guanine). Both possibilities would throw off the coding sequence, leading to faulty protein synthesis.

Some of the factors controlling synthesis of messenger RNA are discussed in the next section, particularly the response of the synthesis system to inhibitors and activators. In a nucleus which is actively replicating its DNA, there is some evidence that the synthesis of RNA may be depressed during this phase. The control mechanisms of the synthesis of transfer RNA and ribosomal RNA are uncertain.

Protein synthesis (review)

A quick review of the machinery for protein synthesis should lay the groundwork for a discussion of the regulatory mechanisms imposed upon this process.

The code for the formation of the amino acid sequence into a biologically active peptide is on the DNA molecule. The code, consisting probably of a triplet of purine and pyrimidine bases (the codon) for each amino acid, is transcribed from the DNA by the formation of the messenger RNA, a strand of nucleotides complementary to a sequence of the DNA, with the uracil substitution for thymine the only exception. The messenger RNA moves to the ribosomes where the protein is synthesized. The ribosomal RNA reads the code, and as the code is translated, the individual amino acids are brought into sequence—each acid carried on a specific transfer RNA. Each messenger RNA can bring about the formation of several copies of the enzyme for which it is coded, but it is then destroyed, and further synthesis depends on the presence of additional messenger RNA. The fact is pivotal in presenting hypotheses about control mechanisms of protein synthesis.

Control of enzyme synthesis

The cell cannot afford to have enzyme activity at peak values during all of its life cycle. There are times when the enzyme activity must be higher than at others; there may be circumstances in which no activity of a particular enzyme is desired. One means of exerting control is to regulate the level of the enzyme responsible for the activity. This implies regulation of the protein synthesis process of the cell. The protein synthesis mechanism is an exacting sequence of events spanning nuclear and cytoplasmic structures. As such, there seem to be only three possibilities for the control site—at the DNA or gene level, on the messenger RNA, and on the ribosomal apparatus. Evidence favors the first alternate.

The concept of repression and induction

The control of enzyme synthesis deals with a phenotypic change in the cellular enzyme makeup, where the genotype remains constant. The phenomenon of discrepancy or variation between phenotype and genotype is a well-known genetic event. At the molecular level, however, it takes on a different view, and the concepts of repression and induction as suggested by Jacob and Monod[1] aid in proposing a more sophisticated model.

By definition, repression is the decrease in the rate of synthesis of an enzyme caused by exposure of the system to a given metabolite. In other words, the presence of a substrate or end product of a reaction chain may cause a decrease in the enzyme or enzymes which are involved in the production of these metabolites. In the sequence

$$A \rightarrow B \rightarrow C \rightarrow D$$

theoretically a large amount of B, C, or D could inhibit formation of the enzyme bringing about the conversion of A. It appears that D, the final distal end product, is capable of repressing synthesis of enzymes for the earlier steps in the chain more effectively than B or C. This repressor substance, then, is a cytoplasmic element which exerts a feedback control to the nuclear DNA.

Induction, conversely, is the increase in synthesis of an enzyme upon exposure of the cell to a given metabolite or substrate. Parallel to repression, the induction process depends on some cytoplasmic compound triggering the production of the enzyme which will metabolize the inducing material. This induction of enzymes is not only a rate-limiting device for controlling the level of the enzyme produced. A substrate is actually capable of inducing production of an enzyme which did not exist before the cell was exposed to the substrate. Yeast, which has no demonstrable lactase enzyme, will develop a high titer of the enzyme if grown in a medium to which lactose has been added. Furthermore, the induction is reversible, in that synthesis of the enzyme is stopped when the inducing compound is removed.

Both the induction and repression may be on the total sequence of enzymes leading to the end product. Unless there are alternate metabolic paths to shunt off the intermediates in a sequence, there would be no advantage in repressing only one step; that is, if the initial enzyme is not repressed, the entire sequence would have to be slowed by repressing all the enzymes in the sequence

$$A \xrightarrow{a} B \xrightarrow{b} C \xrightarrow{c} D$$

If a is repressed, the entire sequence is repressed. On the other hand, if c is the enzyme repressed, a and b would also have to be cut back unless there are alternate paths for B and C. The same holds true for induction, except that if it is the first or last enzyme in the sequence which is induced the cell can only make use of the pathway if all of the enzymes in the sequence are induced.

It would be of no value to induce formation of a or c without induction of b.

A striking example of sequential induction occurs in yeast. Yeast grown anaerobically have no cytochromes. The exposure to oxygen induces formation of the entire cytochrome system.[1] Other examples of sequential induction or repression have occurred in the literature.

Jacob and Monod,[1] at the Institut Pasteur, worked out a model to explain both repression and induction. The first evidence of a control mechanism was the finding that a mutant of *Escherichia coli* was incapable of having the lactase enzyme induced; in fact the lactase was produced as if it were a constitutive enzyme, that is, present at all times. The mutant was apparently a single gene mutant, but the enzyme produced had identical characteristics to the lactase formed in cells where induction occurred. This suggested to these investigators that more than one gene was involved in a protein synthesis sequence, and that one of these genes must be the one which regulates the activities of the others. This was the introduction to the operon idea.

The operon

It has been established that genes occur in a linear fashion along the DNA chain. Most of the genes seem to code for the formation of chemical entities, the enzymes. These genes are called structural genes. There are some genes, however, which seem to have as their prime function control of the activity of other genes; they are called functional genes. One functional gene is the operator gene which coordinates the function of adjacent structural genes. It is probable that the unit which includes one operator gene and several structural genes codes for a single messenger RNA, which in turn dictates the formation of a particular protein structure. The entire complex—the operator plus the structural genes—is termed the operon.

It has been mentioned that not all of the enzymes of the cell are produced in quantities at the same time. This means that all operon units are not "turned on" at once and implies further control. The suggestion by Jacob and Monod of the existence of a separate gene for control did not match the description of the operator gene. Another genetic unit, the regulatory gene, was postulated as the control mechanism of the operon.

Mechanism of action of the regulatory gene

The regulatory gene causes production of a repressor substance (possibly an oligonucleotide or a protein) which functions in control of the operator gene of the operon. The singularly important feature of the repressor molecule is that it works in a negative manner. That is, when it is present in an active form, it prevents the operator gene from stimulating the structural genes to produce messenger RNA. In some manner, this repressor binds at the operator gene site to inhibit its activity.

Two facts seem apparent. The presence of the repressor molecule causes constant inhibition of the function of the operator. This would imply that the normal state within the cell is one of repression. This would be an energy-saving device for the cell. Second, the repressor system would suggest that in order to stimulate production of messenger RNA from the structural genes, the repressor has to be itself repressed. In any control mechanism, initiation of a process can be brought about by direct stimulation or by removal of inhibition. The latter provides a precise control mechanism, a precision necessary in such an important process as enzyme formation.

The concepts embodied in the regulatory repressor molecule, the gene, and the operon can be used to explain the phenomena of enzyme repression and induction. If the repressor molecule is considered to be a specific binding site for compounds which either inhibit or induce enzyme action, the following scheme could be postulated. In a repressible system, the repressor is activated by attachment of some regulatory compound. The activated repressor exerts its inhibition on the operator site, preventing formation of messenger RNA from the structural genes. Conversely, in induction, the regulatory compound would attach to the repressor and effectively inactivate it. Inactivation of the repressor releases the inhibition from the operator gene and the operon becomes functional. In addition to this mechanism for bringing about the derepression of the operator, other genetic mechanisms could accomplish this on a more permanent basis. A mutation of either the regulatory gene (causing a change in the repressor) or the operator gene (affecting its sensitivity to the repressor substance) could bring about the derepression.

Summarized, the repressor system can be outlined as follows (Fig. 31-2):

1. The release of messenger RNA from structural genes is under the influence of a specific operator gene; the complex is called an operon.
2. The operon, itself, is under the control of a regulator gene.
3. This regulator gene causes formation of a repressor molecule which attaches at the operon site and can inhibit its function.
4. The repressor molecule may be activated by contact with some substance from the cytoplasm, presumably a metabolite. The activated repressor causes repression of the operon activity and thus cessation of enzyme synthesis.
5. The repressor molecule also can be inhibited by a substance (metabolite) from the cytoplasm, the net result of this inhibition of the repressor being a stimulation of the operon; that is, enzyme synthesis is induced.

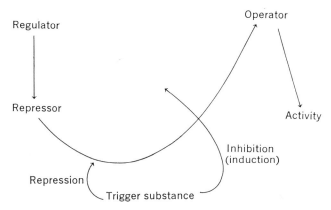

Fig. 31-2. Schematic representation of the repressor system. Regulator produces a repressor substance which becomes active in the presence of a trigger substance. This results in repression of the operator. Other substances may inhibit the repressor, resulting in induction of the final activity.

This remarkable feedback mechanism for control of enzyme synthesis suggests possible application of the concepts to other areas of the cellular processes. The machinery of other physiological functions may be kept in check by a repressor mechanism. For instance, it is not too farfetched to postulate a replicator gene for DNA duplication, a secretor gene, a cell plate–forming gene, and a series of functional genes analogous to the operator gene for enzyme synthesis. All of these would have their respective regulatory genes complete with repressor molecule to maintain inhibition during periods of the cell cycle when the processes are not useful.

How far-reaching is the repressor effect is not certain. In biochemical pathways where shifts of pathway emphasis and activity are almost immediate, other mechanisms probably prevail. For any long-range, semipermanent change, however, the repressor system seems ideally suited. The regulatory control permits a variable phenotypic expression of a genotypic condition.

CONTROL OF ENZYME ACTIVITY (BIOCHEMICAL CONTROL)

The control of synthesis of enzymes only answers part of the challenge of cell regulation. The problem of control of the activity of these protein catalysts after they are formed must also be met. Repression and induction are processes which, for the most part, are too slow to be of immediate use to the cell. As a result, at the risk of losing some precision, mechanisms have arisen for control of enzyme activity at the biochemical level. The concepts of feedback as developed in the previous chapter would seem to apply to cellular control or adjustment at this biochemical level. The input would be the concentration of some member of a sequence, and the output would be a change of rate of the steps leading to the input; thus, output is a controlled rate of reaction. For feedback at the biological level, Chance[2] prefers the term *metabolic control,* which he feels is a more explicit expression of control for living systems.

Metabolic control at the enzyme level implies that the cell contains certain enzymes which may be specific for both the natural substrate and some controlling molecule as well. The parallel with the repressor mechanism is striking. Generally, a positive feedback control is associated with the degradation process and a negative feedback with the biosynthesis. In some pathways, both may exert control, particularly if the enzymes involved are amphibolic, a term coined by Davis[3] to indicate enzymes which can participate equally well in anabolic and catabolic functions.

End product inhibition

One of the basic tenets of negative feedback is that some component along the control scheme inhibits some previous component of the pathway. In biochemical sequences, this means that any intermediate or end product of a pathway can potentially inhibit any previous step in the pathway. The effect is probably on the enzyme which catalyzes the reactions and not on the substrate itself.

Feedback inhibition of an enzyme could be an extremely important facet of cellular control. The mechanism is, first, simple, depending only on the level of the intermediate or end product, and, second, specific, in that only those substances in the pathway normally bring about the inhibition. In addition, this type of mechanism requires expenditure of little or no additional energy. The enzyme has already been synthesized, and the control is merely on the level of activity of the protein. Positive feedback must also involve little expenditure of energy if the mechanism parallels that of the negative feedback.

Many examples of both positive and negative feedback have been found in biological systems. Several specific examples are given:

1. Added tryptophan inhibits the enzyme tryptophan synthetase.
2. In the sequence leading to isoleucine, the pathway begins with threonine. The enzyme inhibited by the presence of L-isoleucine is the first one in the sequence, threonine deaminase. It has not been demonstrated that D-isoleucine has no inhibitory effect at all.
3. The presence of glucose-6-phosphate stimulates the enzyme phosphorylase which causes uridine diphosphate-glucose to be polymerized into glycogen or starch.

These examples demonstrate the simple and direct modes of inhibition (No. 1 and No. 2) and stimulation (No. 3). Somehow, the end products act to bring out the feedback effect.

The allosteric effect

Gerhart and Pardee[4] and Changeux[5] discovered that an enzyme could be heated in such a way that its sensitivity to inhibition or stimulation was lost, but it did not lose its biochemical activity. This immediately suggested that there must be more than one site on the enzyme—one for its biochemical activity and one for attachment of a modifier substance. This possibility, coupled with the parallel of this system with the repressor system, has led to a postulate called the allosteric effect.

Both regulatory enzymes and the repressor molecule have a trait in common, in that both of these substances can recognize the configuration of a specific substrate or metabolite which can either inhibit or activate the enzyme or repressor. In the regulatory enzyme, the recognition process must be by electrostatic and geometric forms of the molecule, and yet, for the most part, the substance recognized bears little resemblance to the natural substrate or product. The theoretical background was laid for the work of Gerhart and Pardee[4] which apparently demonstrates conclusively that in the enzyme with which they worked there are two subunits, each with a specific site. The site on one subunit is specific for the natural substrate; the site on the other subunit apparently recognizes the inhibitor.

The effect of the inhibitor or activator is not on the substrate site, but at a nearby allosteric position. The attachment of the inhibitor or activator, however, definitely affects the activity of the enzyme without actually interfering with the active site *per se*. This theory is compatible with Koshland's[6] suggestion that there are configurational changes in the enzymes (Chapter 14), although he did not suggest this specific allosteric hypothesis.

The concept of the allosteric effect can also be applied to the repressor system. When the repressor substance attaches to the operator site, binding is of such a nature that the operator gene is inhibited. However, when an inducing substance attaches to the repressor first, binding of the repressor to the operator gene is affected in such a way as to release the inhibitory effect of the repressor.

There must be provisions built into the allosteric effect theory for sensitivity to the level of metabolite as well as for its presence. In a metabolic sequence, the end product is produced normally. Only when it reaches a certain level does the inhibition occur. Changeux[5] proposes that there are interactions which occur among the attachment sites of the normal substrate, inhibitor, or activator and that the sum total of the interactions determines the final activity of the enzyme.

The ability of a protein to recognize several biological compounds and to integrate the information they yield upon attachment gives an aura of computerism to these enzymes. How the integration occurs is in the realm of speculation.

Control systems

Every enzyme-catalyzed pathway has a built-in control mechanism; it is a part of the living steady state system. End product inhibition and activation are the expressions of specific allosteric effects. All of these are at the molecular level. There are, however, higher level controls which are also prevalent in the cell.

The Pasteur effect

The relationship between the anaerobic glycolysis and the oxidative respiration cycles was recognized by Pasteur, Meyerhof, Warburg, and other early workers in the field of metabolism. Burk[7] reviewed many of the references to this effect and reemphasized that it has been generally reported that glycolysis is inhibited by oxidative processes, the inhibition being termed the Pasteur effect.

The advantages to the cell of this control device are obvious. The Krebs cycle offers many more potential ATP's to the system than does the glycolytic cycle. Diversion of the metabolic emphasis to oxidative processes permits the cell to glean maximal energy from its metabolites. Second, the shift of primary emphasis to oxidative cycles conserves the reserve glucose and glycogen or starch. A limit will eventually be reached when the cell must generate more acetyl-CoA from carbohydrate sources, but the excess metabolites such as lactic acid are normally used up first.

There is the distinct possibility that this overt inhibition may be a biochemical artifact, and that the glycolysis is not depressed as much as data indicate, but there are more indications that it is a real phenomenon than data which suggest otherwise. If the Pasteur effect is real and predictable, the mechanism is not. Van Eys[8] summarizes the subject by suggesting that no hypothesis can satisfactorily explain the effect. Possibilities which have been suggested include oxidation of sulfhydryl bonds of the glycolytic enzymes and triggering of the pentose shunt by high oxygen tension and the resulting competition for the members of the phosphate pool.

The Crabtree effect

In a few isolated organisms it has been reported that high concentrations of glucose inhibit the oxidative cycles, particularly the Krebs cycle. Whether it is a real phenomenon or an artifact is uncertain. Evidence for its widespread occurrence is shaky, and it is probable that peculiar circumstances led to its original discovery in certain cells. Even if it were the consensus that it is a real control feature, the mechanism for control is more tenuous than the theory itself. It is tempting to dismiss this effect as an artifact, but it still may have some importance to some cells. The effect, real or otherwise, is not prevalent as a major control device.

Alternate pathways as a control

Alternate metabolic pathways are not only control mechanisms. They afford greater flexibility for the cell under a variety of conditions. Their role as control devices should not be overlooked, however. An obvious example is the acetyl-CoA. This ubiquitous compound can enter into many of the major metabolic pathways—Krebs cycle, fatty acid cycle, glycolytic cycle, and various synthesis mechanisms. The control is inherent in the activity of this molecule. If the cell places heavy demands on the Krebs cycle for energy output, the acetyl-CoA is shunted down into this path, essentially preventing the fatty acid synthesis from occurring. By the same token, the glycolytic cycle will not be reversed with the formation of starch. Conversely, if the demand on the Krebs cycle is low, and the glucose intake is maintained, the acetyl-CoA will pile up. Fatty acid synthesis will be spurred, and starch formation will occur. These effects may be expressions of the mass action only in that there is no direct evidence that the enzymes starting these various paths are inhibited or stimulated.

Another example of a metabolite involved in control where the regulation is primarily through alternate pathways is the Krebs cycle intermediate, oxalacetic acid. Like acetyl-CoA, the oxalacetate is at a pivotal point of the metabolic paths, and as such, it can participate in many different reactions. This acid can be formed from three different precursors:

1. Oxidation of malic acid in the Krebs cycle, and under normal circumstances the predominant pathway
2. Pyruvic acid carboxylation in one of the CO_2-fixation mechanisms
3. Transamination in the nitrogen pool from aspartic acid

These are reversible reactions, but primarily the equilibrium favors the formation of the malic acid in No. 1, whereas in No. 2 and No. 3 the equilibrium shifts as the demands on the metabolic mill vary. In addition to these three paths for removal of oxalacetic acid, condensation of the acid with acetyl-CoA occurs, forming citric acid or malonyl-CoA, giving further alternatives. Finally, there are three separate decarboxylation paths for oxalacetic acid (Chapter 17).

The functions of oxalacetic acid are varied and are not, apparently, limited to direct participation in the four reactions mentioned. Since the Krebs cycle is the critical pathway for high-energy ATP production, the regulation of available oxalacetic acid is a definite control mechanism since it is required in the step where acetyl-CoA enters the cycle. There are other controls in which oxalacetic acid is involved. In a feedback relationship, oxalacetic acid inhibits the succinic dehydrogenation step of the Krebs cycle. In other words, if the level of oxalacetic acid becomes high due to formation from other sources, the Krebs cycle production of the acid is inhibited, the inhibition being at the succinic acid $\rightarrow$ fumaric acid step, although the malic acid $\rightarrow$ oxalacetic acid is also reduced. The succinic dehydrogenase inhibition is probably a true end product, or feedback, inhibition. Inhibition of the malic dehydrogenase is most likely a mass action phenomenon. The combination of oxalacetic acid with acetyl-CoA to form malonyl-CoA is the initial step of mitochondrial synthesis of fatty acids. This is the second cycle in which oxalacetate is involved in the critical first step.

The oxalacetic acid, then, is in a state of dynamic balance, with avenues to many paths open. Being at the crossroads of these pathways makes this Krebs cycle intermediate a controlling molecule, a compound whose metabolic shifts can affect the overall metabolism of the cell.

There must be many such examples of biochemical control systems in which the regulation is exerted through the availability of alternate pathways. As in other mechanisms, this type of control requires no energy input. The regulation is by shift of emphasis on the pathways as the demands of the cell change.

Mutual stimulation

There are several examples of mutual stimulation where the metabolism through one pathway stimulates another pathway to activity. One of the best examples is the stimulation of fatty acid synthesis by the pentose shunt. As activity increases in the pentose shunt, a large amount of NADPH·H^+ is formed. This reduced nicotinamide adenine dinucleotide phosphate is a prerequisite for the lipid synthesis pathways. As the lipid pathway increases, pulling the reduced coenzymes from the system, the pentose shunt is further stimulated to undergo the oxidation of glucose, with the further production of NADPH·H$^+$.

Respiratory chain control

Chance and Williams[9] have categorized the major conditions which affect the activity of the respiratory chain. The oxygen requirement is obvious, in that this gas is the only final acceptor of the hydrogens and electrons. The factors which exert a control effect are the level of ADP, the presence of the substrate (reduced coenzyme), and the integrity of the carrier complexes. Assuming availability of the reduced coenzymes and the integrity of the various components of the chain, the level of ADP is apparently the most critical factor in control. It has been demonstrated that there is a sharp increase of respiratory chain activity when amounts of ADP are available; large amounts of ATP have been shown to reverse part of the chain, effecting inhibition. Added glucose stimulates the respiratory chain because it removes the ATP and forms ADP in the initial phosphorylation step:

$$\text{Glucose} + \text{ATP} \longrightarrow \text{Glucose-6-phosphate} + \text{ADP}$$

The activity of the respiratory chain, like any other enzymatic or biochemical sequence, is subject to control. The regulation may not be true feedback inhibition or stimulation, but the demonstrable effects are the same.

Competition effects

Underlying many of the foregoing mechanisms is the tacit competition for available metabolites. The competition for substrate provides the basis for several control mechanisms. A dramatic example of competition occurs in the mitochondria where it is not the metabolites being competed for; the enzymes themselves are the site of competition. The movement of calcium ions across the mitochondrial membranes requires complexing with phosphate ions. The enzymes which provide the phosphate may be identical with those of the ATPase system which provides phosphates for the reversible ATP $\leftrightharpoons$ ADP + P$_i$ reaction. Movement of calcium through the membrane has been demonstrated to interfere with ATP production.[10]

In some instances, there is competition for coenzymes, in particular the NAD, which can act as a shuttle between different pathways. Since a pathway cannot proceed without an available coenzyme to accept the hydrogen, the level and participation of NAD in a pathway may exert a controlling effect on it. Wherever there is competition for metabolites, active sites, enzymes, or coenzymes, the system has the potential of a control system.

·   ·   ·

All of the biochemical control mechanisms are interrelated and none is a separate entity from the others. The advantage of enumerating them is to focus attention on the particular aspects of control. Regulatory devices are in every facet of the biochemistry of the cell; the systems mentioned represent only a few of these control mechanisms.

STRUCTURAL CONTROL

The network of membranes in the cell provides a ready-made mechanism of control. These membranes with their selective permeability can control the influx and efflux of the various compounds from one compartment to the next within the cell. The outer membrane determines which substances get into the cell in the first place. Once within the cell, the substance may only be moved to certain locations because of the regulatory control exerted by the internal membrane system. The impermeability to specific substrates, metabolic intermediates, and coenzymes exerts an immediate control on metabolic processes.

For example, reduced nicotinamide adenine dinucleotide ($NADH \cdot H^+$) cannot penetrate the mitochondrial membrane, even though the facilities for handling the reduced coenzyme are present within the mitochondrion in the form of the respiratory chain. This sets up a cryptic situation and is at once a control device.

The control of metabolic influx and product efflux by the outer membrane was pointed out in Chapter 24. The regulation of ion imbalance by the membranes imparts the characteristic charge to the membrane. The conductivity process is a membrane-controlled event, as are many other cellular processes.

Organelles by their very nature add more control to the cell system. By maintaining separate enzyme systems and functions, there is regulation of activity within the cell. The recent evidences for interrelationships indicate that the organelles do not function as independently as once thought; however, separation of structure and function is there, and it offers added control to the cell.

Control systems, then, are present at the molecular, macromolecular, and structural levels.

DIFFERENTIATION AS AN EXPRESSION OF CONTROL

Cell differentiation is a process whereby a cell becomes specialized for a particular function. This implies a shift in the emphasis of the metabolic pathways and, as a result, implies a shift of control mechanisms. In other words, the differentiation allows a variety of phenotypic expressions of a single genotype. This can only happen if the control mechanisms are present.

In totipotent cells, the physiological processes are those which are basic to any cell without specialization in any one of them. The cell is under steady state control, and the enzyme level is predictable for any set of conditions. As the differentiation process begins, a change in the control mechanism must occur. Certain enzymes are produced at a faster rate, and others are suppressed. The level of activity of the enzymes of certain metabolic pathways is increased, and again, others are repressed. Concomitant permeability changes occur to increase the level of influx of some metabolites and to decrease the level of others. All are outward expressions of the types of control mechanisms afore-mentioned. It is significant that cellular control can denote two basic physio-logical states. One, the *status quo* condition of dynamic equilibrium, is necessary for the steady state existence of cells not undergoing change. Second, con-trolled regulatory shifts allow a cell either to change with the environment or to differentiate into specialized cells. Neither would be possible without control mechanisms.

The indication of any cellular process, whether it be differentiation, secretion, movement, or division, necessitates the presence of control devices. Without these, the processes would be undirected attempts toward a new steady state level.

ABNORMALITIES OF CONTROL

No biological mechanism is infallible, and the control systems of the cell are no exception. Often these control devices do not behave in the ordinary manner, and the manifestations of abnormal control are extraordinary. Neo-plastic cells, for example, have lost some control of the division process. Normal cells are somewhat inhibited from dividing by contact with other surrounding cells. Not so with neoplastic cells. Those cells have lost this contact sensitivity and as a result divide incessantly. Furthermore, the abnormal cells have lost the ability to return to the resting interphase state after division, another aberrant control. Neoplastic cells not only divide more; the span between divisions is shorter than normal cells. All these aberrancies are due to loss or modification of the control mechanisms. There seems to be a state of continual derepression of the synthetic enzymes, which results in the rapid division and high respiratory rates.

The abnormalities of control can lead to other conditions besides neoplasia. The loss of critical control mechanisms may lead to death of the cell and thus probably plays a strong role in cell death and senescence.

SUMMARY

Cell modulation is the ability to reversibly adjust to various physiological states and environments and to maintain a steady state at each level of adjust-ment. The living system must maintain a low entropy level and a high degree of ordered reactions. Both require precise and specific control mechanisms. No level of the cell, molecular, macromolecular, or structural, is free from some form of control. The basic areas of control are genetic, biochemical, and structural.

Genetic control involves both the regulation of synthesis of nucleic acid and synthesis of the enzymes of the cells. The genotype code dictates what kind of enzymes can be made; the cell regulatory mechanisms dictate what enzymes will be made at any point in physiological time. The control of enzyme syn-thesis involves formation of a repressor substance by a regulatory gene. This repressor molecule, which may be either activated or inhibited by various metabolites, specifically attaches to an operator gene. The operator gene, whose function is to control the release of messenger RNA from structural genes in the operon complex, is inhibited if the repressor is activated and is stimulated or induced if the repressor is inhibited.

The control of enzyme activity, or biochemical control in the cell, has many facets. End product inhibition, which has the same result as repression, is inhibition of the activity of an enzyme in a sequence by a metabolite occurring later in the sequence. The pathway is slowed, but the means is direct inhibition and not inhibition of synthesis. Repression, induction, end product inhibition, and stimulation can be explained by the allosteric effect which, in essence, states that an enzyme has one site for enzyme activity and others for attachment of various moderator molecules, with the final action of the enzyme depending on interaction of the substrate and moderator(s) on the protein.

Various biochemical control systems which play a role in intracellular regulation are as follows:

1. The Pasteur effect, in which oxidative metabolism inhibits glycolysis
2. The Crabtree effect, in which high amounts of glucose inhibit the Krebs and other oxidative pathways
3. Alternate pathways as a control
4. Mutual stimulation effects
5. Respiratory chain control by oxygen, ADP-ATP levels, and substrate levels
6. Competition effects of limited substances

Structural control primarily regulates by restricting the metabolites into various compartments of the cell. Selective permeability controls which substances will be in what area of the cell.

Cell differentiation and neoplasia are expressions of a shifted control system. The former is controlled; the latter is uncontrolled.

Literature cited

1. Jacob. F., and J. Monod. 1961. Genetic regulatory mechanisms in the synthesis of proteins. J. Molec. Biol. 3:318.
2. Chance, B. 1961. Control characteristics of enzyme systems, vol. 26, p. 289. In Cellular regulatory mechanisms. Cold Spring Harbor Symposium on Quantitative Biology.
3. Davis, B. D. 1961. Opening address: The teleonomic significance of biosynthetic control mechanisms, vol. 26, p. 1. In Cellular regulatory mechanisms. Cold Spring Harbor Symposium on Quantitative Biology.
4. Gerhart, J. C., and A. B. Pardee. 1964. Aspartate transcarbamylase, an enzyme designed for feedback inhibition. Fed. Proc. 23:727.
5. Changeux, J. 1965. The control of biochemical reactions. Sci. Am. (April), p. 36.
6. Koshland, D. E., Jr. 1964. Conformation changes at the active site during enzyme action. Fed. Proc. 23:719.
7. Burk, D. 1939. A colloquial consideration of the Pasteur and neo-Pasteur effects, vol. 7, p. 420. In Biological oxidations. Cold Spring Harbor Symposium on Quantitative Biology.
8. van Eys, J. 1961. Regulatory mechanisms in energy metabolism. In Bonner, D. M. (editor): Control mechanisms in cellular processes. Ronald Press Co., New York. p. 141.
9. Chance, B., and G. R. Williams. 1956. The respiratory chain and oxidative phosphorylation. Advances Enzymol. 17:65.
10. Brierley, G. P., E. Murer, and D. E. Green. 1963. Participation of an intermediate of oxidative phosphorylation in ion accumulation by mitochondria. Science 140:60.

General references

Allen, J. M. (editor). 1962. The molecular control of cellular activity. McGraw-Hill Book Co., New York.

Bonner, D. M. (editor). 1961. Control mechanisms in cellular processes. The Ronald Press Co., New York.

Brown, G. S., and D. P. Campbell. 1948. Principles of servomechanisms. John Wiley & Sons, Inc., New York.

Cellular regulatory mechanisms. 1961. Cold Spring Harbor Symposium on Quantitative Biology. Vol. 26.

Halvorson, H. O. 1960. The induced synthesis of protein. Advances Enzymol. 22:90.

Herskowitz, I. H. 1965. Genetics, 2nd ed. Little, Brown & Co., Boston.

Lehninger, A. L. 1964. The mitochondrion. W. A. Benjamin, Inc., New York.

Pardee, A. B. 1959. The control of enzyme activity, vol. 1, p. 681. In Boyer, P. D., H. Lardy, and K. Myrbäck (editors): The enzymes. Academic Press, Inc., New York.

Pollack, M. R. 1959. Induced formation of enzymes, vol. 1, p. 619. In Boyer, P. D., H. Lardy, and K. Myrbäck (editors): The enzymes. Academic Press, Inc., New York.

Ritow, I. 1956. A servomechanism primer. Doubleday & Co., Inc., Garden City, New York.

Stent, G. S. 1964. The operon: On its third anniversary. Science 144:816.

Umbarger, H. E. 1964. Intracellular regulatory mechanisms. Science 145:674.

Wilson, A. C., and A. B. Pardee. 1964. Comparative aspects of metabolic control, vol. 6, p. 73. In Florkin, M., and H. S. Mason (editors): Comparative biochemistry. Academic Press, Inc., New York.

Index